TK 2821 T65 1966
WITHDRAWN
3 0250 00331 0674

D1015614

Introduction to the

LOGICAL DESIGN
OF
SWITCHING SYSTEMS

This book is in the
ADDISON-WESLEY SERIES IN
ELECTRICAL ENGINEERING

Consulting Editors

DAVID K. CHENG WILLIAM A. LYNCH

Introduction to the

LOGICAL DESIGN OF SWITCHING SYSTEMS

by

H. C. TORNG

Cornell University

ADDISON-WESLEY PUBLISHING COMPANY

READING, MASSACHUSETTS · PALO ALTO · LONDON · DON MILLS, ONTARIO

Copyright © 1964
ADDISON-WESLEY PUBLISHING COMPANY, INC.

Printed in the United States of America

ALL RIGHTS RESERVED. THIS BOOK, OR PARTS THEREOF, MAY NOT BE REPRODUCED IN ANY FORM WITHOUT WRITTEN PERMISSION OF THE PUBLISHER.

Library of Congress Catalog Card No. 64–14330

Second Printing—October 1966

PREFACE

This book is the outgrowth of the author's lecture notes for a course on Switching Systems, in the School of Electrical Engineering at Cornell University. It is intended to be used both as a text for students in the first course on logical design of computers or switching systems in an engineering curriculum, and also as an aid to practicing engineers in initiating or refreshing their studies in this vital area.

In preparing his lecture notes and subsequently this book, the author has had as his objective the preparation of the reader so that he may pursue advanced studies and practice in the area of computer switching, communication switching, and control switching. The emphasis of the presentation is placed on delineating the reasoning necessary to design a switching system. This book, therefore, is not intended to be a "cook book" or a manual for a switching system designer.

A general survey of switching systems is made in Chapter 1; a common basis is established for switching systems used in computation, communication, and control; and the general approach involved in synthesizing a switching system is outlined.

Switching algebra is introduced in Chapter 2 in its abstract form, so that with proper interpretation, it can be applied to switching systems of a diversified nature. Simple circuits of switches are then represented by switching functions. It is then pointed out that switching functions not only can describe circuits of switches, but also can lead to circuit simplification.

Chapter 3 presents two ways to formulate switching functions for combinational switching circuits. The starting point for formulating a switching function is to identify the relevant inputs and outputs. A truth table relating inputs and outputs is then established. Such a truth table embodies the given specification, or provides the logic, for the circuit.

Two basic forms of switching expressions can then be established: one in terms of standard products and the other in terms of standard sums. The conversion between two basic forms of expressions is discussed.

The topic "Formulation of Switching Functions" is presented at this point to establish a bridge between abstract switching algebra and actual system design. Physical meaning is given when the standard product and the standard sum are introduced. Most important of all, it reflects our opinion that the synthesis of a switching system starts, not from a given set of switching functions, but rather from a given set of clearly defined, sometimes not-so-clearly defined, specifications.

Chapter 4 introduces the concepts of and-gates and or-gates. Any switching function of a combinational switching circuit can be implemented by these gates, provided that all input variables are available.

The relay is then presented and used to realize the and-gates and or-gates. Approaches used in optimizing a given contactor switching circuit are also discussed.

Two basic resistor-diode configurations are shown in Chapter 5. According to a specific truth value, each one of the two configurations is identified with the performance of a specific switching operation. The implementation and optimization of diode switching circuits are then discussed, and the selecting circuits introduced. The coincidence problem in pulsed switching circuits is also illustrated.

Chapter 6 presents two methods of switching function manipulation: the map method and the tabulation method. A map is the graphical representation of switching functions, and the reasoning which lies behind its gradual evolution is discussed. The steps taken in employing the tabulation method are enumerated, and their implications are illustrated by discussing the optimization of two-level diode switching circuits and by introducing the concept of prime implicants.

There are three reasons for presenting the switching function realization by relay gates and diode gates in Chapters 4 and 5, and switching function manipulation in Chapter 6. By presenting the material in this order, we expect first to provide more substantial interpretations for the switching algebra established in Chapter 3; second, to generate motivation and justification for the switching function manipulation methods; third, to facilitate the accompanying laboratory instruction, if any.

Chapter 7 introduces two basic direct-coupled transistor configurations for switching purposes. Not-and-gates and not-or-gates are obtained by adopting a proper truth value. Diode-transistor gates are then presented, and the implementation and optimization of switching functions are discussed.

The advantage and potential of magnetic cores used as switching components are discussed in Chapter 8. Switching gates with magnetic cores are then presented. Considerations involved in realizing a switching function with core gates and subsequent optimization are enumerated. Threshold switching is then presented.

Up to this point, the presentation has concentrated on realizing a switching circuit for a given switching function. Chapter 9 discusses a multiterminal switching circuit used to implement a set of switching functions. Coding in switching systems is also introduced in Chapter 9.

Chapter 10 presents the iterative means of realizing switching functions which have large numbers of input variables. Examples are used to reveal the considerations involved.

At this point, the presentation of systematic approaches for the synthesis of combinational switching circuits is completed.

In initiating the study of sequential switching circuits, Chapter 11 presents first of all the description of a general sequential switching circuit with a finite number of states. The synchronous sequential switching circuit with finite states will be studied in Chapters 11, 12, 13, and 14. We believe that the study of synchronous sequential circuits with finite states provides adequate background for studies of asynchronous switching circuits. The extension to asynchronous switching circuits is done in Chapter 15.

By using what has been presented in previous chapters, Chapter 11 developes the design of a binary storage device, which can be used in the memory of the sequential switching circuit.

Chapter 11 also discusses the design of counters and shift registers. These circuits are discussed not because of their wide applicability, but rather because they are used as a vehicle to convey the general considerations and approaches involved in the design of synchronous sequential switching circuits.

In order to augment in depth the general outline of the synthesis of synchronous switching circuits, the next three chapters expose the difficulties of the synthesis, and reconstruct the thinking necessary to solve them. Chapter 12 shows how to convert a set of given specifications into a state table. Several illustrative examples are introduced in this chapter.

Chapter 13 presents two general approaches for reducing a given state table, completely specified or incompletely specified. The reduction steps to be taken are simple, and explanations are presented in detail to show how these steps are formulated.

Chapter 14 covers the operation of state assignment. Emphasis is again placed on exposing the latent reasonings involved in arriving at the rules and guidelines for achieving an acceptable scheme of state assignment. The illustrative examples, which are initiated in Chapter 12 and continued in Chapter 13, are completed in Chapter 14.

Chapter 15 presents the additional considerations in the design of asynchronous sequential circuits. A list of relevant references is provided at the end of the book. It is, however, by no means exhaustive. The author apologizes for any omission.

A set of problems is included at the end of every chapter. These not only provide opportunities for the reader to use and extend what has just been presented, but also introduce materials which are not covered in the text proper.

The author expresses his thanks to his colleagues in the School of Electrical Engineering at Cornell for their interest; among them Professors

W. E. Meserve, P. Ankrum, H. G. Booker, N. H. Bryant, W. H. Erickson, C. Green, B. Nichols, and N. Vrana. Dr. D. Givone's assistance is also appreciated.

Thanks are extended to the staff of Addison-Wesley for their assistance and cooperation.

The author thanks Mrs. B. Hirshfeld for her editing and Miss J. Manning and Miss S. Westmiller for their patient and careful typing.

The writing of this book would not have been possible without the encouragement and understanding of the author's wife, Bung Fung, to whom this book is dedicated.

H. C. T.

Ithaca, New York
January 1964

CONTENTS

CHAPTER 1

INTRODUCTION

1.1 Automation. Automation is one of the most exciting and challenging developments in technology. Switching systems for communication, control, and computation are the indispensable instruments of automation.

Once, all telephone calls had to be routed by human operators, but automation, in the form of switching circuits, has relieved much of the burden on operators. Direct-distance dialing is becoming commonplace, and other interesting features are being investigated and installed. For example, it is a quite frustrating experience to dial a certain station and get a busy signal every time. A switching system has been devised which will record the number dialed, will keep trying until the connection is made, and then will alert the caller. What a help to some student who would have spent all evening trying to reach a busy number!

In the process of automating telephone circuits, engineers found that a branch of mathematics called *Boolean algebra* could be successfully employed.* The use of Boolean algebra transformed the design of automatic telephone circuits from a cut-and-try process into an orderly procedure, and laid the foundation for swift advancement in the development of switching systems.

It was then reasoned that if switching circuits could be designed to route telephone calls, then it must be possible to implement switching circuits to carry out routine computations. The result of this effort is automatic electronic computers.† These high-speed computers have made it possible to accomplish certain computations that were previously deemed too tedious and time-consuming to be carried out. In fact, machine computation has considerably changed the basic concept of the "solution" of a problem.

Since switching circuits in computation and communication systems execute their tasks by following certain rules, it is only natural that switching circuits are used to execute control functions. Switching systems, or computers, are being used to monitor industrial processes.‡

---

* SH 1. The letter and number designation indicates the reference listed in the bibliography at the rear of the book.

† SC 1 and LE 1.

‡ TO 1, RA 1, and JU 1.

Nuclear reactors and power-generating stations are being operated and controlled by computers with prearranged programs.

1.2 Computer switching: switching systems for computation. A digital computer can be considered to be made up of five interconnected blocks, as shown in Fig. 1.1.

Digital computers, like other switching systems, are a result of men's efforts to reduce routine drudgery. A problem which might take the human mind years to finish can be accomplished in a matter of minutes by a computer. However, if we wish to study the inner working of a computer, we can learn a great deal by examining the process a human operator would follow when approaching such a problem.

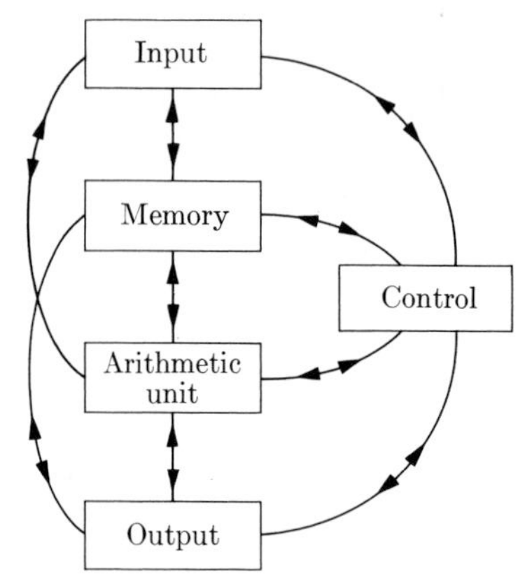

FIG. 1.1. Block diagram of a general-purpose digital computer. (Links between blocks indicate paths of flow of information.)

First of all, he is given a problem and the necessary data. This indicates that an *input device* is needed, i.e., a "device" to impart the necessary information to the operator. If he is an intelligent person and well versed in computing techniques, no step-by-step instruction is necessary. Even if he is given instructions, he might initiate some improvement. However, a computer must be given step-by-step instructions, either by input instructions or by built-in logic.

Upon receiving the input instructions and data, the human calculator will store this information either by memory or in some other form. So does the computer. Thus, a *memory device* is needed.

By means of his thinking mechanism, the human calculator would decide the order of calculation, and accordingly would fetch the appropriate data and determine the relevant arithmetic rules. Such a step is essential in a computer. The unit that performs these functions is termed the *control unit.*

Certainly the human operator should understand and execute arithmetic rules to carry out the calculations. A computer must also perform this function. Thus, an *arithmetic unit* is needed.

When the final result is available, the human operator should be able to present the result in some specified form. A computer should also be capable of performing this operation. Therefore, an *output device* is needed.

In summary, a switching system for computation is divided into five subsystems, each charged with certain functions. For each specified function a switching circuit is designed accordingly to execute it.

1.3 Telephone switching: switching systems for communication. The largest switching system on earth is not a high-speed digital computer. It is the automatic telephone switching system. This switching system reaches almost every home in the United States and every point on the globe. A block diagram of a portion of this gigantic setup is shown in Fig. 1.2.

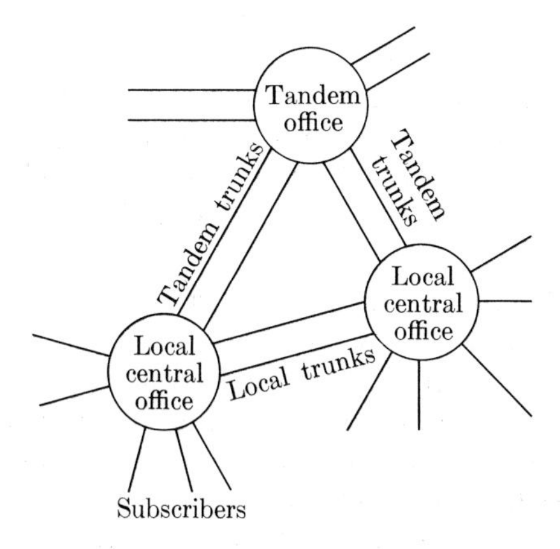

FIG. 1.2. Block diagram for a portion of the automatic telephone switching system.

When a person places a telephone call by dialing a certain number, the switching and control circuits in his local central office record the order and proceed to locate a path in its interconnecting network to reach the called party, if the called party is also located in the same local central office. If the called party belongs to another local central office, the circuits will try to reach him through local trunks, if available, or by way of tandem trunks. In either case, if no path can be established, the calling subscriber's line will be connected to a busy tone.

There are definite rules in processing a call, which are executed by switching and control circuits.

1.4 Control switching: switching systems for control. Switching circuits capable of making decisions according to certain rules are available. These circuits are generally reliable, and they act much faster than a human operator. Therefore, they are being introduced with increasing frequency to monitor industrial processes. A general block diagram is shown in Fig. 1.3.

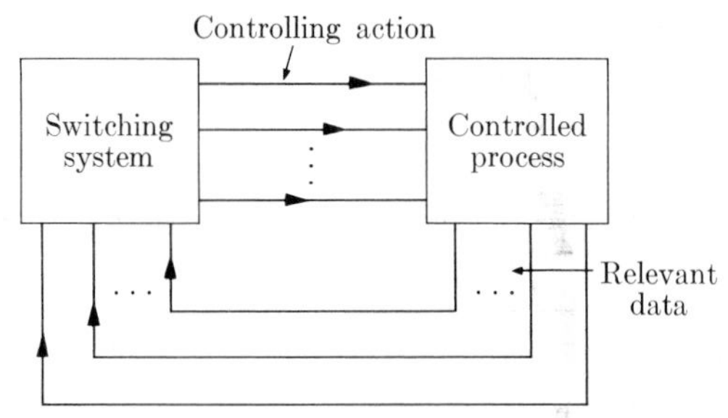

FIG. 1.3. Block diagram for a switching system controlling an industrial process.

To control a chemical process, the relevant data that are sent to the switching system might include temperature, pressure, concentration, and so on. The switching system initiates adequate actions to bring the process within its most optimum conditions and maintains it there.

1.5 A common basis for switching systems. There are so many examples of the marvelous development and wide applications of switching systems that it seems impossible to understand completely their present uses, let alone invent new ones. However, if we could find a common basis for the design of switching systems, the possibilities for application will be much easier to grasp. The object of this section is to try to establish such a common basis upon which all automatic switching systems are built.

In a digital computing machine, the circuits are interconnected in such a way that calculations are performed according to the rules of arithmetic. These rules are followed not because the machine learned them, but because the man who designed the circuits followed the rules. In other words, a set of *predetermined rules* has been built into the computer.

Switching systems used to monitor the operations of industrial processes function like a human operator, who performs his duty by following a set of pertinent instructions. A monitoring switching system "learns" and executes its instructions through adequate programming. It can thus be said that the computer is made to execute a set of certain rules.

The above examples serve to illustrate a very important concept: even though automatic switching systems may differ in their missions and appearances, they can be considered to be fundamentally identical in that they are designed to execute a set of built-in rules. This implies that a common basis can be found for them. A unified approach is thus desirable and attainable.

In a general switching system such as that shown in Fig. 1.4, the number of inputs and outputs is not restricted. The switching system processes the inputs according to its built-in rules. The switching circuits in

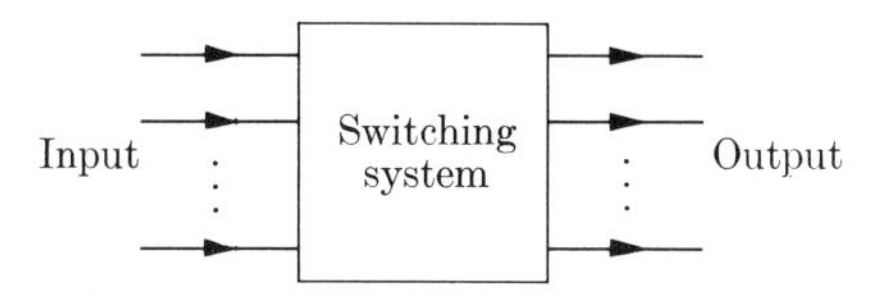

FIG. 1.4. A general switching system.

a telephone central office, by receiving the input pulses produced by dialing, will interpret their meaning and proceed to make the right connection. In a computer, if two numbers a and b are stored and the instructions call for an addition of a and b, the computer will proceed to fetch the numbers a and b from the memory and send them to the arithmetic unit, where the adding circuit will produce the sum. This result might be stored in the memory unit or it might be printed. In carrying out this operation, the computer is following precisely the rule upon which it has been built.

The significance of a common basis is that once it is established, it is then not necessary to study every individual system. Instead, attention can be concentrated on the design theory of a general switching system.

1.6 System synthesis. In order to synthesize a switching system, we follow the steps enumerated below.

First, establish a set of consistent and concise rules for the system.

The set of rules has to be consistent, because under a specific set of input conditions the system can produce only one set of specific outputs. This can best be illustrated by a concrete example. When a switching system is designed to produce the sum of two input numbers, say a and b, the output will always indicate the sum of the inputs. This same system cannot be expected to produce the difference between a and b. The reason is quite clear. Since this system is built to follow the rule of adding two numbers, it will process the two input numbers according to this rule, which is certainly different from the rule for subtraction. These two rules, or the sets of rules involved, are not consistent. Therefore, we cannot design a system that can execute addition and subtraction, *without any alteration*. This last phrase is very important, because we know that a digital computer can certainly do both addition and subtraction. However, the configurations, or interconnections, of the computer for adding and for subtracting operations are not the same.

The set of rules has to be concise, because it has a direct bearing on the complexity of the system to be synthesized. In the later development of this book, much effort will be devoted to the simplification of certain switching expressions, or to making the set of rules as concise as possible.

Second, the designer has to implement the rules established. This implementation should be achieved in the most optimum sense. By *optimum*, it is meant that the system realized should be the simplest, cheapest, fastest, and the most reliable possible. There is no doubt that a designer should strive to achieve these ends. However, these are usually mutually opposed objectives. For example, it can be easily seen that to reduce the cost and to increase the reliability of a switching system cannot be generally achieved at the same time. A compromise has to be reached based on sound and thorough engineering judgement.

The two steps stated above present an immense and interesting challenge. It is the aim of this volume to present the systematic approaches available to achieve these ends. Furthermore, it is expected that the reader will detect the shortcomings of the approaches and offer new and exciting methods.

CHAPTER 2

SWITCHING ALGEBRA

2.1 Introduction. In the previous chapter we established a common basis for various switching systems. This common basis enables us to avoid studying specific systems, and allows us instead to take a general approach, which is more systematic and is applicable to all switching systems.

We further stated that the first step in designing a switching system is to establish a set of consistent and concise rules. It is natural for us to require a set of consistent and concise rules for certain systems, but it is not at all easy to achieve this goal. Painstaking care is needed to avoid ambiguity and redundancy. This same difficulty is faced by logicians. To alleviate it, logicians tried to express logic with symbolic language. From the development of symbolic logic, system designers derive *switching algebra*. By using switching algebra, we can establish and express a given set of rules in the most concise and consistent way possible.

An intuitive approach will be used first. The axiomatic approach will be presented at the end of this chapter.

2.2 Switching variable and truth value. To discuss switching algebra, we must define several terms. Two of these are *switching variable* and *truth value.*

A switching variable is a variable which can assume either one of two distinct values. The value of a switching variable is called its truth value.

Two-valued variables are introduced in the establishment of switching algebra, because, generally speaking, the physical implementation of two-valued variables is more reliable than that of variables of more than two distinct values.

It may also be of interest to point out that the term *truth value* was originally used in the study of symbolic logic and the algebra of proposition, where a variable represents a proposition that is either true or false.

A switching variable will be denoted by either a lower-case or capital letter. Note that the notion of a switching variable is introduced in an abstract form. This leaves room for us to assign appropriate physical interpretations as we see fit in specific situations.

By definition, a switching variable can assume either one of two values. What are these two values? They can be any two values, but generally

0 and 1 are used. Therefore, it can be said that the truth value of a switching variable can be either 0 or 1. Note that we make no indication of how to represent these two values physically. In later chapters it will be shown that they can be physically represented in many ways!

2.3 Operations in switching algebra. In the previous section, switching variable, and truth value are defined. Now the three *operations* in switching algebra are defined.

Or-operation. The *or*-combination of two switching variables has a truth value of 1 if and only if either one or both of the switching variables has a truth value of 1. Let the two switching variables be x and y; their or-combination is denoted by $x + y$. It is sometimes called the sum of x and y.

And-operation. The *and*-combination of two switching variables has a truth value of 1 if and only if both variables have the truth value of 1. Let the two switching variables be x and y; their and-combination is denoted by $x \cdot y$ or xy. It is sometimes called the product of x and y.

Negation. The truth value of the negative, or complement, of a switching variable is 1 if and only if the truth value of the variable is 0. Let the switching variable be x; its negative, or complement, is denoted by x'.

Other symbols are used in published works to denote the or-operation, the and-operation, and negation. The following tabulation illustrates the alternative notations used.

Operation	Notation
or-combination of x and y	$x + y$, $x \vee y$, $x \cup y$
and-combination of x and y	xy, $x \cdot y$, $x \wedge y$, $x \cap y$
negation of x	x', $\bar{x}$, $\sim x$

Note that the three switching operations are defined here in their abstract form. We refrain from assigning specific physical interpretations to them, because we do not want to create the notion that the switching algebra presented here is applicable only in special situations. We have now defined all that has to be defined. Any manipulation, interpretation, or application from here on must conform with what has been defined in this and the previous section.

2.4 Switching functions and truth tables. At this point we have been introduced to switching variables, the truth values of switching variables, and switching operations. The combination of switching variables through switching operations is termed a *switching function.* For example, the or-combination of two switching variables x and y is a switching function. It can be written in the form

$$T = x + y. \tag{2.1}$$

To determine the truth value of the switching function T, we follow the definition of the or-operation and the truth values assumed by x and y. This can be done in a very orderly way by constructing the following table, which is the *truth table* for the switching function defined in Eq. (2.1).

x	0	0	1	1
y	0	1	0	1
T	0	1	1	1

Each column of this table indicates a set of possible truth values assumed by x and y. Since x can take either of the two values and so can y, there are four columns in the table. The value of T in each column is determined by the definition of or-operation.

Now it can be said that the switching function T is a function of switching variables x and y. It is interesting to note that a switching function can also be considered as a switching variable because it can take only one of the two values 0 and 1.

2.5 One form of interpretation. Switching algebra is presented entirely in its abstract form, so that we can apply it without any confusion to switching systems of different switching devices.

In the following, a set of interpretations is made to adapt switching algebra to treat circuits of mechanical switches. This will illustrate that if proper interpretations are made, switching algebra can be used to study actual switching circuits. Furthermore, it is hoped that these interpretations will indicate the advantage of using switching algebra to study switching systems and the need to investigate how to manipulate the representations of switching functions.

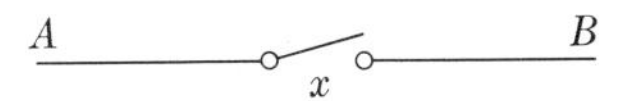

FIG. 2.1. A switch.

In Fig. 2.1, either terminals A and B may be directly connected when the switch x is closed, or terminals A and B may be disconnected when the switch x is open. There are two physical entities in this setup that are of interest to us. One is the status of the connection between terminals A and B: is it connected or not connected? The other is the status of the switch: is it closed or open? Since each entity has only two possibilities, one can immediately see that they can be represented by two switching variables T and x, defined as follows.

T stands for the status of the connection between terminals A and B. If terminals A and B are connected, T is assigned a truth value of 1, or simply $T = 1$; if terminals A and B are not connected, T is assigned a truth value of 0, or simply $T = 0$.

x stands for the status of the switch x. If switch x is open, x is assigned a truth value of 0, or simply $x = 0$; if switch x is closed, x is assigned a truth value of 1, or simply $x = 1$.

What we have accomplished is that we can use switching variables to represent physical entities. At this point, it might seem that one switching variable can represent only events of two possible states; for example, T represents whether there is a connection between terminals A and B or not. Actually, we can use combinations of switching variables to represent events with more than two states. This point will be further explained later.

Let us now examine the simple setup shown in Fig. 2.1. Since the physical connection of terminals A and B depends on the status of the switch, we would expect that T should be a function of x. We can now proceed to develop the relationship between T and x by constructing the following truth table.

x	0	1
T	0	1

The number of columns in such a truth table depends on the number of independent switching variables involved. In the present case, only one independent variable, x, has to be considered; therefore, there are only two columns. The corresponding value for T in each column is of course found by considering the physical situation. For instance, $x = 0$ means that the switch is open; obviously there is no connection between terminals A and B, so $T = 0$.

It might seem that the table exhibits exhaustively the relationships between T and x. However, it is obvious that the table representation is somewhat cumbersome. From examining the table, we realize that $T = 1$ only when $x = 1$; therefore, the table can actually be represented by the equation

$$T = x. \tag{2.2}$$

In other words, Eq. (2.2) stands for the actual circuit in Fig. 2.1.

Let us consider next the case of two mechanical switches connected in parallel, as in Fig. 2.2. Two switching variables x and y can be used to represent the two switches, and the switching variable T can be used to represent the connection between terminals A and B. To find out how T, x, and y are related, we construct the following truth table.

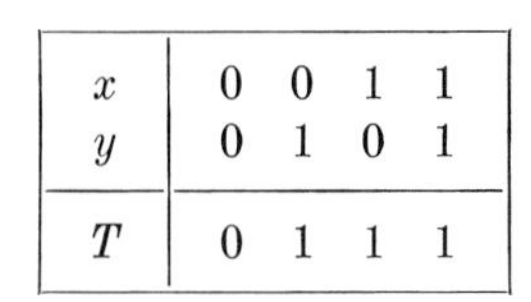

x	0	0	1	1
y	0	1	0	1
T	0	1	1	1

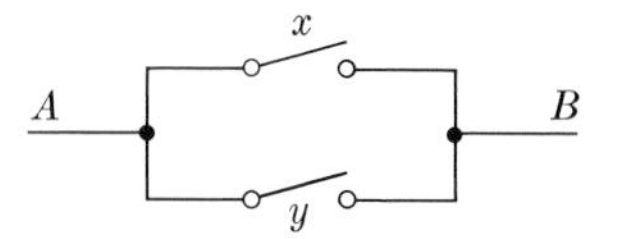

Fig. 2.2. Two switches connected in parallel.

Since there are two independent variables x and y, there are four columns in the truth table. By examining the table, we see that $T = 1$ when either x or y or both are 1. This can be expressed by the equation

$$T = x + y. \tag{2.3}$$

Equation (2.3) actually represents the circuit shown in Fig. 2.2.

Two switches x and y connected in series, as shown in Fig. 2.3, can be represented by the following truth table.

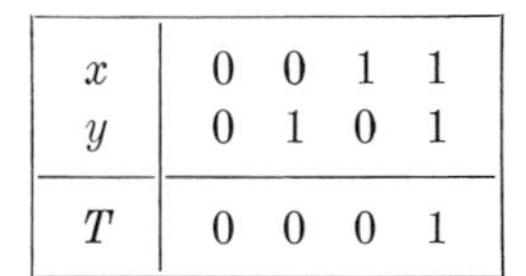

x	0	0	1	1
y	0	1	0	1
T	0	0	0	1

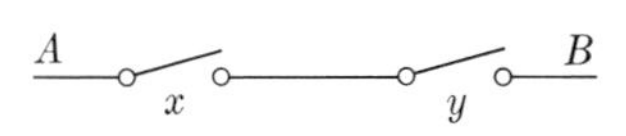

Fig. 2.3. Two switches connected in series.

Since $T = 1$ if and only if x and y are 1, the following equation is established:

$$T = xy. \tag{2.4}$$

The circuit shown in Fig. 2.3 is, therefore, represented by Eq. (2.4).

Up to this point we have shown that simple circuits of switches can be satisfactorily described by switching functions. By using the same technique to treat another simple circuit, we intend to show not only that we can use switching functions to represent actual circuits, but also that we can manipulate the representations of switching functions to simplify actual circuits.

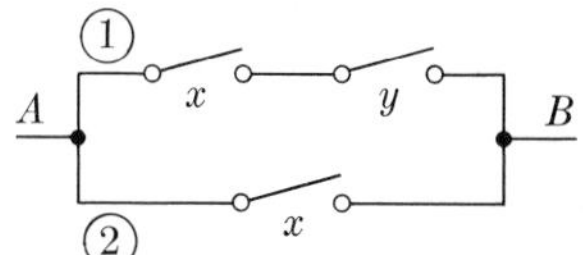

Fig. 2.4. A simple circuit of switches.

Let us examine the simple circuit shown in Fig. 2.4. Two switches designated by the same letter, x, means that when one switch is open, the other is also open; when one is closed, the other is also closed.

The switching function for branch 1 is established in Eq. (2.4), and the switching function for branch 2 is established in Eq. (2.2). Since the two branches are connected in parallel, the switching function for the entire circuit can be found from Eq. (2.3) as the or-combination of the switching functions of the two branches:

$$T = xy + x. \tag{2.5a}$$

A truth table for the switching function shown in Eq. (2.5a) can be constructed.

x	0	0	1	1
y	0	1	0	1
T	0	0	1	1

When we examine the table we see immediately that x is the only independent variable which actually determines the value of T. In other words, this table can be reduced to the table for Fig. 2.1. This implies that the switching function in Eq. (2.5a) is equivalent to that in Eq. (2.2):

$$T = xy + x = x. \tag{2.5b}$$

We can, therefore, conclude that the circuits in Figs. 2.1 and 2.4 are equivalent so far as the connection between terminals A and B is concerned. When we recognize the existence of Eq. (2.5b), we can immediately replace the circuit in Fig. 2.4 with that in Fig. 2.1. This amounts to a welcome simplification.

2.6 Theorems in switching algebra. In the previous section, we see that by using a set of proper interpretations, we can represent actual switching circuits by switching functions. Furthermore, by manipulating representations of the switching functions, we can simplify a given circuit.

In this section, we intend to present certain theorems which are useful in such manipulation.

1. Absorption Theorem

Let x be a switching variable; then

$$x + x = x. \tag{2.6}$$

This theorem can be justified by constructing the following truth table.

x	0	1
$x + x$	0	1

This table is obtained from the definition of the or-operation. In the present case, since there is only one independent switching variable x, there are two entries in the table. For each truth value of x, the corresponding truth value of $x + x$ is found. It can then be concluded that the two expressions on both sides of Eq. (2.6) are equal, because for any truth value assigned to x, the value of these two functions are the same.

$$x \cdot x = x. \tag{2.7}$$

The justification for Eq. (2.7) can be found by constructing a truth table as we did for Eq. (2.6).

2. Commutative Theorem

$$x + y = y + x. \tag{2.8}$$

$$xy = yx. \tag{2.9}$$

3. Associative Theorem

$$x + y + z = (x + z) + y = (x + y) + z = x + (y + z). \tag{2.10}$$

$$xyz = (xy)z = x(yz) = y(xz). \tag{2.11}$$

One can justify these two rules by constructing truth tables.

4. Universal-Unity Theorems

$$x + x' = 1. \tag{2.12}$$

$$xx' = 0. \tag{2.13}$$

This theorem is obvious.

5. Functions Involving 1

$$x \cdot 1 = x. \tag{2.14}$$

$$x + 1 = 1. \tag{2.15}$$

6. Functions Involving 0

$$x \cdot 0 = 0. \tag{2.16}$$

$$x + 0 = x. \tag{2.17}$$

Theorems 5 and 6 can be proved by constructing relevant truth tables.

7. Distributive Theorem

$$x(y + z) = xy + xz. \tag{2.18}$$

This theorem looks like one in ordinary algebra. However, it should be justified by constructing the following truth table.

x	0	1	0	0	1	1	0	1
y	0	0	1	0	1	0	1	1
z	0	0	0	1	0	1	1	1
$x(y + z)$	0	0	0	0	1	1	0	1
$xy + xz$	0	0	0	0	1	1	0	1

Note that there are three explicit switching variables x, y, and z present. Each variable can assume one of the two values. The number of entries in the truth table is, therefore, equal to eight (which is of course $2 \times 2 \times 2$). For each entry, the truth values for both sides of Eq. (2.18) are independently evaluated. These two expressions are considered to be equal, because for every one of the eight possible entries, they have the same truth values.

$$x + yz = (x + y) \cdot (x + z). \tag{2.19}$$

Equation (2.19) can be proved by constructing a truth table. It can also be approached by using the theorems established above.

Let us start from the right-hand side and justify each step taken by the theorems already established:

$$\begin{aligned}
(x + y)(x + z) &= (x + y)x + (x + y)z && \text{by Eq. (2.18)} \\
&= x(x + y) + z(x + y) && \text{by Eq. (2.9)} \\
&= xx + xy + zx + zy && \text{by Eq. (2.18)} \\
&= x + xy + zx + yz && \text{by Eq. (2.7)} \\
&= x(1 + y) + zx + yz && \text{by Eq. (2.18)} \\
&= x + zx + yz && \text{by Eq. (2.15)} \\
&= x(1 + z) + yz && \text{by Eq. (2.18)} \\
&= x + yz && \text{by Eq. (2.15).}
\end{aligned}$$

It is hoped that this step-by-step derivation will illustrate how the theorems developed can be used.

The theorems developed in this section are to be used for switching function simplification and manipulation.* All these theorems are justi-

* Note that previously the expression "simplification or manipulation of the representation of switching functions" is used, because a switching function indicates a basic statement or specification which can be neither simplified nor manipulated. However, a switching function can be expressed in different forms. One can, therefore, manipulate or simplify its representation. It is to be understood that "switching function simplification and manipulation" means "simplification and manipulation of the *representation* of a switching function."

fied by the fact that the truth values of both sides are equal under any circumstances. In fact, the last comment is the only criterion that has to be observed.

2.7 Illustrative examples. The examples provided below demonstrate how to employ the theorems developed to simplify given switching functions. Each step taken is justified by the theorem cited. It is also of interest to note that the truth values of the simplified functions are equal to those of the original functions with any set of values for the switching variables involved.

The results of the first two examples can be considered as theorems because of their frequent applicability.

EXAMPLE 2.1. Simplify the switching function

$$T = x + x'y. \tag{2.20}$$

$$\begin{aligned} x + x'y &= (x + x')(x + y) && \text{by Eq. (2.19)} \\ &= x + y && \text{by Eq. (2.12).} \end{aligned}$$

$$x + x'y = x + y. \tag{2.21}$$

The proof of Eq. (2.21) is very simple; however, this is one of the simplifying tools that may be overlooked.

It is of interest to check the validity of Eq. (2.21) by constructing a truth table. Since there are two explicit switching variables in the equation, the truth table will consist of 4 entries, as shown at the right.

x	0	0	1	1
y	0	1	0	1
$x + x'y$	0	1	1	1
$x + y$	0	1	1	1

Under any set of values for the switching variables x and y, the truth values for both sides are always equal. This proves the validity of the equation. ▲

EXAMPLE 2.2. Simplify the switching function

$$T = xy + x'z + yz. \tag{2.22}$$

$$\begin{aligned} xy + x'z + yz &= xy + x'z + (1)yz && \text{by Eq. (2.14)} \\ &= xy + x'z + (x + x')yz && \text{by Eq. (2.12)} \\ &= xy + x'z + xyz + x'yz && \text{by Eq. (2.18)} \\ &= xy(1 + z) + x'z(1 + y) && \text{by Eq. (2.18)} \\ &= xy + x'z && \text{by Eq. (2.15).} \end{aligned}$$

$$xy + x'z + yz = xy + x'z. \blacktriangle \tag{2.23}$$

EXAMPLE 2.3. Simplify the switching function

$$T = (y + z + x)(y + z + x') + xy + yz.$$

$$\begin{aligned}
&(y + z + x)(y + z + x') + xy + yz \\
&\quad = [(y + z) + x][(y + z) + x'] + xy + yz && \text{by Eq. (2.10)} \\
&\quad = (y + z + xx') + xy + yz && \text{by Eq. (2.19)} \\
&\quad = y + z + xy + yz && \text{by Eq. (2.13)} \\
&\quad = y(1 + x) + z(1 + y) && \text{by Eq. (2.18)} \\
&\quad = y + z && \text{by Eq. (2.15).} \blacktriangle
\end{aligned}$$

EXAMPLE 2.4. Simplify the switching function

$$T = x + xyz + yzx' + x'y + wx + w'x.$$

$$\begin{aligned}
&x + xyz + yzx' + x'y + wx + w'x \\
&\quad = x + (yz)x + (x'y)z + x'y + wx + w'x && \text{by Eq. (2.11)} \\
&\quad = x(1 + yz) + (x'y)(1 + z) + x(w + w') && \text{by Eq. (2.18)} \\
&\quad = x + x'y + x(w + w') && \text{by Eq. (2.15)} \\
&\quad = x + x'y + x && \text{by Eq. (2.12)} \\
&\quad = x + x'y && \text{by Eq. (2.6)} \\
&\quad = x + y && \text{by Eq. (2.21).} \blacktriangle
\end{aligned}$$

It should be stated that the simplification process for any given switching function is not unique. This can be shown by working Example 2.4 in a different way. The switching function

$$\begin{aligned}
T &= x + xyz + yzx' + x'y + wx + w'x \\
&= x(1 + yz + w + w') + x'y(1 + z) && \text{by Eq. (2.18)} \\
&= x + x'y && \text{by Eq. (2.15)} \\
&= x + y && \text{by Eq. (2.21).}
\end{aligned}$$

2.8 Negation theorem. In this section, two theorems which deal with the operation of negation are presented.

1. $$(x')' = x. \tag{2.24}$$

This theorem is self-evident, because the negative of the negative certainly must be the original switching variable itself.

2. NEGATION THEOREM *

This theorem is to be presented first in the form of two specific problems and then the generalization will be drawn.

---

* This theorem is also known as DeMorgan's Theorem.

Problem 1. Find the negative of the switching function $x + y$.

$$(x + y)' = x'y'. \tag{2.25}$$

Equation (2.25) is validated by the following truth table.

x	0	0	1	1
y	0	1	0	1
$x + y$	0	1	1	1
$x'y'$	1	0	0	0

Problem 2. Find the negative of the switching function xy.

$$(xy)' = x' + y'. \tag{2.26}$$

The justification of Eq. (2.26) is left to the student.

With Eqs. (2.25) and (2.26) established, we can arrive at the generalization. If we consider the cases of three switching variables, connected by "or" or "and" operations, we obtain

$$\begin{aligned} (x + y + z)' &= [(x + y) + z]' && \text{by Eq. (2.10)} \\ &= (x + y)'z' && \text{by Eq. (2.25)} \\ &= x'y'z' && \text{by Eq. (2.25).} \end{aligned}$$

The above derivation shows that

$$(x + y + z)' = x'y'z'. \tag{2.27}$$

Using the same process, we can obtain

$$(xyz)' = x' + y' + z'. \tag{2.28}$$

In treating a function of n switching variables, we can group the $n - 1$ variables as one variable and proceed to yield the following general expression of DeMorgan's theorem:

$$(x + y + z + \cdots)' = x'y'z' \ldots, \tag{2.29}$$

$$(xyz \ldots)' = x' + y' + z' + \cdots. \tag{2.30}$$

It is of interest to note that in Section 2.6, pairs of two equations are grouped together. By using the Negation Theorem, we can obtain one from the other. For example, we can apply the Negation Theorem to both sides of Eq. (2.12):

$$(x + x')' = (1)', \qquad (x)'(x')' = 0, \qquad xx' = 0.$$

The result obtained is Eq. (2.13).

2.9 Illustrative examples. The Negation Theorem presented in the previous section can also be used to simplify switching functions, as is shown in the following example.

EXAMPLE 2.5. Simplify the switching function

$$T = x + x'y.$$

This problem is worked out in Example 2.1. However, it can be simplified by using the Negation Theorem.

Taking the negative of T, we obtain

$$\begin{aligned} T' &= (x + x'y)' \\ &= x'[(x'y)'] \\ &= x'(x + y') \\ &= x'y'. \end{aligned}$$

At this stage, we convert the negative of T' and regain the original T:

$$\begin{aligned} T = (T')' &= (x'y')' \\ &= (x')' + (y')' \\ &= x + y. \blacktriangle \end{aligned}$$

EXAMPLE 2.6. Simplify the switching function

$$T = w'x'y' + wx'y' + (w + x + y')' + wx'y + wxy + (w' + x' + y)'.$$

The simplification is effected by first using the Negation Theorem as follows:

$$\begin{aligned} T &= w'x'y' + wx'y' + w'x'y + wx'y + wxy + wxy' \\ &= (w' + w)x'y' + (w' + w)x'y + wx(y + y') \\ &= x'y' + x'y + wx \\ &= x'(y' + y) + wx \\ &= x' + wx \\ &= x' + w. \end{aligned}$$

Using another approach, we take the negative of the given function first:

$$\begin{aligned} T' &= (w'x'y')'(wx'y')'(w'x'y)'(wx'y)'(wxy)'(wxy')' \\ &= [(w + x + y)(w' + x + y)(w + x + y')(w' + x + y') \\ &\quad (w' + x' + y')(w' + x' + y)]. \end{aligned}$$

Using the theorem expressed by Eq. (2.19), we obtain

$$\begin{aligned} T' &= [ww' + (x + y)][ww' + (x + y')][(w' + x') + yy'] \\ &= (x + y)(x + y')(w' + x') \\ &= x(w' + x') \\ &= xw'. \end{aligned}$$

We then take the negative of T' to obtain the original switching function:

$$\begin{aligned} T = (T')' &= (xw')' \\ &= x' + w. \blacktriangle \end{aligned}$$

2.10 A formal presentation.* A heuristic approach is used in the previous sections of this chapter to present switching algebra. In this section, an axiomatic approach is used to present Boolean algebra. This formal presentation will also enable us to appreciate how a mathematical system is erected and studied.

The definition of a general Boolean algebra is as follows.

A class of elements C together with two operations $(+)$ and $(\cdot)$ is a Boolean algebra if and only if the following postulates † hold.

P1: The operations $(+)$ and $(\cdot)$ are binary. If two elements a and b are members of C, then $a \cdot b$ is a member of C and $a + b$ is also a member of C.

P2: The operations $(+)$ and $(\cdot)$ are commutative. If a and b are members of C, then

$$a + b = b + a, \tag{2.31a}$$

$$a \cdot b = b \cdot a.\ddagger \tag{2.31b}$$

P3: There exist in C distinct identity elements 0 and 1 relative to the operations $(+)$ and $(\cdot)$, respectively. For every element a in C,

$$a + 0 = 0 + a = a, \tag{2.32a}$$

$$a \cdot 1 = 1 \cdot a = a. \tag{2.32b}$$

P4: Each operation is distributive over the other. For three elements a, b, and c in C,

$$a + (b \cdot c) = (a + b) \cdot (a + c), \tag{2.33a}$$

$$a \cdot (b + c) = (a \cdot b) + (a \cdot c). \tag{2.33b}$$

P5: For every a in C, there exists an element a' in C such that

$$a + a' = 1, \tag{2.34a}$$

$$a \cdot a' = 0. \tag{2.34b}$$

All other theorems and rules can be derived from the definitions and postulates given above. To illustrate this point, certain theorems in Section 2.6 are proved below.

---

* WH 1, BI 1, BO 1, and BO 2.

† These postulates are given by Huntington, HU 1 and HU 2.

‡ $a \cdot b$ can be written as ab.

1. ABSORPTION THEOREM

Equations (2.6) and (2.7) are repeated below:

$$x + x = x, \tag{2.6}$$

$$x \cdot x = x. \tag{2.7}$$

Proof of Eq. (2.6):

$$\begin{aligned} x &= x + 0 && \text{P3, Eq. (2.32a)} \\ &= x + xx' && \text{P5, Eq. (2.34b)} \\ &= (x + x)(x + x') && \text{P4, Eq. (2.33a)} \\ &= (x + x)(1) && \text{P5, Eq. (2.34a)} \\ &= x + x && \text{P3, Eq. (2.32b).} \end{aligned}$$

Proof of Eq. (2.7):

$$\begin{aligned} x &= x \cdot 1 && \text{P3, Eq. (2.32b)} \\ &= x(x + x') && \text{P5, Eq. (2.34a)} \\ &= xx + xx' && \text{P4, Eq. (2.33b)} \\ &= xx + 0 && \text{P5, Eq. (2.34b)} \\ &= xx && \text{P3, Eq. (2.32a).} \end{aligned}$$

2. FUNCTIONS INVOLVING 1

Equation (2.14) is presented as a postulate. Equation (2.15) is repeated below:

$$x + 1 = 1. \tag{2.15}$$

Proof.

$$\begin{aligned} 1 &= x + x' && \text{P5, Eq. (2.34a)} \\ &= x + x'(1) && \text{P3, Eq. (2.32b)} \\ &= (x + x')(x + 1) && \text{P4, Eq. (2.33a)} \\ &= (1)(x + 1) && \text{P5, Eq. (2.34a)} \\ &= x + 1 && \text{P3, Eq. (2.32b).} \end{aligned}$$

3. FUNCTIONS INVOLVING 0

Equation (2.17) is considered a postulate. Equation (2.16) is repeated below:

$$x \cdot 0 = 0. \tag{2.16}$$

Proof.

$$\begin{aligned} 0 &= xx' && \text{P5, Eq. (2.34b)} \\ &= x(x' + 0) && \text{P3, Eq. (2.32a)} \\ &= x \cdot x' + x0 && \text{P4, Eq. (2.33b)} \\ &= 0 + x \cdot 0 && \text{P5, Eq. (2.34b)} \\ &= x \cdot 0 && \text{P3, Eq. (2.32a).} \end{aligned}$$

A general Boolean algebra is established above. Note that there is no restriction given concerning the number of elements in C. If we specify that C contains two elements, 0 and 1, the resultant algebra is the switching algebra established in the previous sections.

An interesting and valuable feature is noticed when we examine Eqs. (2.15) and (2.16). Equation (2.16) can be obtained from Eq. (2.15) by replacing the operation $(+)$ by the operation $(\cdot)$ and replacing the element 1 by the element 0. Conversely, Eq. (2.15) can be obtained from Eq. (2.16) by replacing the operation $(\cdot)$ by the operation $(+)$ and replacing the element 0 by the element 1. Equations (2.15) and (2.16) are considered to form a duality pair. Using the same reasoning, we see that Eqs. (2.6) and (2.7) also form a duality pair.

This characteristic can be summarized by the *principle of duality.*

Every theorem or identity deducible from the postulates of a Boolean algebra remains valid if the operations $(+)$ and $(\cdot)$ and the identity elements 0 and 1 are interchanged throughout.

The proof of this principle lies in the fact that the postulates given are symmetrical in nature with respect to the operations $(+)$ and $(\cdot)$ and the identity elements 0 and 1.

The principle of duality has a profound influence on the development in the following chapter.

PROBLEMS

2.1 Construct relevant truth tables to justify the Commutative Theorem and the Associative Theorem.

2.2. Construct a truth table to justify the following Distributive Theorem:

$$x + yz = (x + y)(x + z).$$

2.3. Simplify the following switching functions.

(a) $xy + xy'$
(b) $x + xyz$
(c) $ab + (b' + c')' + a'c$
(d) $w + w'xyz + w'xy'z' + w'xyz' + w'xy'z$

2.4. Simplify the following switching functions.

(a) $abcd + abc' + abd'$
(b) $(a + b + c)(a + b + c')$
(c) $xyz + xyz' + xy'z + xy'z' + x'z$
(d) $(x + y)(x + yz) + x'y' + x'z'$

2.5. Find the negatives of the switching functions in Problem 2.3 and also the negatives of the simplified expressions obtained. Justify that the corresponding pairs are equivalent.

2.6. Find the negatives of the switching functions in Problem 2.4 and also the negatives of the simplified expressions obtained. Justify that the corresponding pairs are equivalent.

2.7. Simplify the following switching functions.

(a) $w'x' + y'z + yz + wz$
(b) $ac' + a'c' + a'b' + c'd'$

2.8. Prove that the following two equations are true:

$$f(x_1, x_2, \ldots, x_n) = x_1 f(1, x_2, \ldots, x_n) + x_1' f(0, x_2, \ldots, x_n),$$
$$f(x_1, x_2, \ldots, x_n) = [x_1 + f(0, x_2, \ldots, x_n)][x_1' + f(1, x_2, \ldots, x_n)],$$

where $f(x_1, x_2, \ldots, x_n)$ is any switching function of n switching variables $x_1, x_2, \ldots, x_n$.

The above equations are two forms of representation of the *expansion theorem,* which can be used to develop the normal form of representation of switching functions in Chapter 3. [*Hint:* The expansion theorem can be proved by evaluating the truth values of both sides of the equations.]

2.9. Prove that the following two equations are true:

$$x_1 \cdot f(x_1, x_2, \ldots, x_n) = x_1 f(1, x_2, \ldots, x_n),$$
$$x_1 + f(x_1, x_2, \ldots, x_n) = x_1 + f(0, x_2, \ldots, x_n),$$

where $f(x_1, x_2, \ldots, x_n)$ is a switching function of n switching variables $x_1, x_2, \ldots, x_n$.

2.10. Prove that the following two equations are true:

$$x_1' f(x_1, x_2, \ldots, x_n) = x_1' \cdot f(0, x_2, \ldots, x_n),$$
$$x_1' + f(x_1, x_2, \ldots, x_n) = x_1' + f(1, x_2, \ldots, x_n),$$

where $f(x_1, x_2, \ldots, x_n)$ is a switching function of n switching variables $x_1, x_2, \ldots, x_n$.

2.11. Use the definitions and postulates given in Section 2.10 to prove the following:

$$x + xy = x,$$
$$x(x + y) = x,$$

where x and y are elements in Boolean algebra C.

2.12. Use the definitions and postulates given in Section 2.10 and the results of Problem 2.11 to prove that the operations (+) and (·) are associative, i.e., prove the following:

$$(x + z) + y = (x + y) + z = x + (y + z),$$
$$(xy)z = x(yz) = y(xz),$$

where x, y, and z are elements in Boolean algebra C.

2.13. Use the definitions and postulates given in Section 2.10 to prove that

$$(xy)' = x' + y',$$
$$(x + y)' = x'y',$$

where x and y are elements in Boolean algebra C. [*Hint:* Try to establish that P5 of Section 2.10 is satisfied and also that the element a' associated with the element a in a Boolean algebra is unique.]

2.14. Employ an axiomatic approach to prove the following:

$$ab + a'c + bc = ab + a'c,$$
$$(a')' = a,$$

where a, b, and c are elements in C. The proof must be carried out in such a way that every step can be justified by a given postulate.

CHAPTER 3

FORMULATION OF SWITCHING FUNCTIONS

3.1 Introduction. In the previous chapter, switching algebra is introduced. The development presented in this chapter concerns the relationship between switching circuits and switching algebra. In other words, it deals with the topic: how shall a set of rules to be embodied in the circuits be expressed in terms of switching variables?

The expression of the pertinent set of rules in terms of switching variables must be the first step in the design of switching systems. After the rules to be embodied have been expressed in terms of switching variables, we can manipulate and simplify the switching functions* obtained. At the same time, we should be able to interpret the abstract switching functions in terms of switching components. This interpretation will serve as the guide line to function manipulation. Examples will follow which illustrate this problem.

3.2 Number systems. To find an adequate switching function for a given set of rules constitutes the first step in switching system design. A discussion of the design of switching circuits for a binary adder will be our first example. It is obvious that circuits for addition are the most basic and indispensable unit in a digital computer.

In discussing the design of arithmetic units, we must consider first of all the number system to be used. It is true that everyone is familiar with the decimal system. By using decimal digits 0, 1, 2, . . . , 8, 9, every quantity can be represented and easily processed. But there is nothing sacred about the decimal system. If two human hands did not possess ten fingers, there might be serious doubt about whether the decimal system would have been so popular.

When we try to implement quantities in the decimal system in a computer, we are confronted with the problem of finding a device that can represent the ten digits reliably and economically. This is not an easy task indeed. On the other hand, we realize that there are many switching devices that can be used to implement two distinct digits, say 0 and 1. This immediately brings about two possibilities: one is to code each decimal digit by 0's and 1's (this will be discussed in Chapter 9); the

---

* The expression "manipulate and simplify the switching functions" actually means "manipulate and simplify the *representation* of the switching functions."

other is to express quantities in terms of 0 and 1, that is, to use the binary system.

First of all, let us investigate how any quantity can be represented by the binary system. In the binary system, there are only two digits, 0 and 1, available. A number $a_n a_{n-1} a_{n-2} \cdots a_2 a_1 a_0$ in the binary system, in which each of the $n + 1$ digits can be either 0 or 1, can be converted to the decimal system by the equation

$$N = a_n 2^n + a_{n-1} 2^{n-1} + a_{n-2} 2^{n-2} + \cdots + a_1 2^1 + a_0 2^0. \tag{3.1}$$

According to this scheme, 3 in the decimal system corresponds to 11 in the binary system, because Eq. (3.1) allows the conversion

$$N = 1 \cdot 2^1 + 1 \cdot 2^0 = 2 + 1 = 3. \tag{3.2}$$

Secondly, let us investigate how the arithmetic operations are performed in the binary system.

Addition: The operation of addition in the binary number system is essentially the same as that in the decimal system. It is summarized by the following two tables.

Addend \ Augend	0	1
0	0	1
1	1	0

Sum Table

Addend \ Augend	0	1
0	0	0
1	0	1

Carry Table

Subtraction: The operation of subtraction in the binary number system can likewise be summarized by the following two tables.

Subtrahend \ Minuend	0	1
0	0	1
1	1	0

Difference Table

Subtrahend \ Minuend	0	1
0	0	0
1	1	0

Borrow Table

Multiplication and division: The operations of multiplication and division are carried out in the binary system following the same rules as used in the decimal system, except that it is even simpler. This is obvious by examining the following multiplication table.

Multiplier \ Multiplicand	0	1
0	0	0
1	0	1

This multiplication table is certainly simpler than that in the decimal system.

3.3 Modes of operation.* No matter what kind of number system is used, there are two basic modes available to carry out the operation. One is the *parallel* mode and the other is the *serial* mode. The two modes are explained in the following.

Let A be the augend and B be the addend, i.e.,

$$A = a_n a_{n-1} a_{n-2} \cdots a_2 a_1 a_0,$$

$$B = b_n b_{n-1} b_{n-2} \cdots b_2 b_1 b_0.$$

If the decimal system is used, the a's and b's can be 0, 1, 2, . . . , 9. If the binary system is employed, they can be either 0 or 1.

Parallel mode addition calls for the addition of corresponding digits at the same time. This means that the following operations are carried out in parallel:

$$a_0 + b_0,$$
$$a_1 + b_1,$$
$$\vdots$$
$$a_n + b_n.$$

The actual operation needed is not so simple as it looks. It would be simple if it were only necessary to build identical switching circuits for each one of the $n + 1$ digits. However, the circuit is good only for the first digits, a_0 and b_0. The addition of a_0 and b_0 may produce a carry, and this carry must be entered in the addition of a_1 and b_1. By the same reasoning, the switching circuits for the addition of other digits must also have provisions for possible carries from previous stages.

* RI 1.

Note that the addition of a_1 and b_1 is not completed until the carry produced by the previous addition, that is the addition of a_0 and b_0, is taken into account. This points out that the statement, "All corresponding digits can be processed at the same time," is questionable. It is actually correct. Even though the circuits will be quite complicated, the carries can be anticipated and the operation can be completed in the shortest time possible. The block diagram of such a parallel adder is shown in Fig. 3.1.

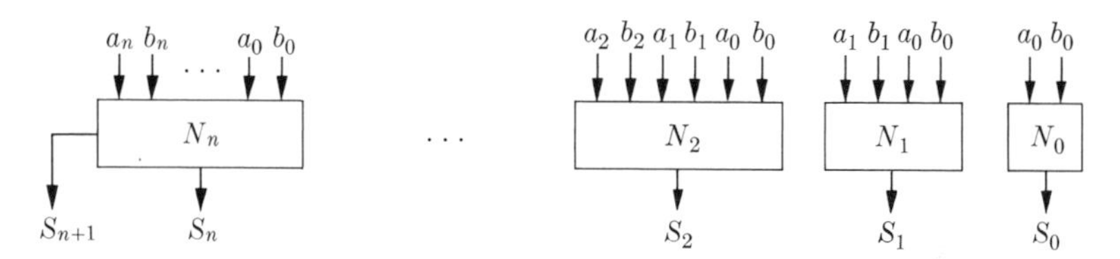

FIG. 3.1. Block diagram of a strictly parallel adder.

As shown in Fig. 3.1, a_0 and b_0 alone determine the least significant digit of the sum. The next digit, S_1, is determined not only by a_1 and b_1, but also by a_0 and b_0. The inclusion of a_0 and b_0 in the N_1 block assures the anticipation of the carry. The increasing number of inputs to other blocks can be explained in the same way.

All the arguments above lead to the following realization: the output of a switching circuit, in the present example the sum of two numbers, is determined entirely by the inputs to the circuit at that time. In the example cited above, the inputs are $a_0, a_1, \ldots, a_n, b_0, b_1, \ldots, b_n$. A circuit whose output at any time is determined only by the inputs at that time is called a *combinational circuit*.

Observe that an addition carried out in the parallel mode is fast, but at the same time, it demands complicated switching circuits. If we look into this parallel operation, we note that it is quite alien to the process we adopt with paper and pencil. A human calculator would first add the two most insignificant digits, a_0 and b_0, to obtain the most insignificant digit, S_0, for the sum and forward a carry c_0 to a storage. At the next instant, a_1, b_1, and the stored carry c_0 from the previous operation are added to generate S_1 and a carry c_1. This process is continued until all digits are properly added. A block diagram for such an addition is shown in Fig. 3.2.

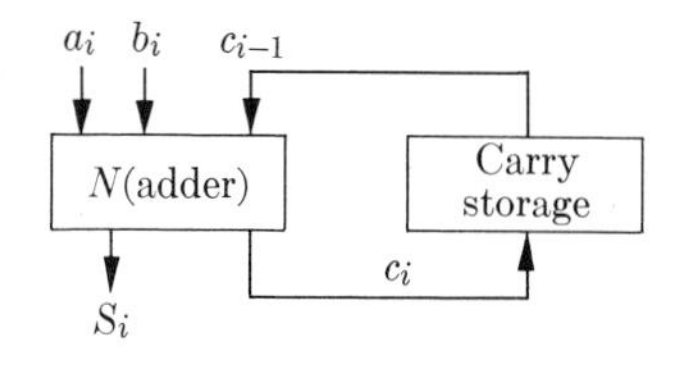

FIG 3.2. Block diagram of a serial adder.

It is obvious that the completion of the operation in such an arrangement takes more time than it does in a parallel adder. But the same switching circuit can be used over and over again. This certainly indicates a possibility of saving in the number of switching components needed.

This addition scheme is termed *serial mode* addition. Such an adder is termed a *serial adder*. The output of the circuit not only depends on the inputs to the circuit at that time, but also depends on the carry stored in the memory, which in turn is a function of the previous inputs.

A circuit whose output at any time is determined not only by the inputs at that time, but also by the previous inputs to the circuit, is called a *sequential circuit*. The study of sequential circuits is made in Chapters 11 through 15.

3.4 Switching functions for a binary adder I. The number systems and the modes of operation for an adder are discussed in the previous two sections. The next step is to formulate switching functions for an adder. The implementation of the adder will follow the formulation of necessary switching functions.

Let us now try to formulate the switching functions necessary for an adder circuit that processes three binary digits, as shown in Fig. 3.2.

The starting point of this formulation is to identify the inputs and also the outputs for such a circuit. The inputs are a_i, the ith digit of the augend; b_i, the ith digit of the addend; and c_{i-1}, the carry forwarded by the carry storage. The outputs are S_i, the ith digit in the sum, and c_i, the carry to be forwarded to the carry storage.

Since the relevant inputs and outputs are identified, we now relate the inputs to the outputs, or establish a set of rules which produce the outputs with any given set of inputs. It seems to be a difficult task. The most reliable and the most exhaustive way of doing this is to consider every possible input combination and determine the corresponding outputs under each circumstance, i.e., to construct a truth table. Since there are three inputs, and since each one can be either 1 or 0, there should be eight entries in the table, as shown in Table 3.1.

In the first column, $a_i = 0$, $b_i = 0$, and $c_{i-1} = 0$; the sum and the carry will be zero as shown. In the fifth column, $a_i = 1$, $b_i = 1$, and

TABLE 3.1

a_i	0	1	0	0	1	1	0	1
b_i	0	0	1	0	1	0	1	1
c_{i-1}	0	0	0	1	0	1	1	1
S_i	0	1	1	1	0	0	0	1
c_i	0	0	0	0	1	1	1	1

$c_{i-1} = 0$; a carry will be produced and the sum will be zero as shown. The other columns can be explained in the same way.

Now the problem has been brought into focus. In designing an adder circuit, the set of rules, expressed in the form of a truth table, must be incorporated into the circuit. An attempt to put this set of rules into verbal statements will not only be tedious, but also it will be hard to put them in the most exact and complete form. It is here that the mathematical formulation enters.

Note that a_i, the ith digit of the augend, can assume only two values, 0 or 1. It is entirely logical to consider a_i as a switching variable. By using the same reasoning, b_i and c_i can also be considered as switching variables.

Let us examine the second column of Table 3.1. The input combination is $a_i = 1$, $b_i = 0$, and $c_{i-1} = 0$. This demands that the sum should be 1. This requirement can be met if the switching function for the sum circuit has the form

$$S_i = a_i b'_i c'_{i-1} + S_{i1}(a_i, b_i, c_{i-1}). \tag{3.3}$$

There are two points to be stated here. First, if the input condition $a_i = 1$, $b_i = 0$, and $c_{i-1} = 0$ prevails, the term $a_i b'_i c'_{i-1}$ will be 1, and subsequently the sum will be 1. Secondly, we do not intend to specify what the switching function S_{i1} is, because at this time we just want to make sure that whenever the input combination shown in column two is applied, the sum should be 1. This is certainly accomplished by Eq. (3.3).

We now examine the third column of Table 3.1. This column indicates that whenever the input combination $a_i = 0$, $b_i = 1$, and $c_{i-1} = 0$ is true, the sum should be 1. To accomplish this, we can partially specify S_{i1} and rewrite the switching function for the sum as

$$S_i = a_i b'_i c'_{i-1} + a'_i b_i c'_{i-1} + S_{i2}(a_i, b_i, c_{i-1}). \tag{3.4}$$

There is no need to specify the function $S_{i2}(a_i, b_i, c_{i-1})$, because the presence of $a'_i b_i c'_{i-1}$ is adequate to meet the requirement of column three.

We can use the same reasoning to treat the cases represented in columns four and eight. This can be accomplished by partially specifying $S_{i1}(a_i, b_i, c_{i-1})$ to obtain

$$S_i = a_i b'_i c'_{i-1} + a'_i b_i c'_{i-1} + a'_i b'_i c_{i-1} + a_i b_i c_{i-1} + S_{i4}(a_i, b_i, c_{i-1}). \tag{3.5}$$

In Eqs. (3.3) and (3.4), the functions S_{i1} and S_{i2} are not specified. This is done to leave room to accommodate additional requirements. When we reach Eq. (3.5), we can and should specify S_{i4}, because all input combinations that call for an output of 1 have been taken into account. We can set $S_{i4} = 0$, because there is no other input combination that demands an output of 1. The final expression for the sum circuit is, therefore,

$$S_i = a_ib_i'c_{i-1}' + a_i'b_ic_{i-1}' + a_i'b_i'c_{i-1} + a_ib_ic_{i-1}. \tag{3.6}$$

The same technique can be used to treat the carry circuit and obtain the following switching function for the carry circuit:

$$c_i = a_ib_ic_{i-1}' + a_ib_i'c_{i-1} + a_i'b_ic_{i-1} + a_ib_ic_{i-1}. \tag{3.7}$$

What we have achieved here is that we can express the rules of binary addition in terms of switching variables and switching operations. This is the first step in switching system design.

3.5 Standard product: basic form I. Something interesting can be learned from Eqs. (3.6) and (3.7). Each equation has four terms connected by or-operators. Each one of the four terms contains every input variable either in its unprimed form or in its primed form. In the present example, the three input variables provide eight different combinations, corresponding to the eight entries in the truth table.

Each one of these variations is termed a *standard product.* A standard product is a product of all the switching variables, either primed or unprimed. Such a product is also called a *canonical minterm* or a *minterm.* This immediately brings forth the problem: how do we distinguish or identify any specific standard product? This question will be answered later.

Let us now look at cases of more than three variables. Suppose that there are n switching variables involved in a circuit. How many standard products are there?

Each switching variable is binary in nature. Each one can assume one of the two possible forms, primed or unprimed. There will be 2^n variations; therefore, there will be 2^n standard products.

To interpret or to attach physical significance to this situation, we can say that each of the 2^n standard products corresponds to one of the 2^n possible input combinations. Whenever the truth value of any standard product is 1, it signifies that its corresponding input combination exists. For example, consider three switching variables a, b, and c. When the product abc is 1, that the input combination $a = 1$, $b = 1$, and $c = 1$ exists is indicated. No other input combinations can exist at the same time.

One important point deserves further explanation. Given a standard product, how can we proceed to identify its corresponding input combination, or vice versa? The answer actually depends on the physical significance we attach to a standard product. According to what has been specified in the previous paragraph, we can state the following rule. If a switching variable appears in the product in the unprimed form, the truth value of this variable in the corresponding input combination should be 1; if a switching variable appears in the primed form, the truth value of the variable in the corresponding input combination should be 0.

If we adopt this rule, we can easily deduce that the corresponding input combination of product abc should be $a = 1$, $b = 1$, and $c = 1$. It can be easily seen that when $abc = 1$, the condition in which $a = 1$, $b = 1$, and $c = 1$ is indicated. This conforms with what has been specified.

What has been presented in this section can be summarized as follows. The concept of standard product is introduced. Each standard product is shown to represent one input combination. Switching functions are formulated by connecting relevant standard products by or-operators. Such functions are said to be in *disjunctive normal form*. It can then be said that the standard product serves as a basic form in switching expressions.

3.6 Representation of standard products. It is pointed out in the previous section that there is a need for identifying the products. Let us now start with three variables x, y, and z. There are eight standard products. The tabulation in Table 3.2 is an exhaustive one. In Table 3.2,

TABLE 3.2

Standard product	Binary notation	m notation
$x'y'z'$	000	m_0
$x'y'z$	001	m_1
$x'yz'$	010	m_2
$x'yz$	011	m_3
$xy'z'$	100	m_4
$xy'z$	101	m_5
xyz'	110	m_6
xyz	111	m_7

besides the listing of all the products, there are two columns for identification purposes. Note that for each primed variable, a 0 is assigned. For each unprimed variable, a 1 is assigned. The binary notation for each variable is placed in the position corresponding to the variable itself. That is why $x'y'z'$ is represented by 000. This kind of binary notation is quite satisfactory for identifying the products; however, it is also obvious that it is a very cumbersome scheme. For a product of n variables, we must write a sequence of n binary digits to represent a product, and nothing has been saved at all! But this leads directly to a simplified scheme.

Let us now examine column three of Table 3.2. The binary notation 000 represents the product $x'y'z'$. Note that the binary number 000 is equivalent to 0 in the decimal system. The thinking process is as follows: 000 represents the product $x'y'z'$, and 0 in the decimal system is equivalent to 000 in the binary system. Therefore, m_0 is used to represent the product $x'y'z'$. One question might be asked: why is there a need for the m notation? At this time the only explanation needed is that there is another basic form available (a natural consequence from the principle of duality). m is used to denote the standard product.

Using the argument stated above, it is not difficult to realize that the product $xy'z$ can be represented by the binary notation 101, and also by m_5. A systematic process has been developed to represent a standard product by the notations adopted in Table 3.2. The reversing process is also important, and can be described as follows. If a standard product of a certain number of variables is given, we should be able to appreciate what the actual product looks like.

To achieve this appreciation, first note that m stands for the standard product. Second, the binary equivalent of the decimal number is found. At this point use will be made of the number of variables given. In the binary equivalent, wherever there is a 1, an unprimed variable is implied. Wherever there is a 0, a primed variable is needed. This process can best be illustrated by an example.

It is known that m_{14} is a function of four variables, w, x, y, and z. Find the function in terms of w, x, y, and z.

Following the process stated above, note that m stands for the standard product. The next task is to find the binary number equivalent to 14, which is 1110. One question might be asked: why is it not 01110? This is where the number of variables comes in. If the binary equivalent is taken as 01110, then five switching variables will be involved. Since it is given in the problem that there are only four variables, the equivalent must be 1110. Following the rule that 1 implies an unprimed variable and 0 implies a primed variable, the product in question can be written as $wxyz'$.

The representation scheme presented in this section can be used to simplify the writing of Eqs. (3.6) and (3.7).

Equation (3.6) can be written as

$$S_i(a_i, b_i, c_{i-1}) = m_4 + m_2 + m_1 + m_7,$$

or

$$S_i(a_i, b_i, c_{i-1}) = \sum m\ 1, 2, 4, 7.$$

Where standard products are clearly meant, the expression can be simplified to

$$S_i(a_i, b_i, c_{i-1}) = \sum 1, 2, 4, 7.$$

Using the same reasoning, we can write Eq. (3.7) as

$$c_i(a_i, b_i, c_{i-1}) = m_6 + m_5 + m_3 + m_7,$$

or

$$c_i(a_i, b_i, c_{i-1}) = \sum m\ 3, 5, 6, 7,$$

or

$$c_i(a_i, b_i, c_{i-1}) = \sum 3, 5, 6, 7.$$

3.7 Switching functions for a binary adder II. As stated in Section 3.4, the starting point for the switching function formulation is the identification of the inputs and outputs. A truth table is then constructed to relate the inputs and outputs.

The approach used in Section 3.4 forms a standard product to represent each input combination. If any input combination calls for the output to be 1, the corresponding standard product is entered into the final expression through the or-operation. Whenever any input combination prevails, its corresponding standard product will have a truth value of 1. Its inclusion in the final expression through the or-operation ensures that whenever that input combination prevails, the output will be 1. The number of standard products contained in the final expression is equal to the number of input combinations whose corresponding outputs will be 1.

The above is not the only approach applicable to forming switching functions. Instead of paying attention to the input combination that will produce an output of 1, consider those input combinations that will produce an output of 0. Let us again examine the truth table for the binary adder, Table 3.1. In the first column, the input combination is $a_i = 0$, $b_i = 0$, and $c_{i-1} = 0$, requiring the sum to be 0. That is to say, whenever this input combination prevails, the sum must be 0. This can be assured if the final expression for the sum circuit takes the form

$$S_i = (a_i + b_i + c_{i-1})S_{i1}(a_i, b_i, c_{i-1}). \tag{3.8}$$

In Eq. (3.8), the function $S_{i1}(a_i, b_i, c_{i-1})$ is not specified because we only want to make sure that whenever $a_i = 0$, $b_i = 0$, and $c_{i-1} = 0$, the sum will be 0. This requirement is certainly met by the inclusion of the term $(a_i + b_i + c_{i-1})$ through the and-operator.

Having taken care of column one, we can move to column five, which also presents an input combination to make the sum 0. That is, whenever

$a_i = 1$, $b_i = 1$, and $c_{i-1} = 0$, the sum must be 0. This additional requirement can be met by modifying Eq. (3.8) as follows:

$$S_i = (a_i + b_i + c_{i-1})(a_i' + b_i' + c_{i-1})S_{i2}(a_i, b_i, c_{i-1}). \quad (3.9)$$

There is no need at this time to specify the function $S_{i2}(a_i, b_i, c_{i-1})$, because the presence of $(a_i' + b_i' + c_{i-1})$ suffices to meet the specification of column five.

The same reasoning can be applied to treat the cases represented in columns six and seven. In doing this, we must modify Eq. (3.9) to the form

$$S_i = [(a_i + b_i + c_{i-1})(a_i' + b_i' + c_{i-1})(a_i' + b_i + c_{i-1}') \\ (a_i + b_i' + c_{i-1}')S_{i4}(a_i, b_i, c_{i-1})]. \quad (3.10)$$

In Eqs. (3.8) and (3.9), the functions S_{i1} and S_{i2} are not specified because it is necessary to leave space to accommodate additional requirements. At this point, we can and should specify S_{i4}, because all input combinations that call for an output of 0 have been taken into account. Since there is no other input combination that requires the sum to be zero, S_{i4} is set to be 1. The final expression for the sum circuit is, therefore,

$$S_i = (a_i + b_i + c_{i-1})(a_i' + b_i' + c_{i-1})(a_i' + b_i + c_{i-1}')(a_i + b_i' + c_{i-1}'). \quad (3.11)$$

The same technique can be used to treat the carry circuit and obtain the following expression:

$$c_i = (a_i + b_i + c_{i-1})(a_i' + b_i + c_{i-1})(a_i + b_i' + c_{i-1})(a_i + b_i + c_{i-1}'). \quad (3.12)$$

3.8 Standard sum: basic form II. Examining the switching functions in Eqs. (3.11) and (3.12), we observe that each equation has four terms connected by and-operators. Each one of the four terms contains every input variable, either in its unprimed form or in its primed form. To form such a term, all the input variables, primed or unprimed, are connected by or-operators. Such a term is called a *standard sum*. A standard sum is a sum of all the switching variables, either primed or unprimed. It is also called a *canonical maxterm* or a *maxterm*.

In the case of n switching variables, there are 2^n variations in forming a standard sum; therefore, there are 2^n standard sums. To interpret or to attach physical significance to the situation, we can claim that each of the 2^n standard sums corresponds to one of the 2^n possible input combinations. When the truth value of a standard sum is 0, that its corresponding input combination exists is indicated. To put this in another way, when the truth value of a standard sum is 1, that its corresponding input combination does not exist is indicated.

Now the following question should be answered: "Given a standard sum, how can we proceed to identify its corresponding input combination, or vice versa?" According to what has been specified in the previous paragraph, the following rule can be stated. If a switching variable appears in the sum in the unprimed form, the truth value of this variable in the corresponding input combination should be 0; if a switching variable appears in the primed form, the truth value of the variable in the corresponding input combination should be 1.

For example, consider the three switching variables a, b, and c. The corresponding input combination for the sum $a' + b' + c'$ is $a = 1, b = 1$, and $c = 1$. The condition $a' + b' + c' = 0$, implies that $a = 1, b = 1$, and $c = 1$. The condition $a' + b' + c' = 1$, undoubtedly suggests that its corresponding input combination, $a = 1, b = 1$, and $c = 1$, cannot be true.

Up to this point, the concept of standard sum is introduced. Each standard sum is also shown to represent one input combination. Switching functions are formulated by connecting relevant standard sums by and-operators. Such functions are said to be in *conjunctive normal form.*

The representations of standard sums can be handled in the same way as the representations of standard products. Let us now study three switching variables, x, y, and z. As with standard products, there are eight standard sums, which are tabulated in Table 3.3.

TABLE 3.3

Standard sum	Binary notation	M notation
$x' + y' + z'$	000	M_0
$x' + y' + z$	001	M_1
$x' + y + z'$	010	M_2
$x' + y + z$	011	M_3
$x + y' + z'$	100	M_4
$x + y' + z$	101	M_5
$x + y + z'$	110	M_6
$x + y + z$	111	M_7

The same binary notations are used for the standard sums. In decimal notation, M is used to denote the standard sum. It is not hard at all to extend this case to that involving n switching variables.

Using the notation developed, we can express Eq. (3.11) as

$$S_i(a_i, b_i, c_{i-1}) = M_7M_1M_2M_4,$$

or

$$S_i(a_i, b_i, c_{i-1}) = \prod M\ 1, 2, 4, 7.$$

Equation (3.12) can of course be written as

$$c_i(a_i, b_i, c_{i-1}) = M_7M_3M_5M_6 = \prod M\ 3, 5, 6, 7.$$

3.9 Conversion between basic forms. Two basic forms, standard product and standard sum, have been introduced. This is another manifestation of the principle of duality. It has been established that the switching function for a given problem can be expressed either in the disjunctive normal form or in the conjunctive normal form. Either expression can be used as a starting point for manipulation. There is another interesting aspect which will be fully exploited in the next chapter; that is, each form implies a different scheme of implementation. For certain problems, it is advantageous to express the switching function as the sum of standard products. In certain other situations, it is more economical to write the switching function as the product of standard sums.

In this section, attention will be concentrated on the conversion of basic forms. Two theorems which are important to conversion technique will be presented first.

THEOREM 1. The negative of a switching function can be obtained by joining the standard products not contained in the original function by or-operators.

Proof. Let the number of switching variables involved be n. Then the number of standard products will be 2^n, which can be represented by $m_0, m_1, m_2, \ldots, m_{2^n-1}$. This theorem actually states that the 2^n products can be divided arbitrarily into two groups. Each group is joined by or-operators; then the two switching functions thus obtained are negative to each other. Let the two switching functions thus obtained be

$$A = m_0 + m_a + m_b + \cdots,$$
$$B = m_\alpha + m_\beta + m_\gamma + \cdots.$$

To prove the theorem, one has only to prove that A and B are negative to each other. In order to show this, the following two equations have to be satisfied:

$$A + B = 1, \tag{3.13}$$

$$AB = 0. \tag{3.14}$$

In the case of n switching variables, there will always be one and only one standard product which has a truth value of 1, because there is only one input combination true at any given time. Let this product be m_x. This term can be grouped into either A or B. Whenever A has this term, A will have a truth value of 1 and B will have a truth value of 0. Whenever B has this term, B will have a truth value of 1 and A the truth value of 0. Since both Eqs. (3.13) and (3.14) are satisfied, A and B are certainly negative to each other.

An example illustrates how Theorem 1 can be applied.

EXAMPLE 3.1. Given a switching function of three variables,

$$f(a, b, c) = m_1 + m_2 + m_3 + m_7; \tag{3.15}$$

find f' in terms of standard products.

This problem can be approached by taking the negative of the right-hand side of Eq. (3.15). However, with the theorem just developed available, we can write down the answer immediately.

Corresponding to three switching variables, there are eight standard products, namely, m_0, m_1, m_2, m_3, m_4, m_5, m_6, and m_7, with m_1, m_2, m_3, and m_7 used in the expression for f. Then its negative must be

$$f' = m_0 + m_4 + m_5 + m_6. \blacktriangle \tag{3.16}$$

THEOREM 2. The negative of a function can be obtained by joining the standard sums not contained in the original function by and-operators.

Proof. Let the number of switching variables involved be n. The number of standard sums will be 2^n, which are represented by M_0, M_1, . . . , M_{2^n-1}. Theorem 2 actually claims that the 2^n sums can be divided arbitrarily into two groups, that each group is joined together by and-operators, and that the two switching functions thus obtained are negative to each other.

The two switching functions formed by grouping can be expressed as

$$A = M_0 M_a M_b \ldots,$$

$$B = M_\alpha M_\beta M_\gamma \ldots.$$

In order to verify the theorem, we need only to justify that the following two equations are true:

$$A + B = 1, \tag{3.17}$$

$$AB = 0. \tag{3.18}$$

This task turns out to be very easy. In the case of n switching variables, there will always be one and only one standard sum which has a value of 0 under any circumstances, because there is only one input combination true at any given time. Let this sum be M_x. This term can be grouped into either A or B. Whenever A contains this term, then A will have a truth value of 0 and B will have a truth value of 1. If B contains this term, then the opposite is true. With this reasoning, the validity of Eqs. (3.17) and (3.18) can be established.

EXAMPLE 3.2. Given a switching function of four variables,

$$f(a, b, c, d) = M_{15}M_{14}M_{13}M_{12}M_7M_5M_9M_8M_1;$$

find $f'(a, b, c, d)$.

Using Theorem 2, the negative of the given function can be written by taking the product of those standard sums which are not included in the given function:

$$f'(a, b, c, d) = M_{11}M_{10}M_6M_4M_3M_2M_0. \blacktriangle$$

With Theorems 1 and 2 established, we can investigate the conversion between basic forms. The conversion is carried out by reasoning that if a switching function is negated twice, the original function will result.

The approach used can best be illustrated by examples.

EXAMPLE 3.3. Convert the switching function in Eq. (3.6) from an expression of standard products to one of standard sums:

$$\begin{aligned} S_i &= a_ib'_ic'_{i-1} + a'_ib_ic'_{i-1} + a'_ib'_ic_{i-1} + a_ib_ic_{i-1} \\ &= m_4 + m_2 + m_1 + m_7. \end{aligned} \tag{3.6}$$

Start the conversion by negating the expression to obtain

$$S'_i = (m_4 + m_2 + m_1 + m_7)' = m'_1m'_2m'_4m'_7. \tag{3.19}$$

Before the second negation is performed, find out what the negative of a standard product is:

$$\begin{aligned} m'_1 &= (a'_ib'_ic_{i-1})' = a_i + b_i + c'_{i-1} = M_6, \\ m'_2 &= (a'_ib_ic'_{i-1})' = a_i + b'_i + c_{i-1} = M_5, \\ m'_4 &= (a_ib'_ic'_{i-1})' = a'_i + b_i + c_{i-1} = M_3, \\ m'_7 &= (a_ib_ic_{i-1})' = a'_i + b'_i + c'_{i-1} = M_0. \end{aligned} \tag{3.20}$$

The expressions in Eq. (3.20) suggest that the following is true:

$$m'_\alpha = M_{2^n-1-\alpha}, \tag{3.21}$$

where n is the number of switching variables involved.

Using the development in Eq. (3.20), we can rewrite Eq. (3.19) as

$$S_i' = M_0M_3M_5M_6. \tag{3.22}$$

The second negation is applied to Eq. (3.22) to recover the original switching function:

$$(S_i')' = S_i = (M_0M_3M_5M_6)'. \tag{3.23}$$

Instead of using the theorem on negation, use Theorem 2 to obtain

$$S_i = M_1M_2M_4M_7. \tag{3.24}$$

The conversion from an expression of standard products to one of standard sums is accomplished. It is natural indeed that the expression in Eq. (3.24) is the same as that of Eq. (3.11).

In the conversion process above, the Negation Theorem is used first and then Theorem 2. This order can actually be reversed.

Applying Theorem 1 to Eq. (3.6), we obtain

$$S_i' = m_0 + m_3 + m_5 + m_6. \tag{3.25}$$

We now apply the Negation Theorem to Eq. (3.25), and obtain

$$\begin{aligned}(S_i')' = S_i &= (m_0 + m_3 + m_5 + m_6)' \\ &= m_0'm_3'm_5'm_6' \\ &= M_1M_2M_4M_7. \end{aligned} \tag{3.26}$$

The expressions in Eqs. (3.24) and (3.26), of course, have to be the same.▲

In Example 3.3, the conversion from an expression of standard products to one of standard sums is illustrated. The same technique can be used to convert in the opposite direction, as shown in Example 3.4.

Example 3.4. A switching function of four variables is written in terms of standard sums:

$$F = M_{11}M_{10}M_6M_4M_3. \tag{3.27}$$

Convert the function into an expression of standard products.

There are two approaches available. The first approach is to use Theorem 2 first. The negative of the given function is

$$F' = M_0M_1M_2M_5M_7M_8M_9M_{12}M_{13}M_{14}M_{15}. \tag{3.28}$$

To recover the original function, take the negative of the function in Eq. (3.28):

$$\begin{aligned} F = (F')' &= (M_0M_1M_2M_5M_7M_8M_9M_{12}M_{13}M_{14}M_{15})' \\ &= M'_0 + M'_1 + M'_2 + M'_5 + M'_7 + M'_8 + M'_9 \\ &\quad + M'_{12} + M'_{13} + M'_{14} + M'_{15}. \end{aligned} \tag{3.29}$$

A relationship similar to that expressed in Eq. (3.21) can be established.

$$M'_\alpha = m_{2^n-1-\alpha}. \tag{3.30}$$

The given function can then be written in terms of products by making use of Eqs. (3.29) and (3.30):

$$\begin{aligned} F = m_{15} &+ m_{14} + m_{13} + m_{10} + m_8 + m_7 + m_6 \\ &+ m_3 + m_2 + m_1 + m_0. \end{aligned} \tag{3.31}$$

In this approach, the negative of the given function is obtained by using Theorem 2 first. The given function is then recovered by using the Negation Theorem.

The second approach to be presented adopts the reverse order. Applying the Negation Theorem to Eq. (3.27), we obtain

$$\begin{aligned} F' &= (M_{11}M_{10}M_6M_4M_3)' \\ &= M'_{11} + M'_{10} + M'_6 + M'_4 + M'_3. \end{aligned} \tag{3.32}$$

Equation (3.30) can then be used to rewrite Eq. (3.32):

$$F' = m_4 + m_5 + m_9 + m_{11} + m_{12}. \tag{3.33}$$

Now, Theorem 1 can be used to recover the original function:

$$\begin{aligned} F = m_{15} &+ m_{14} + m_{13} + m_{10} + m_8 + m_7 + m_6 \\ &+ m_3 + m_2 + m_1 + m_0. \end{aligned} \tag{3.34}$$

Equations (3.31) and (3.34) show the same result.▲

3.10 Switching functions for a binary multiplier. Sections 3.4 through 3.8 present the approaches available for establishing switching functions for a combinational switching circuit. The presentation is carried out by finding the switching functions for a binary adder. In this section, the switching function for a binary multiplier will be established. This is done not only to show how multiplication is carried out in a computer, but also to illustrate once again how switching functions for switching systems are established.

The two operands are defined as follows:

$$N_1 \text{ (multiplicand)} = a_{n-1}a_{n-2} \cdots a_1a_0,$$

$$N_2 \text{ (multiplier)} = b_{n-1}b_{n-2} \cdots b_1b_0.$$

Basically, multiplication is a repeated addition process; therefore, it can be executed by repeated addition. However, in order to increase speed, some other schemes are used on modern computers. One of them takes its origin from the way multiplication is performed when paper and pencil are used. This process can be illustrated by an example.

EXAMPLE 3.5. Let the multiplicand be 1101 and the multiplier be 1010. The first step is to multiply the multiplicand by the least significant digit of the multiplier, in the present case 0. A partial product 0000 is thus obtained. Then the second digit from the right of the multiplier, 1, is multiplied by the multiplicand and a second partial product, 1101, is obtained. This second partial product is shifted to the left by one digit and added to the first partial product to produce the first partial sum. This process is repeated until the final result is obtained, as shown in the following tabulation.

```
                     1101
                     1010
                     ----
                     0000  First partial product
                    1101   Second partial product shifted
                             to the left by one digit
                   -------
Accumulated sum     11010
                  1101
                  --------
                  10000010▲
```

Multiplication involves the multiplication of two binary digits, the operation of shifting to the left, and the subsequent additions.

From the above discussion, it is clear that a binary multiplier needs a switching circuit to generate the partial products, units which will store the partial products and do appropriate shifting (to be discussed in Chapter 11), and a binary adder (which has already been discussed). This section will concentrate on the switching circuit which generates the partial product. The schematic diagram of such a circuit is shown in Fig. 3.3.

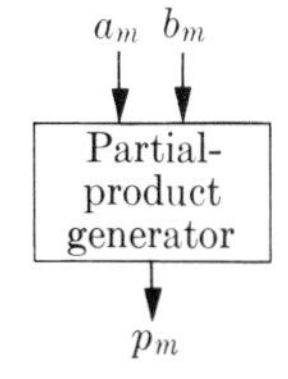

FIG 3.3. Block diagram of a partial-product generator.

First, identify the inputs and outputs. There are two inputs, a_m and b_m; therefore,

TABLE 3.4

a_m	0	0	1	1
b_m	0	1	0	1
p_m	0	0	0	1

there are four possible input conditions. Corresponding to each one of the four input conditions, there is an output determined by the multiplication rule. The results are tabulated in Table 3.4.

If we follow the approach presented in Section 3.4, we immediately note that the input combination in column four of Table 3.4 is the only one which produces a product of 1. Its corresponding standard product is $a_m b_m$ or m_3. The switching function for the product circuit can be written as

$$p_m(a_m, b_m) = m_3. \tag{3.35}$$

If we adopt the approach presented in Section 3.7, we see that the input combination in column one of Table 3.4 produces a product of 0. Its corresponding standard sum is $(a_m + b_m)$ or M_3. The input combinations in columns two and three of Table 3.4 also produce a product of 0. Their corresponding standard sums are $(a_m + b'_m)$ or M_2 and $(a'_m + b_m)$ or M_1, respectively. The switching function for the product circuit can be written as

$$p_m(a_m, b_m) = M_1 M_2 M_3. \tag{3.36}$$

Equations (3.35) and (3.36) are certainly equivalent, but Eq. (3.35) is much simpler than Eq. (3.36). This points out the fact that for a specific set of rules, one form of expression may be more suitable than another.

PROBLEMS

3.1. Express the following decimal numbers in the binary system. Establish a general approach to convert any number in the decimal system into the binary system.

(a) 9820 (b) 1961

3.2. Find the quotient for each one of the following fractions. Both the dividend and the divisor are expressed in the binary system:

$$\frac{1000}{100}, \quad \frac{100000}{1000}, \quad \frac{1111}{11}, \quad \frac{1011010}{11}.$$

3.3. Construct a truth table and establish the switching function in both disjunctive normal form and conjunctive normal form for a circuit which will be closed when any two and only two of the five switches are closed.

3.4. Construct a truth table and establish the switching function in both disjunctive normal form and conjunctive normal form for a circuit which will be closed when any three and only three of the five switches are closed.

3.5. The block diagram of a serial adder is shown in Fig. 3.2. Establish the block diagram for a binary serial subtractor. Find the switching function for the circuit which produces the difference, and that for the circuit which produces the borrow. Express them in both disjunctive and conjunctive normal forms.

3.6. Express the following switching functions in terms of standard products. In other words, write the following switching functions in the disjunctive normal form.

(a) $T(w, x, y, z) = x + y + z + w$
(b) $T(a, b, c) = (a + b)' + c$
(c) $T(w, x, y, z) = w'(x + y) + yz$
(d) $T(A, B, C) = AB + BC + CA$
(e) $T(w, x, y, z) = (w' + x')y + zw$
(f) $T(a, b, c, d) = (ab + cd)' + bc$

Note: There are several ways to express a given switching function in the disjunctive normal form. (1) A truth table can be established for a given function. Each combination which makes the truth value of the given switching function be 1 corresponds to a standard product in the final expression. (2) A given switching function can always be expressed in the form of a sum of products by using the theorems developed in Chapter 2. At this stage, each product does not have to be a standard product. In other words, certain switching variables might be missing from a product. For example, the switching function

$$T(a, b, c) = a(c + b)$$

can be expressed as

$$T(a, b, c) = ac + ab,$$

which is in the form of a sum of two products. In the product ac, the switching variable b is missing and a term $(b + b')$ can be introduced into the product. For the product ab, the variable c is missing and a term $(c + c')$ can likewise be introduced. The given switching function is then of the form

$$T(a, b, c) = ac(b + b') + ab(c + c'),$$

which can be easily expanded to obtain

$$T(a, b, c) = abc + ab'c + abc'.$$

3.7. Express the following functions in terms of standard sums. In other words, write the following switching functions in the conjunctive normal form.

(a) $T(x, y, z) = x(yz + y'z')$
(b) $T(a, b, c, d) = ab' + cd$
(c) $T(a, b, c) = a + b'c$
(d) $T(x, y, z) = xy + x'y' + x'z$
(e) $T(x, y, z) = xyz$
(f) $T(a, b, c, d) = (a + b)(c + d)$

Note: There are several ways to express a given switching function in the conjunctive normal form. (1) A truth table can be established for a given function. Each combination which makes the truth value of the given switching function be 0 corresponds to a standard sum in the final expression. (2) A given switching function can always be expressed in the form of a product of sums. It should, however, be pointed out that each sum is not necessarily a standard sum. In other words, certain switching variables might be missing from a sum. For example, the switching function

$$T(a, b, c) = ab + c$$

can be expressed as follows by using the Distributive Theorem (or postulate):

$$T(a, b, c) = (c + a)(c + b),$$

which is in the form of a product of two sums. In the sum $(c + a)$, the switching variable b is missing and subsequently a term bb' is introduced into the sum. By the same reasoning, a term aa' is introduced into the sum $(c + b)$. The given function is then of the form

$$T(a, b, c) = (a + c + bb')(aa' + c + b),$$

which can be expanded to obtain

$$T(a, b, c) = (a + b + c)(a + b' + c)(a' + b + c).$$

3.8. It is established in Problem 2.8 that the following Expansion Theorem is true:

$$f(x_1, x_2, \ldots, x_n) = x_1 f(1, x_2, \ldots, x_n) + x_1' f(0, x_2, \ldots, x_n),$$

where $f(x_1, x_2, \ldots, x_n)$ is a switching function of switching variables $x_1, x_2, \ldots, x_n$. Try to make use of this theorem to show that any switching function of n variables can be expressed in the disjunctive normal form. Furthermore, try to make use of the theorem to develop a systematic approach to express any given switching function in the disjunctive normal form.

3.9. It is established in Problem 2.8 that the following Expansion Theorem is true:

$$f(x_1, x_2, \ldots, x_n) = [x_1 + f(0, x_2, \ldots, x_n)][x_1' + f(1, x_2, \ldots, x_n)],$$

where $f(x_1, x_2, \ldots, x_r)$ is a switching function of switching variables $x_1, x_2, \ldots, x_n$. Make use of this theorem to show that any switching function of n variables can be expressed in the conjunctive normal form. Furthermore, try to make use of this theorem to develop a systematic approach to express any given switching function in the conjunctive normal form.

3.10. Express the negatives of the switching functions given in Problem 3.6 in the disjunctive normal form.

3.11. Express the negatives of the switching functions given in Problem 3.7 in the conjunctive normal form.

3.12. Convert the answers obtained in Problem 3.6 into expressions in the conjunctive normal form.

3.13. Convert the answers obtained in Problem 3.7 into expressions in the disjunctive normal form.

3.14. In Section 3.9, the conversion between basic forms is discussed. Note that for a given switching function, there are always two ways of doing the conversion. (1) Use Theorem 1 (Theorem 2), Section 3.9, and then the Negation Theorem. (2) Use the Negation Theorem first and then Theorem 1 (Theorem 2), Section 3.9. How do you decide which way to follow when you are given a switching function in the disjunctive (conjunctive) normal form to be converted to an expression in the conjunctive (disjunctive) normal form?

CHAPTER 4

CIRCUIT REALIZATION I: RELAY LOGIC

4.1 Primitive implementation. The establishment of switching algebra enables us to imbed a given set of rules into switching functions. We expect that the resultant function will lead to actual implementation, and also that such a function will help the designer to achieve the best possible circuit. These two points will be illustrated in this and subsequent chapters.

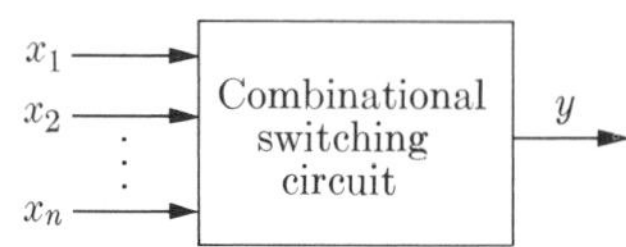

FIG 4.1. General scheme of a combinational circuit with one output.

The presentation in the previous chapter shows that for a general combinational switching circuit with one output (Fig. 4.1), the output y can be expressed in terms of inputs $x_1, x_2, \ldots, x_n$, in either one of two basic forms.

It can be expressed as the sum of standard products:

$$y(x_1, x_2, \ldots, x_n) = \sum_{k=0}^{2^n-1} a_k m_k, \tag{4.1}$$

where each m_k represents a standard product and a_k is its corresponding coefficient, which can be either 0 or 1. The question now becomes very clear: can the switching function in Eq. (4.1) be implemented?

Since the designer has $x_1, x_2, \ldots, x_n$ as inputs, he needs a device that can perform the and-operation in order to produce a standard product. Such a device is termed an *and-gate*. After the standard products are generated by and-gates, a device that is capable of performing the or-operation, termed an *or-gate*, is needed to generate the switching function. The general schematic diagram of such a setup is shown in Fig. 4.2. In a specific problem, if any a_k equals 0, that branch is to be omitted. If any a_k equals 1, its corresponding standard product must be processed by the or-gate.

Another basic form for a given switching function is

$$y(x_1, x_2, \ldots, x_n) = \prod_{k=0}^{2^n-1} (a_k + M_k). \tag{4.2}$$

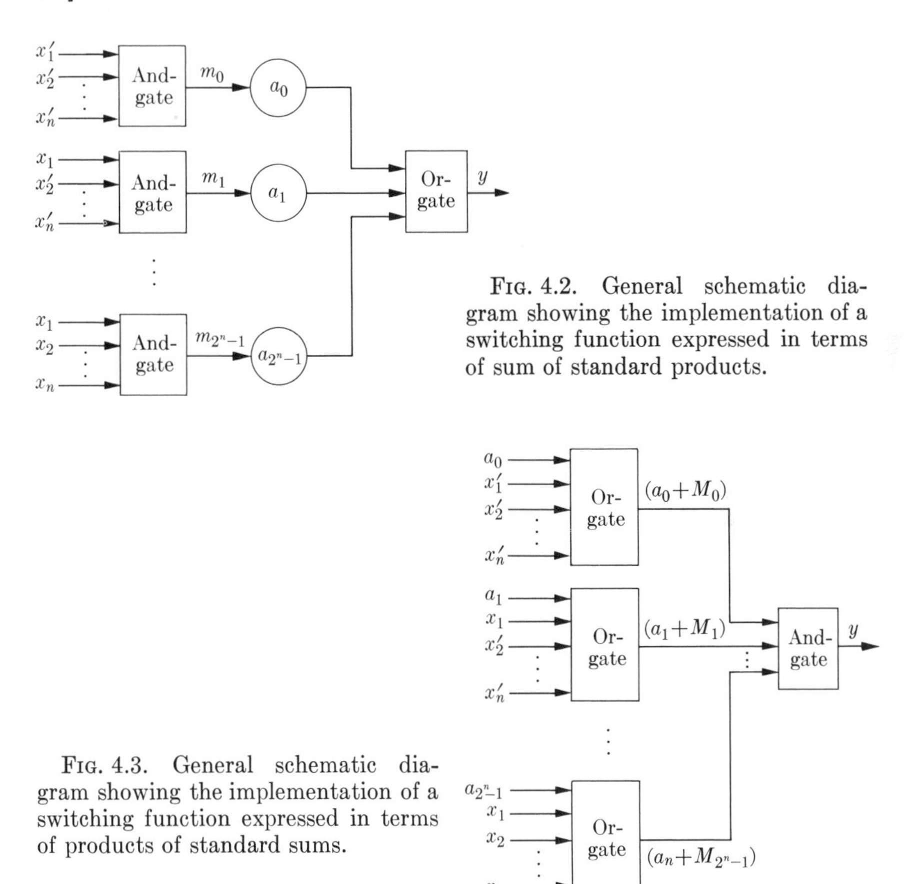

FIG. 4.2. General schematic diagram showing the implementation of a switching function expressed in terms of sum of standard products.

FIG. 4.3. General schematic diagram showing the implementation of a switching function expressed in terms of products of standard sums.

The implementation of this basic form also requires the use of both and-gates and or-gates. The or-gates are used first to generate standard sums, which are then processed by an and-gate to produce the switching function. The general schematic diagram of such a setup is shown in Fig. 4.3. Note that in a given problem, if any a_k is equal to 1, that branch must be omitted.

The above discussion establishes that the switching function of a combinational switching circuit can be implemented by using either one of the two general schemes. The devices needed are and-gates and or-gates. The next question certainly will be: how are and-gates and or-gates realized? This problem will be dealt with in this and the following chapters.

Another point that should be stated is that the circuit obtained by using either the general scheme shown in Fig. 4.2 or that shown in Fig. 4.3 serves as a faithful implementation of a given switching function. But, is it the "best" implementation for that given function? In order to answer this question, we must define what we mean by the "best" implementation. In general, a better circuit than those shown in either Fig. 4.2 or Fig. 4.3 can be found for a given switching function. They merely serve as the starting point for the actual realization of switching functions, and are therefore called "primitive implementations."

4.2 Relay gates. The previous section made the point that and-gates, or-gates, or both are necessary to implement a switching function. This section introduces a switching device, the relay, which makes both these gates possible. In selecting a switching component, one essential requirement must be met: the component to be chosen must possess the capability of representing unambiguously two distinct states. Further, the transition from one state to the other can and must be controlled. Also, its operating characteristic, its reliability, and its cost must all be considered. Relays meet these criteria and are used extensively in automatic telephone switching systems, in control switching, and in computers.

The schematic diagram of an electromagnetic relay* is shown in Fig. 4.4. A relay consists of two parts. The first part is formed by the coil and the core, which control the position of the center spring; the second part is formed by two sets of contacts mounted on springs. When these (or the movable spring) assume their quiescent position, the terminals, or nodes, a and b' are connected. This pair of contacts is termed the *normally closed contact*. When there is a sufficient amount of current, I, flowing in the coil, the center spring moves to connect terminals, or nodes, a and b. This pair of contacts is termed the *normally open contact*. The contact shown in Fig. 4.4 is termed a *transfer contact*. A normally open or a normally closed contact needs two springs. A transfer contact requires three. There are two physical entities that are of interest to the designer: the connection between terminals, and the existence of a current in the coil. The whole setup can be represented by one switching variable, x, which is defined as follows.

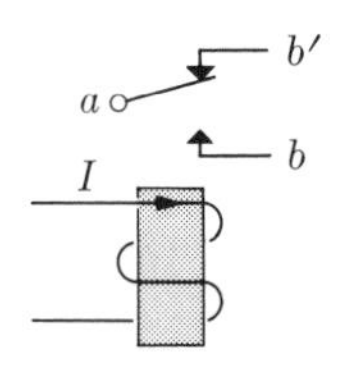

FIG. 4.4. Schematic diagram of an electromagnetic relay.

$x = 1$ implies that there is a current I flowing in the coil; the terminal pair ab is closed and the terminal pair ab' is open.

$x = 0$ implies that there is no current flowing in the coil; the terminal pair ab is open and the terminal pair ab' is closed.

The above discussion reveals that a relay can be used as the physical realization of a switching variable. The value of the switching variable can be set by applying or not applying current to the coil, and the value

* For further information on relays see PE 2.

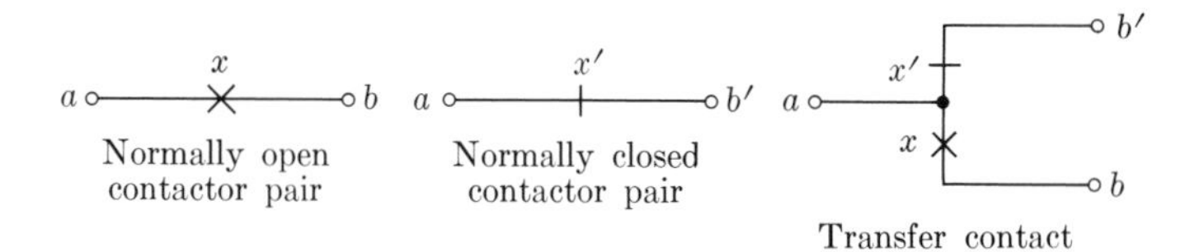

FIG. 4.5. Symbolic representations of relays.

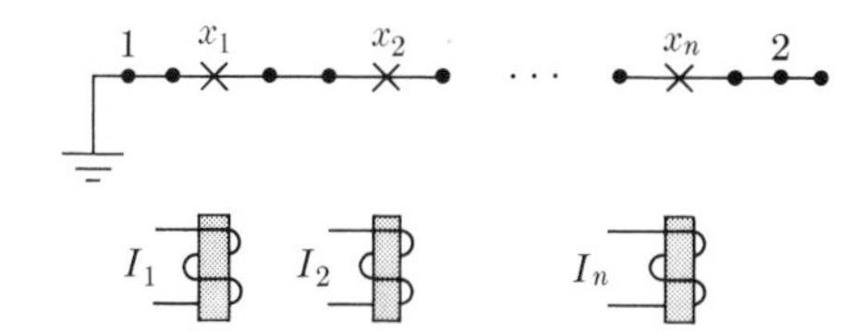

FIG. 4.6. A relay and-gate generating $x_1x_2 \cdots x_n$.

of the variable can be observed by examining the connection between terminal pair *ab* or *ab′*.

A set of representations for relays is introduced in Fig. 4.5.

From the above discussion it can be seen immediately that a relay and-gate of n variables can be constructed by connecting n pairs of relay contacts in series. A typical one, producing $x_1x_2 \cdots x_n$ is shown in Fig. 4.6. The truth value of the product $x_1x_2 \cdots x_n$ can be determined by examining the connection between terminals 1 and 2. If terminals 1 and 2 are connected, the product has a truth value of 1; if otherwise, 0. In order to facilitate the sensing of the output of the gate, terminal 1 is grounded. The appearance of ground at terminal 2 would indicate that the product has a truth value of 1; if otherwise, 0. This convention will be used throughout the book, unless specified otherwise.

A relay or-gate of n variables can be constructed by connecting n pairs of relay contacts in parallel. A typical one, producing $x_1 + x_2 + \cdots + x_n$ is shown in Fig. 4.7. The truth value of the sum $x_1 + x_2 + \cdots + x_n$ can be determined by examining the connection between terminals 1 and 2. If terminals 1 and 2 are connected, the sum has a truth value of 1; if otherwise, 0. In order to facilitate the sensing of the output of the gate, terminal 1 is permanently grounded. The presence of ground at terminal 2 would indicate that the sum has a truth value of 1; if otherwise, 0. This convention will be used throughout the book, unless specified otherwise.

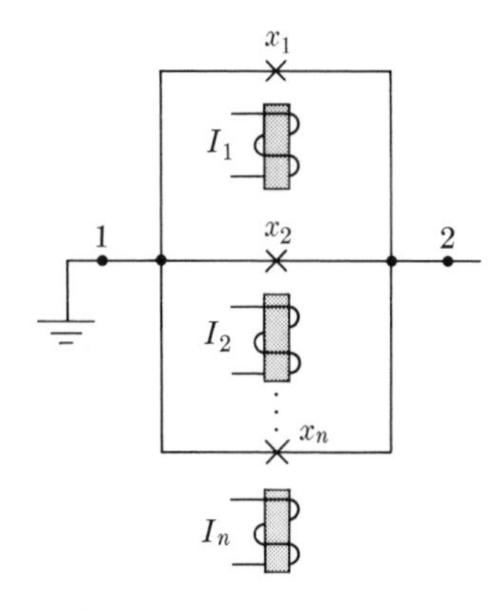

FIG. 4.7. A relay or-gate generating $x_1 + x_2 + \cdots + x_n$.

4.3 A problem of lamp switching. It is pointed out in Section 4.1 that any switching function of a combinational switching circuit can be implemented by using and-gates and or-gates. It is shown in Section 4.2 that relays can be used to construct and-gates and or-gates. The conclusion can be drawn from the above that any switching function of a combinational switching circuit can be realized by using relays. It should be pointed out that such a realization is a primitive one, but from this starting point an optimal circuit can be achieved. To illustrate the above, the following example is given.

A switching circuit is to be designed which can turn a lamp on or off at three different locations independently. To most readers, this is a familiar problem indeed. By using a trial-and-error approach, this problem can be solved, but let us see how this circuit can be designed by using what has been presented so far.

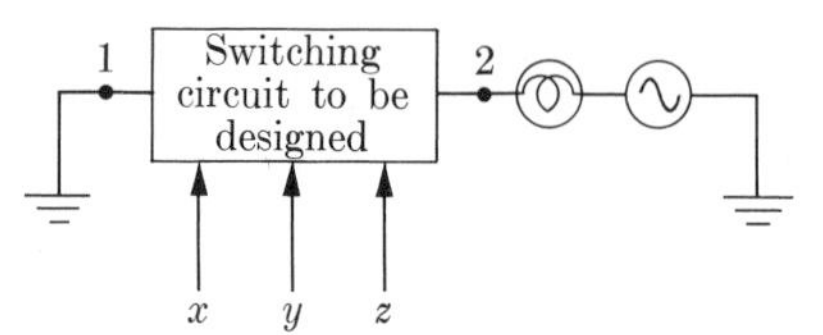

FIG. 4.8. General scheme for a lamp-switching problem.

Let the switches at the three locations be designated as x, y, and z. These are the input variables to be considered. The general outline of the setup is shown in Fig. 4.8. In order to satisfy the condition that any switch can turn the lamp on or off alone, we specify that the truth value of the switching circuit should be 1 whenever the number of operated switches is odd. This is a good specification, because by operating any switch alone, we can dictate the number of operated switches to be even or odd.

Following this specification, we can construct the truth table shown in Table 4.1.

TABLE 4.1

x	0	0	0	0	1	1	1	1
y	0	0	1	1	0	0	1	1
z	0	1	0	1	0	1	0	1
T	0	1	1	0	1	0	0	1

We find the switching function by examining Table 4.1 and noting that there are four cases when the truth value will be 1:

$$T = x'y'z + x'yz' + xy'z' + xyz. \tag{4.3}$$

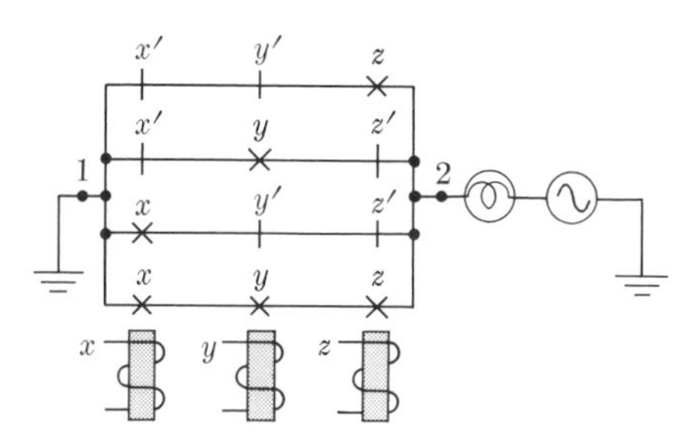

FIG. 4.9. Schematic diagram of the primitive implementation of the lamp-switching problem.

The switching function for the circuit can of course also be expressed in terms of standard sums. Following the general scheme shown in Fig. 4.2, we can implement the switching function of Eq. (4.3) by the circuit in Fig. 4.9. This circuit meets the basic specification of the lamp-switching problem, but it cannot be considered as the optimum solution available.

At this point, let us define clearly what an optimum system is. There are many factors, the operating characteristic, the cost, the reliability, and others, to be considered. In a contactor switching circuit, the following criterion is often adopted. The contactor switching circuit, if any, which employs the least number of springs to implement a given switching function is considered to be the optimum one.*

With this criterion in mind, it is easy to see why the circuit in Fig. 4.9 is considered a primitive one. It is primitive because no effort has been made at this point to reduce the number of springs needed. Now we want to investigate the possibility of reducing the number of springs.

In order to meet the criterion of the "least number of springs" in designing the optimum contactor switching circuit, two simplifications should always be tried. First, reduce the number of *literals* in the switching function. A *literal* is a switching variable in either the primed or unprimed form. Second, employ transfer contacts wherever possible. The reason for this is obvious. A normally open contact and a normally closed contact require four springs, while a transfer contact needs only three.

If we aim to reduce the number of literals in Eq. (4.3), we can rewrite Eq. (4.3) as

$$T = x'(y'z + yz') + x(y'z' + yz). \tag{4.4}$$

The number of literals on the right-hand side of Eq. (4.3) is 12, while

* Another important consideration in relay circuit optimization is discussed in Problem 4.4.

the number of literals on the right-hand side of Eq. (4.4) is 10. The implementation of the switching function in Eq. (4.4) is shown in Fig. 4.10.

An and-gate is used to produce $y'z$, and another to generate yz'. An or-gate is used to implement $y'z + yz'$. In order to have $x'(y'z + yz')$ available, an and-gate is used. The entire implementation can be explained in the same way. Note the effect of reducing the number of literals. One contactor instead of two is employed to implement x', and also one contactor instead of two is employed to implement x. The primitive implementation shown in Fig. 4.9 demands 24 springs, while the one in Fig. 4.10 needs only 20.

The next step is to investigate the possibilities of using one transfer contact to replace one normally closed and one normally open contact. This, generally, can be accomplished by inspection. In the circuit in Fig. 4.10, the x' contact and the x contact have one terminal in common. They can be replaced by a transfer contact. The same reasoning can be applied to other contacts. The circuit in Fig. 4.10 can actually be implemented by five transfer contacts. The number of springs needed is reduced to 15. This circuit is certainly better than the primitive implementation.

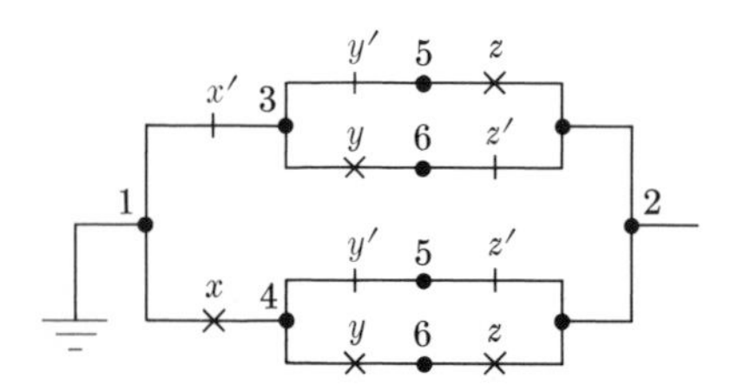

Fig. 4.10. Schematic diagram of the implementation of the switching function in Eq. (4.4).

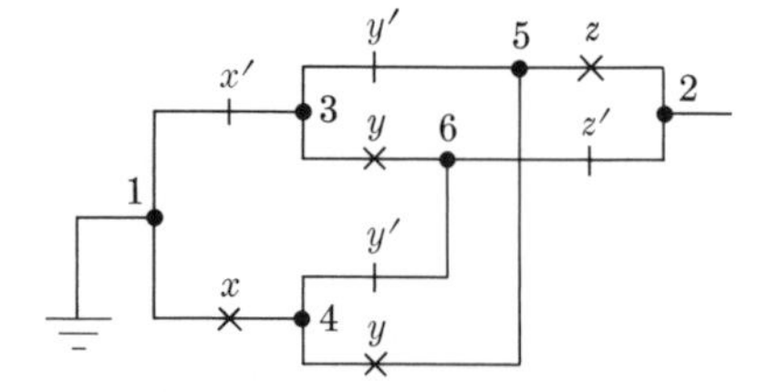

Fig. 4.11. Schematic diagram of the final solution of the lamp-switching problem.

Once these two simplifications have been effected, further improvement can still be made. Unfortunately, there is no general guide line available, but unnecessary springs should be sought. On inspection, we note that Eq. (4.4) contains three switching variables, x, y, and z. The variable x appears in both primed and unprimed forms, and a single transfer contact is provided. So long as x appears in both forms, this is the best we can do. Let us now examine the situation with respect to z. It also appears in both primed and unprimed forms, but *two* transfer contacts are used. Upon investigation we find that one transfer contact is enough to implement the switching variable z, as shown in Fig. 4.11. The same attempt should be made concerning y, but it proves unsuccessful. This circuit, which performs the lamp-switching problem properly, needs only 12 springs.

There is one point which deserves special attention. In simplifying the circuit in Fig. 4.10 to obtain that in Fig. 4.11, we should in no way alter the switching function between terminals 1 and 2. This caution is offered in the last step, because this step is carried out entirely by inspection.

TABLE 4.2

Number of path	Points involved	Corresponding switching function
1	(1, 3, 5, 2)	$x'y'z$
2	(1, 3, 6, 2)	$x'yz'$
3	(1, 4, 6, 2)	$xy'z'$
4	(1, 4, 5, 2)	xyz
5	(1, 3, 5, 4, 6, 2)	$x'y'yy'z' = 0$
6	(1, 3, 6, 4, 5, 2)	$x'yy'yz = 0$
7	(1, 4, 6, 3, 5, 2)	$xy'yy'z = 0$
8	(1, 4, 5, 3, 6, 2)	$xyy'yz' = 0$

In order to check whether any contactor circuit is a faithful realization of a given switching function, we should be able to identify the switching function for a given contactor switching circuit. In a contactor switching circuit, this can best be accomplished by exhaustively connecting the paths provided by the circuit through which the ground can be transmitted. For the circuit in Fig. 4.11, the paths listed in Table 4.2 are available.

The switching function for the contactor circuit can be obtained by taking the or-combination of the switching function listed in Table 4.2. It is interesting to note that the first four paths listed in Table 4.2 are those provided by the circuit in Fig. 4.10. The four other paths were not present in the original circuit; fortunately, their corresponding switching functions are 0. Therefore, the switching function between terminals 1 and 2 is not altered, and the circuit in Fig. 4.11 is acceptable.

The contactor circuit in Fig. 4.11 is the optimum solution for the lamp-switching problem. It can also, however, be considered as the realization of the switching function of Eq. (4.3). If we examine the switching function for the sum circuit of a binary adder, which is found in Eq. (3.6), we note that it is exactly the same as that of Eq. (4.3) if x, y, and z are replaced by a, b, and c, respectively. Therefore, if we intend to realize the sum circuit with relay contacts, the circuit in Fig. 4.11 is the answer.

4.4 Contactor circuit optimization. The previous section shows how a contactor switching circuit can be realized for a given problem. We see that it is not hard at all to realize a contactor circuit; it is, however, very difficult to realize an optimum circuit. We have suggested that in optimizing a contactor switching circuit, we should try to reduce the number of literals in the switching function, try to use as many transfer contacts as possible, and, finally, try to simplify further by inspection. This section presents another example that again illustrates how the optimization of contactor circuits can be accomplished.

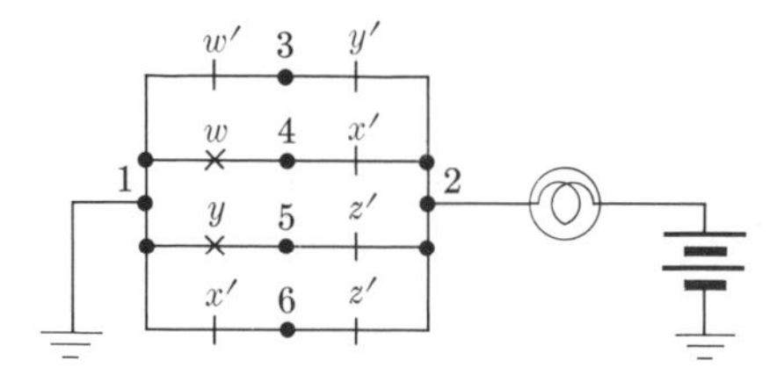

FIG. 4.12. The contactor circuit for Example 4.1.

EXAMPLE 4.1. Optimize the contactor circuit in Fig. 4.12, so that a minimum number of springs is needed.

The first step in optimization is to find the switching function between terminals 1 and 2. This can be accomplished by enumerating the paths available for transmitting the ground from 1 to 2, as in Table 4.3.

TABLE 4.3

Number of path	Points involved	Corresponding switching function
1	(1, 3, 2)	$w'y'$
2	(1, 4, 2)	wx'
3	(1, 5, 2)	yz'
4	(1, 6, 2)	$x'z'$

The switching function between terminals 1 and 2 can then be obtained by combining the switching functions in Table 4.3 by or-operators:

$$T_{12} = w'y' + wx' + yz' + x'z'. \tag{4.5}$$

With the switching function established, we now proceed to try to reduce the number of literals contained. The steps are shown in the following:

$$\begin{aligned} T_{12} &= w'y' + wx' + yz' + x'z'(w + w') \\ &= w'y' + wx' + yz' + wx'z' + w'x'z' \\ &= w'y' + wx'(1 + z') + yz' + w'x'z' \\ &= w'y' + wx' + yz' + w'x'z'(y + y') \\ &= w'y' + wx' + yz' + w'yx'z' + w'y'x'z' \\ &= w'y'(1 + x'z') + wx' + yz'(1 + w'x') \\ &= w'y' + wx' + yz'. \end{aligned} \tag{4.6}$$

Equation (4.6) shows that the path (1, 6, 2) involving $x'z'$ is redundant and, therefore, can be omitted.

Next we try to replace the normally open or normally closed contacts with transfer contacts. Immediately we see that the w' contact and the w contact have a common terminal in 1, and, therefore, can be replaced by a transfer contact. Since x and z appear only in primed forms, there is no need to investigate the possibility of using transfer contacts. However, since the switching variable y appears in both primed and unprimed forms, it seems advisable to see if a transfer contact can be employed. As the circuit stands now, the y and y' contacts do not have common terminals; therefore, we cannot employ a transfer contact. However, note that the positions of y and z' contacts can be interchanged without any alteration of the switching function. This makes it possible to employ a transfer contact and thus save one spring. The final circuit is shown in Fig. 4.13.

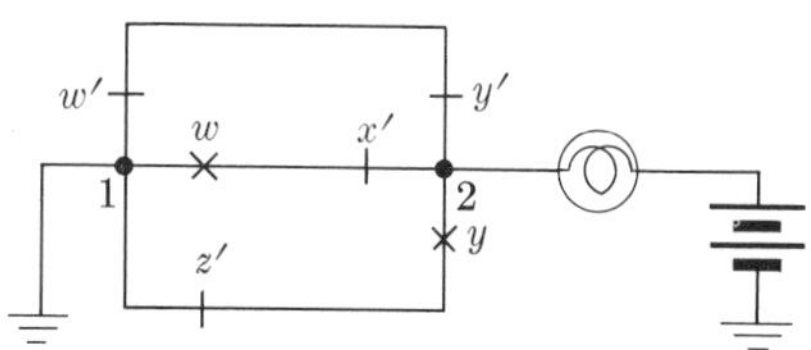

FIG. 4.13. The final circuit for Example 4.1.

Switching variables x and z both appear in primed form and each is realized with two springs. Both w and y appear both in primed and unprimed forms, and each is realized with three springs. This achieves the absolute minimum.

By following the above procedure, the original circuit of 16 springs has been reduced to one of 10.

There might be one question in the reader's mind. It is true that the steps taken to rewrite the switching function in Eq. (4.5) to that in Eq. (4.6) are correct. By doing this, we have reduced the number of literals in the given switching function from 8 to 6. But, merely by examining

Eq. (4.5), how do we know where to start in the simplification process? To put it another way, how can we know that the and-combination of $x'z'$ and $w + w'$ will lead to eventual simplification? This question, or difficulty, can be resolved by the orderly simplification methods to be introduced in Chapter 6. At present, we will have to be content with the cut-and-try approach.

Another alternative in optimizing contactor switching functions is preferred by many who have experience with switching circuits. This approach effects optimization entirely by inspection, and it is carried out on the circuit diagram alone. If we do this, we must be careful not to change the switching function between terminals 1 and 2. It might seem that the contactor circuit in Fig. 4.14 is the answer to the original problem. It is quite understandable how this circuit is reached, because from inspecting the original circuit in Fig. 4.12, we see that four paths have to be provided. By retaining the first three and then connecting nodes 3 and 5 to create the fourth path $x'z'$, nothing seems to have been changed.

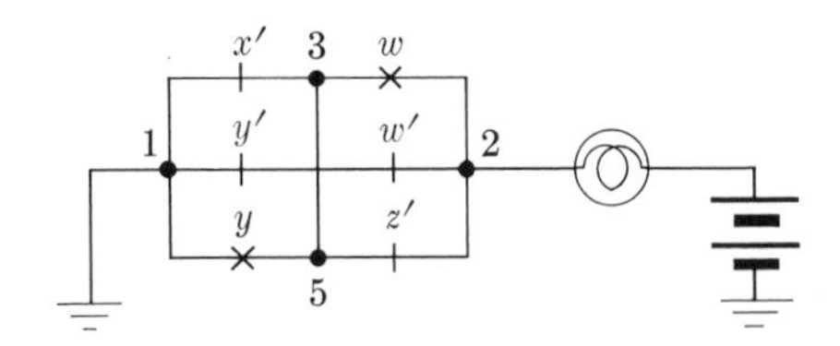

FIG. 4.14. A wrong answer for Example 4.1.

It might be said that the inspection approach, correctly used, is much more direct, because no switching function needs to be written and simplified. But, painstaking care must be exercised to make sure that the switching function is not changed. In the present example, the circuit in Fig. 4.14 is not a correct answer, because it yields a different switching function between terminals 1 and 2. This can be detected by noting that a new path (1, 5, 3, 2) is created. This additional path brings a term yw into the switching function. That is to say, since the switching function between terminals 1 and 2 has been changed, the resultant circuit certainly cannot be the correct answer.▲

4.5 Bridge networks. We have discussed the realization and optimization of contactor switching circuits in the two previous sections. If we examine the resultant circuits in Figs. 4.11 and 4.13, we note a very interesting feature. That is, each contact transmits the ground in only one direction. For example, in Fig. 4.11, the ground always passes through the x' contact from left to right. It is certainly true that a contactor can transmit the ground in both directions, but this bilateral characteristic is not exploited in the previous two sections. An example will be given to illustrate this point.

EXAMPLE 4.2. Use relays to implement the switching function

$$T = xz'v + xw + yz'w + yv. \tag{4.7}$$

In order to reduce the number of literals in Eq. (4.7), we rewrite it as

$$T = x(w + z'v) + y(v + z'w). \tag{4.8}$$

The implementation of the switching function in Eq. (4.8) is shown in Fig. 4.15. This circuit needs 16 springs. Further attempts should be made to optimize the circuit. Because the switching variables w, x, y, and v appear only in unprimed form and the switching variable z appears only in primed form, the smallest possible number of springs needed is 10. Even though it is not absolutely possible that one can attain a circuit of 10 springs, it is worthwhile to try.

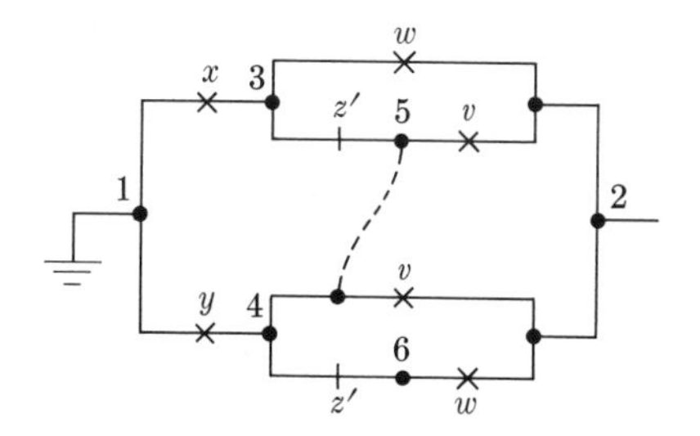

FIG. 4.15. Contactor circuit for the switching function of Eq. (4.8).

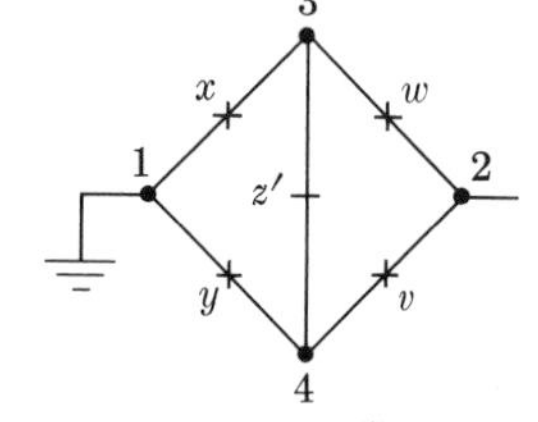

FIG. 4.16. The final circuit for Example 4.2.

We examine the circuit in Fig. 4.15, and note that two normally open contacts (four springs) are used to implement the single variable v. Now, let us attempt to eliminate one of the two v contacts. We make a connection between nodes 4 and 5, which should eliminate the v-contact between nodes 5 and 2. The original path (1, 3, 5, 2) is replaced by the path (1, 3, 5, 4, 2). Before we begin to rejoice at the saving, we should check to see if any unwanted path has been created in the process. It immediately comes to our attention that a path (1, 4, 5, 3, 2) has come into being. In order to see whether this path is unwanted or not, we must identify its corresponding switching function, $yz'w$. Fortunately, one original path (1, 4, 6, 2) also has a corresponding switching function $yz'w$. We easily conclude that we can eliminate the branch (4, 6, 2). The resultant circuit is shown in Fig. 4.16. Since the number of springs needed is 10, which is the absolute minimum, the optimization process is terminated.▲

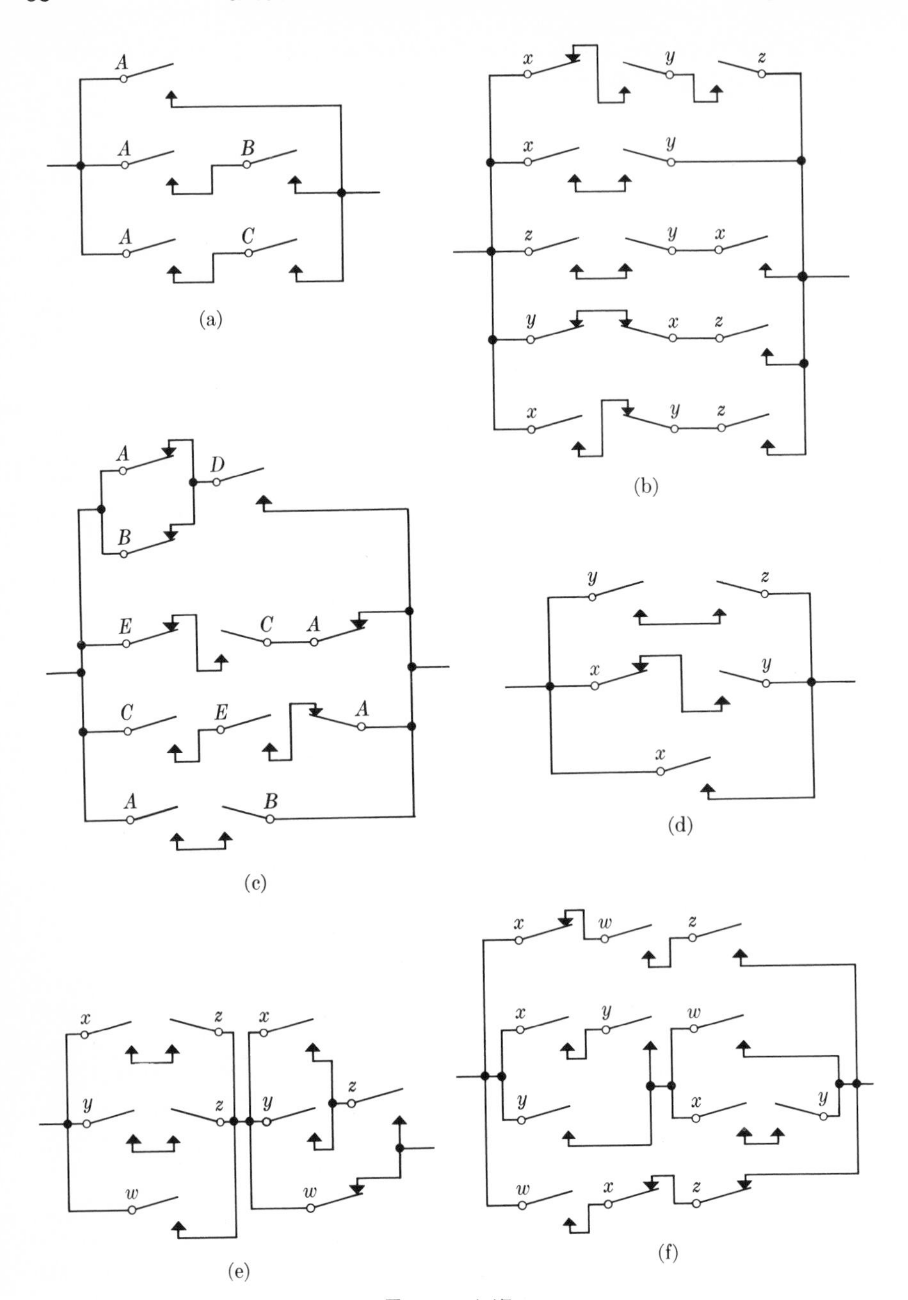
A
A B
A C
(a)
x y z
x y
z y x
y x z
x y z
(b)
A D
B
E C A
C E A
A B
(c)
y z
x y
x
(d)
x z x
y z y z
w w
(e)
x w z
x y w
y x y
w x z
(f)

FIGURE 4.17

It is interesting to examine the z' contact in the final circuit, Fig. 4.16. The ground can be propagated downward through the z' contact by following the path (1, 3, 4, 2). The ground can also be transmitted upward by tracing the path (1, 4, 3, 2). The bilateral characteristic of the z' contact has been advantageously used. Such a circuit is termed a *bridge circuit.*

While bridge circuits generally provide optimum implementation for a given switching function, it is not true at all that every given switching function will have a corresponding bridge circuit. Even if a switching function does have one, there is no orderly process available to attain it.*

Problems

4.1. Implement the following switching functions with relay circuits. Optimize the circuits in the sense that the number of springs needed is a minimum.

(a) $T(A, B, C, D) = m_4 + m_5 + m_6 + m_7 + m_8 + m_9 + m_{10} + m_{11}$
(b) $T(x, y, z) = M_0M_1M_2M_3M_4M_5$
(c) $T(x, y, z) = M_2M_3M_4M_5$
(d) $f(A, B, C, D) = m_0 + m_1 + m_2 + m_3 + m_4 + m_5 + m_6 + m_7 + m_8 + m_9 + m_{10} + m_{11} + m_{12} + m_{13}$

4.2. Optimize the relay switching circuits in Fig. 4.17 so that the number of springs required in each case is the minimum.

4.3. (a) Given four relays, numbered 1 through 4. Design a switching circuit which will be closed when two and only two relays are operated.

(b) Given four relays, numbered 1 through 4. Design a switching circuit which will be closed when (i) no relay is operated, or (ii) all the four relays are operated, or (iii) the number of operated relays is odd.

[*Hint:* The following steps are recommended: (1) Construct the truth table. (2) Write the switching function for the circuit in terms of standard products or sums (you have to make a good choice). (3) Implement and optimize the circuit.]

4.4. In our previous discussion on contactor circuit optimization, efforts were made to reduce the number of springs used in the entire circuit. Another important consideration which should always be kept in mind is the number of pairs of contacts required for each relay. Physically there is a definite limit on the number of pairs of contacts that a relay can have. It is also generally true that the speed of a relay unit is adversely affected by the number of pairs of contacts. In designing a relay contactor switching circuit, efforts should be made to distribute, as evenly as possible, the number of pairs of contacts to all

* Further discussions on contactor circuit optimization and bridge networks can be found in CA 2 and KE 1. The matrix method, SE 1, HO 1, HO 2, possesses promise that a systematic synthesis procedure might be attainable.

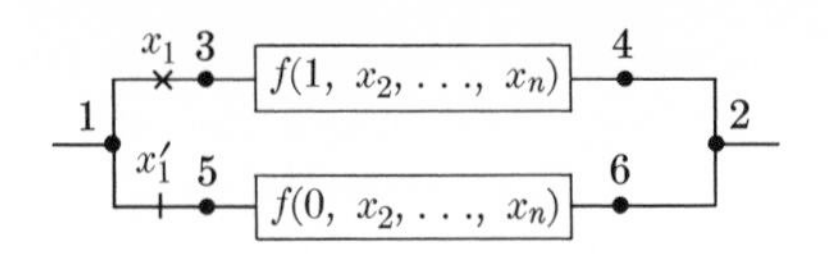

FIGURE 4.18

relays and to merge a pair of normally closed contacts and a pair of normally open contacts into transfer contacts.

By using the Expansion Theorem (see Problem 2.8), a given switching function of n switching variables can be expressed in the following two forms:

$$f(x_1, x_2, \ldots, x_n) = x_1 f(1, x_2, \ldots, x_n) + x_1' f(0, x_2, \ldots, x_n) \quad (1)$$

$$f(x_1, x_2, \ldots, x_n) = [x_1 + f(0, x_2, \ldots, x_n)][x_1' + f(1, x_2, \ldots, x_n)]. \quad (2)$$

Equation (1) suggests the following contactor circuit shown in Fig. 4.18. Note that the circuit between nodes 3 and 4 contains only the remaining $n - 1$ variables, namely $x_2, x_3, \ldots, x_n$. The same statement can be made concerning the circuit between nodes 5 and 6.

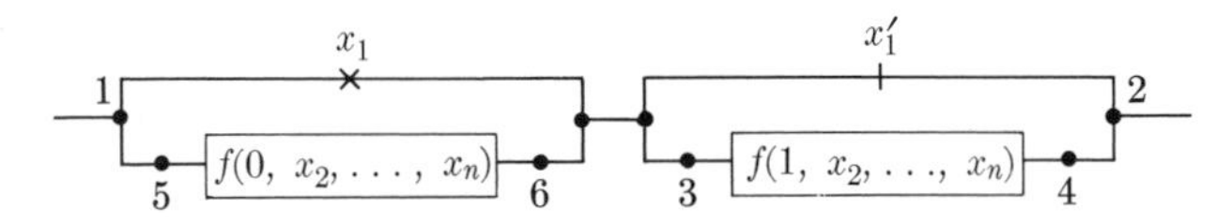

FIGURE 4.19

Equation (2) suggests the contactor circuit shown in Fig. 4.19. The above development indicates that any switching variable in a given switching function can be implemented by a set of transfer contacts.

Implement the following switching functions with transfer contacts only.

(a) $x_1x_2' + x_1'x_2$ (b) $x_1x_2 + x_1'x_2'$

(c) $x_1x_2x_3 + x_1'x_2'x_3'$ (d) $x_1x_2'x_3 + x_1'x_2x_3'$

(e) $x_1'x_2x_3x_4' + x_1x_2'x_3'x_4$

4.5. Implement the following switching functions with contactor bridge networks if possible.

(a) $T = vyz' + xyw' + xv + vwy$
(b) $T = adef + ac'f + a'b'e + b'f + a'b'c'd$

4.6. A small corporation has 100 shares of stock, and *each share* entitles its owner to one vote at a stockholders' meeting. The 100 shares of stock are owned by four people as follows:

Mr. Alcuim:	10 shares
Mr. Baker:	20 shares
Mr. Cornell:	30 shares
Mr. Day:	40 shares

At the stockholders' meeting, it is necessary to have a two-thirds majority in favor of a measure in order to have it pass. Each of the above men has a switch he closes to vote "yes" for all his shares and opens to vote "no" for all his shares. Design an optimum switching circuit (minimum number of springs) which will light a light if and only if the measure passes.

4.7. There is a group of eight relays, designated as A, B, C, D, E, F, G, and H. Design an optimum (least number of springs) switching circuit with these relays. The circuit is to be closed whenever there are four and only four relays excited. [*Note:* The resultant switching function and its corresponding circuits are likely to be very complicated. Do the best you can. However, it might be noted that the switching function in its normal disjunctive or conjunctive forms has a very interesting characteristic.]

4.8. Establish an optimum (least number of springs) circuit between terminals 3 and 4 (Fig. 4.20), so that the switching function between terminals 3 and 4 is the negative of that between terminals 1 and 2.*

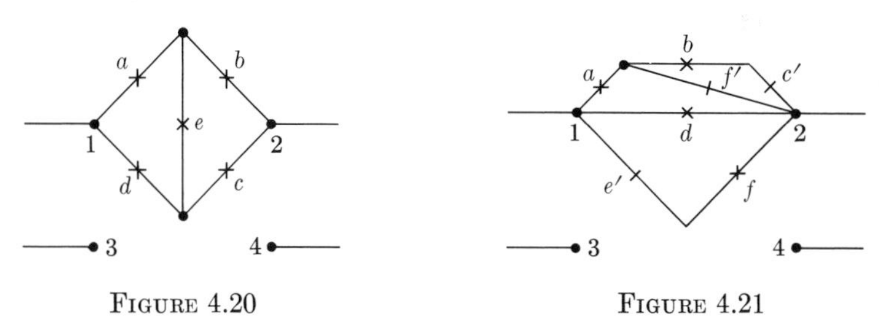

FIGURE 4.20 FIGURE 4.21

4.9. Establish an optimum (least number of springs) circuit between terminals 3 and 4 (Fig. 4.21), so that whenever terminals 1 and 2 are connected, terminals 3 and 4 are not connected, and vice versa.*

* For a general discussion, see SH 3.

CHAPTER 5

CIRCUIT REALIZATION II: DIODE LOGIC

5.1 Introduction. The previous chapter demonstrates that relays can be advantageously used to implement switching circuits. In certain applications, however, relays are not considered to be suitable. Compared with a diode, a relay is generally heavier, bulkier, and slower. The relay is slower, because the switching has to be accomplished by the mechanical motion of the spring.

A *diode* is defined as a device that possesses the characteristic shown in Fig. 5.1(a). Therefore, it can be either a thermionic device or a semiconductor device, so long as its terminal characteristic exhibits the form shown in Fig. 5.1(a).*

It will be shown in the following sections that diodes and resistors can be used to implement switching functions. Diode switching gates generally occupy less space and switch much faster than relays. However, diode gates also possess many undesirable features, which will be discussed.

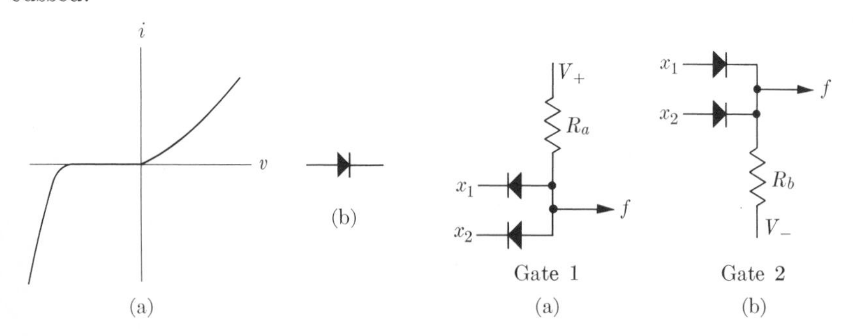

FIG. 5.1. The (a) characteristic and (b) representation of a diode.

FIG. 5.2. The two general diode-resistor configurations for switching purposes.

5.2 Diode gates. We mentioned in the previous section that diodes and resistors can be combined to execute switching operations. There are two general diode-resistor configurations, shown in Fig. 5.2.

Before we identify the switching operations performed respectively by gate 1 and gate 2, we should decide how the truth value of a switching variable is implemented physically. In relay gates, the presence or ab-

* Further discussion on diodes can be found in AN 1 and MI 1.

sence of the ground at a specific terminal is used to represent 1 and 0, respectively. In diode gates, voltage levels (or currents) are generally employed. In such an implementation, there are many variations possible.

Let us now consider the situation in which two voltage levels, V_+ and V_-, are employed to represent the two truth values of a switching variable, and in which V_+ is sufficiently higher than V_-. We have not, however, decided whether V_+ is going to represent 1 or 0.

In gate 1 of Fig. 5.2, x_1 and x_2 are the inputs, and f denotes the point where the value of the output is sensed. The voltage level at point f, as a function of the input levels, is expressed in Table 5.1.

TABLE 5.1

x_1	V_-	V_-	V_+	V_+
x_2	V_-	V_+	V_-	V_+
f	V_-	V_-	V_-	V_+

In the case represented by column four of Table 5.1, V_+ is applied to both x_1 and x_2. No current will flow through the resistor R_a. Consequently, the voltage level of f is V_+, as shown. When V_+ is applied at x_1 and V_- at x_2 (column three of Table 5.1), there is a current flowing through R_a to x_2, and the voltage at f is

$$V_f = V_- + (V_+ - V_-) \frac{r_f}{r_f + R_a}, \tag{5.1}$$

where r_f is the forward resistance of the diode. Note from Eq. (5.1) that the voltage at f can be approximated to be V_- only when r_f is very, very small. By this approach, we see that V_f, listed in the first three columns of Table 5.1, serves only as an approximation.

It is known that r_f, the forward resistance of the diode, can never be 0. Under any one of the three conditions represented by the first three columns of Table 5.1 the voltage at the output will be slightly higher than V_-. In other words, the difference between the two voltage levels, representing 0 and 1, is reduced. This is one of the causes which bring about the signal attenuation in diode gates.

The physical characteristic of gate 1 in Fig. 5.2 has been discussed. Now we investigate the logical operation that the gate performs. This actually depends on the assignment the gate is given. There are two ways to assign the representation of 0 and 1. The first scheme is that V_+ stands for 1 and V_- stands for 0. This convention is employed in this book. With this representation, Table 5.1 becomes Table 5.2.

TABLE 5.2

x_1	0	0	1	1
x_2	0	1	0	1
f	0	0	0	1

TABLE 5.3

x_1	1	1	0	0
x_2	1	0	1	0
f	1	1	1	0

Table 5.2 clearly indicates the relationship

$$f = x_1x_2. \tag{5.2}$$

Therefore, gate 1 can be considered as an and-gate under the first scheme.

The second scheme is to make V_+ stand for 0 and V_- for 1. With this representation, Table 5.1 becomes Table 5.3.

The relationship between the output f and the inputs x_1 and x_2 can be written by examining Table 5.3:

$$f = x_1 + x_2. \tag{5.3}$$

Under the second scheme, gate 1 in Fig. 5.2 should be considered as an or-gate.

The above discussion shows that one physical setup can be used as an and-gate under one assignment scheme, and as an or-gate under another. In this book, the first assignment is implied if no explicit statement is made. Under the first scheme, gate 1 in Fig. 5.2 is, of course, an and-gate.

The operation of gate 2 in Fig. 5.2 can be summarized by Table 5.4.

TABLE 5.4

x_1	V_-	V_-	V_+	V_+
x_2	V_-	V_+	V_-	V_+
f	V_-	V_+	V_+	V_+

It should be stated that Table 5.4 is constructed under the assumption that the forward resistance of the diode is negligible.

Using the first assignment scheme, where V_+ stands for 1 and V_- for 0, gate 2 in Fig. 5.2 executes the or-operation. If the second assignment scheme is used, the same gate will be considered as an and-gate. The same analysis can be employed to show that voltage level deterioration also exists in this gate.

In the above discussion, only two inputs, x_1 and x_2, are considered. It is not necessary to restrict the number of inputs to each gate. With appropriate inputs, a diode and-gate can produce a standard product, and a diode or-gate can produce a standard sum. In the subsequent discussion, the symbols shown in Fig. 5.3 will be used to represent and-gates and or-gates.

It is of interest to point out that negation cannot be performed by diode gates.

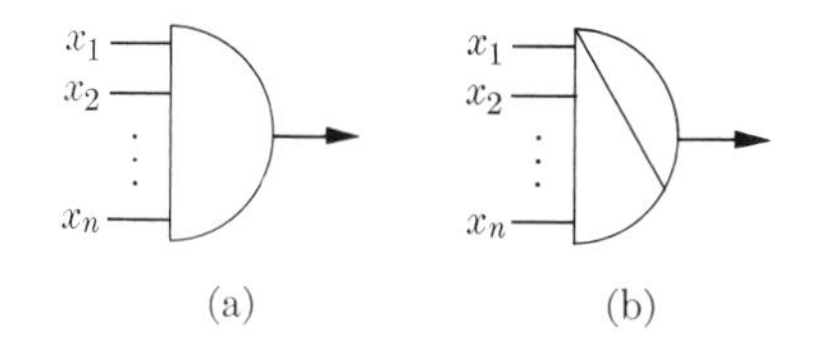

FIG 5.3. (a) A diode-resistor and-gate, $f = x_1x_2 \cdots x_n$. (b) A diode-resistor or-gate, $f = x_1 + x_2 + \cdots + x_n$.

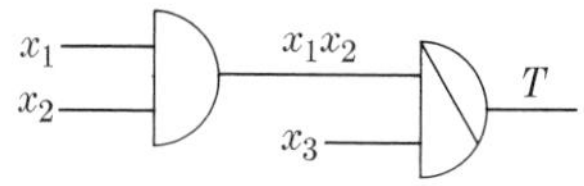

FIG. 5.4. The symbolic representation of the switching circuit for Example 5.1.

5.3 Signal deterioration in diode gates. It is pointed out in the previous section that voltage level deterioration occurs in diode gates. The forward resistance of the diode is not, however, the only cause of this undesirable result. The following example will reveal some other considerations that have to be taken into account by the designer.

EXAMPLE 5.1. Use diode gates to implement the switching function

$$T = x_1x_2 + x_3. \tag{5.4}$$

To start the implementation, we must assume the availability of inputs x_1, x_2, and x_3. An and-gate has to be used to generate the term x_1x_2. With x_1x_2 available, an or-gate is then used to produce T. The symbolic representation of the final circuit is shown in Fig. 5.4. This symbolic representation can be easily drawn, but it conceals several important points that are of interest to a designer. To reveal them, the actual physical schematic diagram is shown in Fig. 5.5.

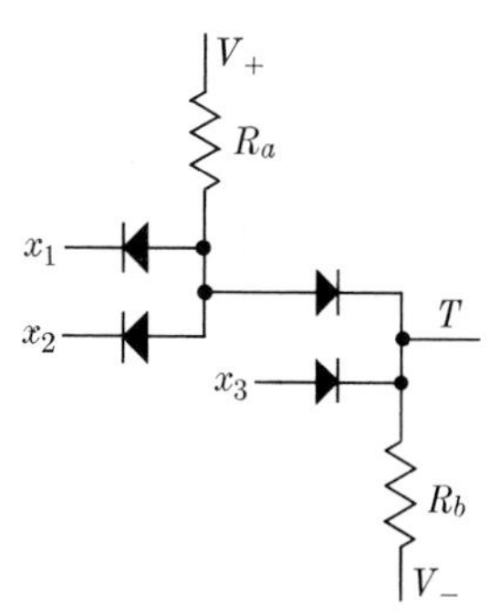

FIG. 5.5. The physical schematic diagram of the switching circuit for Example 5.1.

Let us consider one possible situation where $x_1 = 1$, $x_2 = 1$, and $x_3 = 0$. Under this input condition, the output of the circuit, T, should be 1. In the actual circuit, the input condition corresponds to the situation where V_+ is applied to the two inputs of the and-gate, and V_- is applied to one of the input terminals of the or-gate. Since the output T should be 1, we would expect that the voltage should be V_+ at the output terminal. However, this is not the case. The voltage actually appearing at the output is

$$V_T = V_- + (V_+ - V_-) \frac{R_b}{R_b + R_a + r_f}. \tag{5.5}$$

Since the fraction $R_b/(R_b + R_a + r_f)$ is always less than 1, V_T will be somewhere between V_+ and V_-. This, of course, indicates that voltage level deterioration exists. Note that this is brought about not because of the nonzero r_f (it, of course, aggravates the situation), but because of the interaction between successive gates. In order to reduce this deterioration, the resistors R_a and R_b have to be carefully chosen to produce reasonably detectable output voltage levels. In this circuit, the inputs x_1 and x_2 are sent to one and-gate; this constitutes one level. The output of the and-gate is sent to an or-gate. This or-gate is considered to constitute another level. Such a switching circuit is termed a two-level switching circuit.▲

Because of the interaction between diode gates, it is advisable that the output of a two-level switching circuit be sent to a device which is capable of restoring adequate voltage level. In general practice, three-level switching circuits can be achieved but are seldom attempted. In this book, a two-level switching circuit is implied if no other explicit statement is made.

Another problem which deserves our attention is the delay developed within the gates. The delay is defined as the time interval between the instant that the inputs are applied and the instant that the output voltage level reaches its detectable level. Obviously, the more levels a circuit has, the more delay it will develop. Not only does the delay at each gate have a direct effect on the total switching speed of the circuit, but also it introduces into the pulsed switching circuit the coincidence problem, which will be discussed in Section 5.6.*

5.4 An example of optimization. The development of Example 5.1 demonstrates that it is important to avoid excessive interaction between successive diode gates, and leads us to the conclusion that only two-level switching circuits are to be attempted. In the following example, we intend to show the considerations involved in optimizing a diode switching circuit.

* Discussions on diode gates can be found in MI 1.

EXAMPLE 5.2. Use diode-gates to implement the switching function

$$T(x, y, z) = (x + y + z')(x + y' + z)(x' + y + z)(x' + y' + z)(x' + y' + z'). \tag{5.6}$$

Five or-gates are needed to generate the five standard sums, and one and-gate is used to produce the product of the five sums. The circuit is shown in Fig. 5.6. This is certainly a two-level switching circuit. Also it clearly indicates that it is a primitive implementation of the switching function in Eq. (5.6).

Next comes the task of optimization. Recall that in the process of optimizing a relay switching circuit, we try to reduce the number of springs needed. In the case of a diode switching circuit, there is no such clear-cut criterion available. We must consider the cost involved, possible interaction between gates, and the delay developed, and then reach a compromise. The cost of a diode switching circuit can generally be evaluated by examining the number of diodes used. The delay developed and possible interaction can generally be predicted by the number of levels involved. If a two-level diode switching circuit is prescribed, the number of diodes needed serves generally as a good measuring rod.

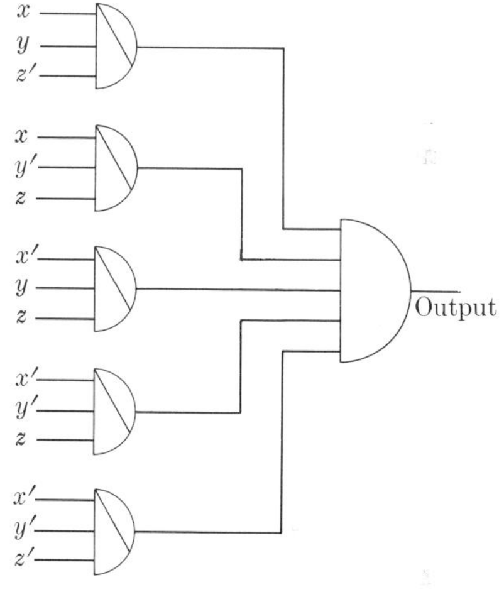

FIG. 5.6. The circuit for Example 5.2.

The first step in optimization is to change the configuration of the circuit. The circuit in Fig. 5.6 is of an or-and scheme. This means that or-gates are used in front of and-gates. This corresponds to the situation in which the switching function is expressed as the product of appropriate standard sums. Another possibility is the use of and-gates preceding that of the or-gate. This is termed the and-or scheme, which corresponds to the situation in which the switching function is expressed as the sum of appropriate standard products.

When we examine the switching function in Eq. (5.6), we see the opportunity to convert it into an expression in terms of standard products. It is a function of three switching variables, and it is composed of five standard sums. This means that under five different input conditions the function will be zero. In other words, there are three input conditions in which the function should be 1. If we try to express it in terms of products, only three terms are necessary. Following the approach shown in Section 3.9, we can immediately write

$$T' = (x + y + z)(x' + y + z')(x + y' + z'),$$
$$T = x'y'z' + xy'z + x'yz. \tag{5.7}$$

The same switching function, according to Eq. (5.7), can be implemented by using three and-gates, each one having three inputs, and one or-gate which also has three inputs. The circuit diagram shown in Fig. 5.7 is also a primitive one. It requires 12 diodes; three for each and-gate and three for the or-gate. This compares very favorably with the other primitive implementation shown in Fig. 5.6, which needs 20 diodes; three for each or-gate and five for the and-gate.

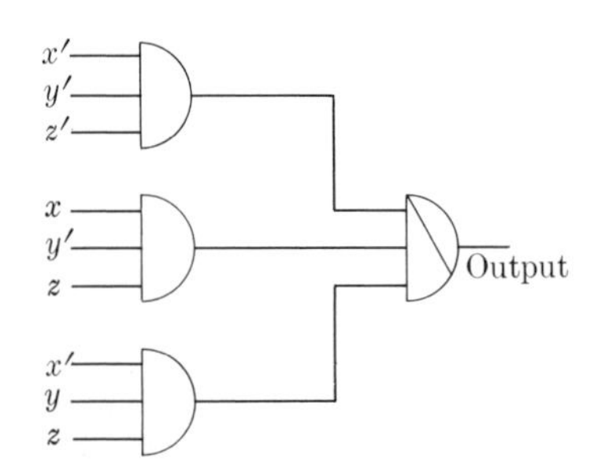

FIG. 5.7. Alternative circuit for Example 5.2.

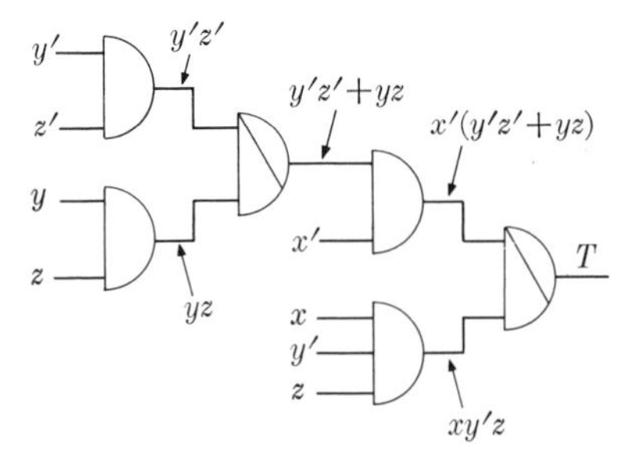

FIG. 5.8. Alternative implementation for Example 5.2.

There is another important consideration which does not come into this problem. Always examine the availability of the input variables in each circuit. In the two circuits shown, all the variables, in both their primed and unprimed forms, are needed. In certain cases, one design might require more input variables than another. Since diodes do not perform the negation operation, the availability of certain variables in certain forms might influence the design.

At this point let us attempt to reduce the number of literals in Eq. (5.7). We obtain

$$T = x'(y'z' + yz) + xy'z. \tag{5.8}$$

The implementation of the switching function in Eq. (5.8) is shown in Fig. 5.8. This implementation is far inferior to the one in Fig. 5.7, because it calls for a four-level circuit and requires 13 diodes.▲

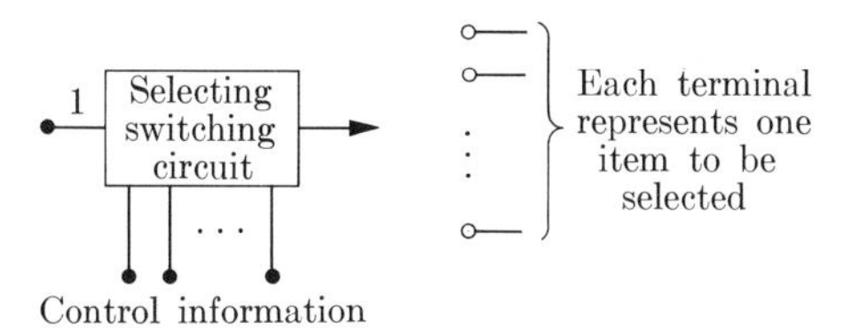

FIG. 5.9. Block diagram of a selecting switching circuit.

5.5 Selecting switching circuits. In this section the very important and interesting switching problem of design of *selecting switching circuits* is discussed. Its name implies that this circuit is capable of selecting one item from many possibilities, depending on the control information received. Its function can be illustrated by the diagram in Fig. 5.9.

The mission of the selecting switching circuit is to establish a connection between terminal 1 and a proper terminal on the right-hand side, which represents the item demanded by the control information. Selecting switching circuits are used in automatic telephone switching to establish a path between the calling and called stations. Selecting switching circuits are also widely used in computer switching.* They are used to select the appropriate register to which certain information is sent or from which certain information is fetched. It is also used as a decoding device to determine the content of a given instruction. This decoder is discussed below.

A computer, in general, is capable of carrying out many arithmetic and related operations, and each operation is represented by a coded message in terms of switching variables. Suppose that a computer is designed to perform sixteen basic operations. Each operation can then be represented by a message of four binary digits; 0000 can be assigned to stand for addition, 0001 for subtraction, and so on. These coded messages are written on the instruction and stored in the memory unit. When the control unit receives such a message, it must have a gating circuit to decode the message. Such a circuit is called a *decoder* and can be constructed with diode gates.

The general plan of an operation decoder is shown in Fig. 5.10. The number of lines used to transmit coded messages, indicating the operation to be executed, between memory and the decoder is determined by the number of binary digits in such a message. The number of binary digits necessary is in turn dictated by the number of operations which can be performed by the computer. The number of lines between the operation decoder and the control signal generator is equal to the number of operations designed into the computer. Each line corresponds to a specific

---

* For further discussion, see LE 1 and PH 1.

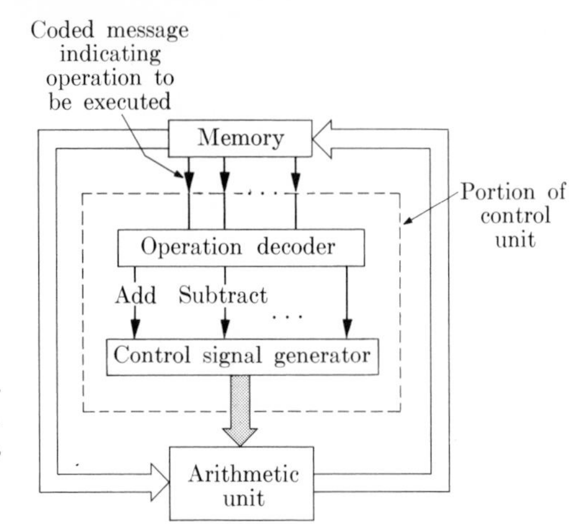

FIG. 5.10. General schematic diagram showing the function of an operation decoder in a computer.

operation. If the line, labelled "add," is energized, this means that an addition is to be executed. The arrow "$\Rightarrow$" just indicates the flow of information between different units of a computer.

Let us now design an operation decoder for a hypothetical computer which can perform sixteen operations. Each message has to have at least four binary digits, designated as D_1, D_2, D_3, and D_4, respectively. Each message, representing a corresponding operation, can be considered as a standard product of the four switching variables. The decoder can be implemented by the one-level switching circuit shown in Fig. 5.11. This circuit requires 64 diodes, since there are 16 diode and-gates, and each and-gate has four inputs. If the "add" operation is coded as 0000, then whenever an "add" operation is to be executed, the voltage level V_+ will appear at the output of gate 0. It can also be said that the output of gate 0 is energized.

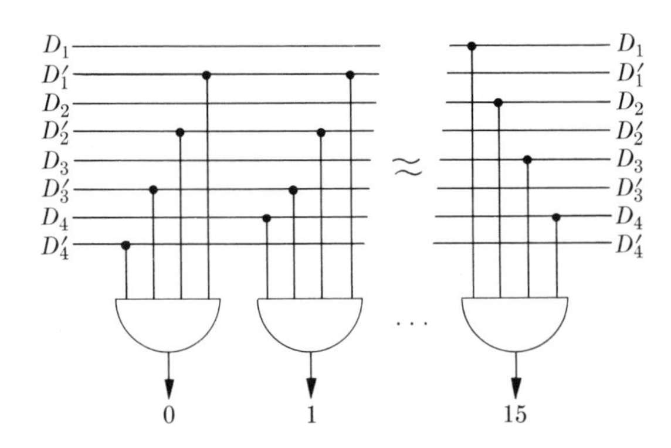

FIG. 5.11. A one-level diode switching circuit used as a computer decoder.

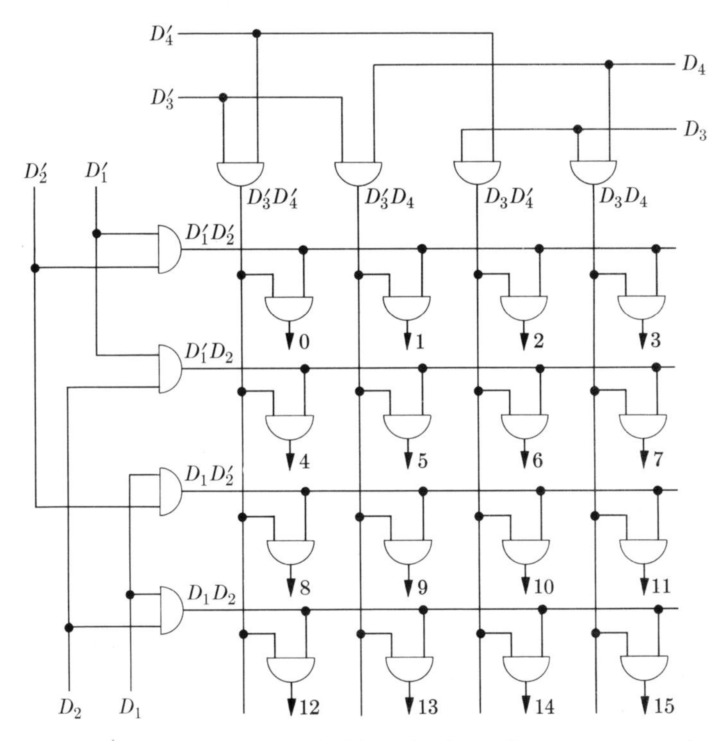

FIG. 5.12. A two-level diode switching circuit used as a computer decoder.

This computer decoder can also be implemented by the two-level switching circuit shown in Fig. 5.12. This circuit has 24 diode and-gates and each and-gate has two inputs. Therefore, 48 diodes are needed. The two-level implementation is sometimes called a decoder matrix. Its circuit diagram explains why it is so called.

Selecting switching circuits are, in general, implemented with relays, diodes, and other switching components. The fact that we have introduced them in this chapter does not mean that diode gates alone are used in realizing selecting switching circuits.

5.6 Pulsed switching circuits. Up to this point the truth values of switching variables have been represented physically in switching circuits by voltage levels V_+ and V_-. This is what is generally termed the *level logic*. The output is not sensed until the steady state is reached. Voltage levels are, however, not the only scheme of truth value implementation. The truth values of switching variables can be represented by pulses of finite width. A pulse of amplitude V_+ is used to stand for 1, a pulse of amplitude V_- for 0. The converse can also be adopted.

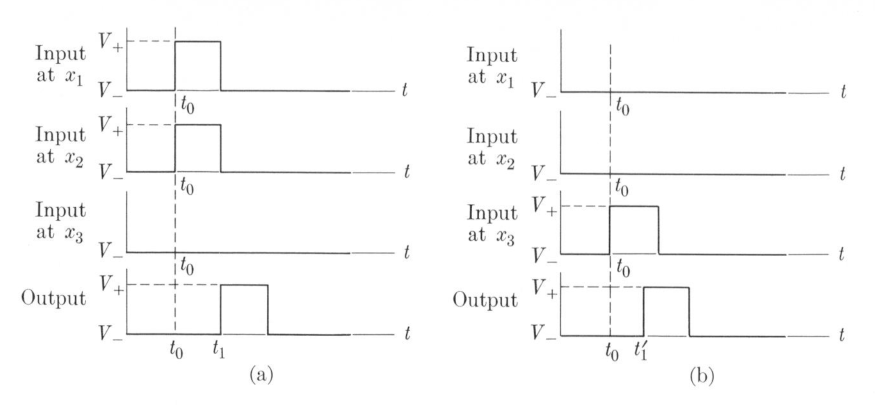

FIG. 5.13. Input and output waveforms of a pulsed switching circuit shown in Fig. 5.4. (a) $(t_1 - t_0)$: the delay developed in the and-gate and the or-gate. (b) $(t_1' - t_0)$: the delay developed in the or-gate alone.

Superficially this designation scheme does not offer any problem. Let us examine again the circuit in Fig. 5.4. If the input condition is $x_1 = 1$, $x_2 = 1$, and $x_3 = 0$, and finite-width pulses are used, the actual inputs to the circuit are shown in Fig. 5.13(a). The corresponding output is also shown. The delay introduced by the and-gate and then by the or-gate is exaggeratedly shown. Another input condition, $x_1 = 0$, $x_2 = 0$, $x_3 = 1$, also produces an output of 1. If this set of input values is implemented by finite-width pulses, the input and output waveforms are as shown in Fig. 5.13(b). The output pulse of amplitude V_+ appears at t_1' instead of t_1. This happens because the delay in this situation is contributed by the or-gate alone. The above illustration shows that the output of a pulsed switching circuit appears at different instants for different input conditions.

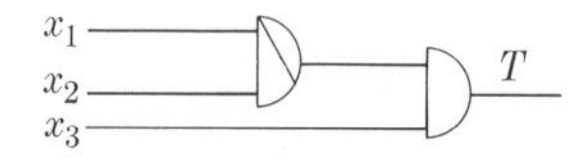

FIG. 5.14. A switching circuit employed to illustrate the coincidence problem.

Let us now examine another switching circuit (Fig. 5.14). If the input conditions are $x_1 = 1$, $x_2 = 0$, $x_3 = 1$, and finite-width pulses are used to represent them, the input and output waveforms are as shown in Fig. 5.15. Note that the and-gate has two inputs. The input from the or-gate does not arrive until t_1 because of the delay developed in the or-gate, while the input from x_3 arrives promptly at t_0. The result of this staggered arrival is known as the *coincidence problem.* The width of the output pulse is reduced. This is certainly not desirable. Furthermore, if

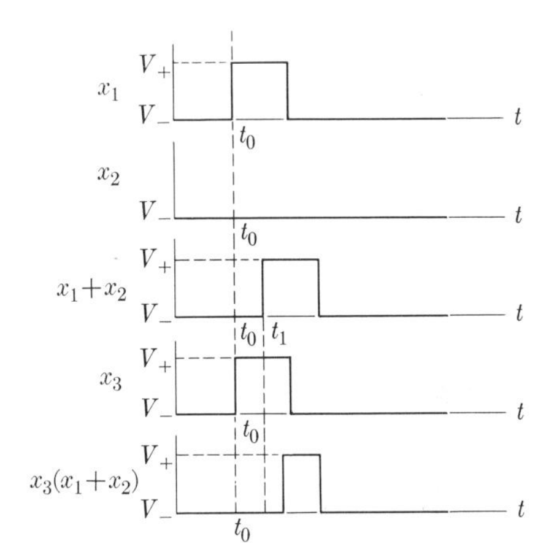

FIG. 5.15. Input and output waveforms for the circuit in Fig. 5.14.

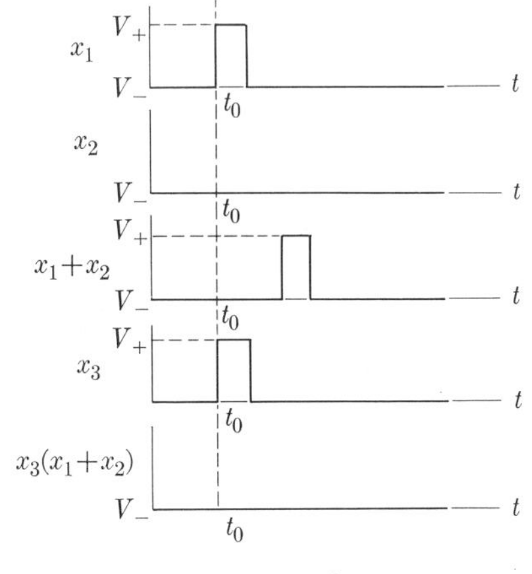

FIG. 5.16. Input and output waveforms illustrating the coincidence problem in a pulsed switching circuit.

the delay developed in the or-gate is larger than the input pulse width, the circuit might produce an entirely incorrect result, as shown in Fig. 5.16. Figure 5.16 shows that the output of the or-gate is so delayed that it does not appear until the input at x_3 has vanished. This brings about a 0 output instead of the correct 1 output. To remedy this situation, one can deliberately introduce a delay into the x_3 input, so that the situation shown in Fig. 5.16 will not occur.

The above discussion illustrates one point. In using finite-width pulses to represent truth values of switching variables, the coincidence problem must be kept in mind.

PROBLEMS

5.1. Implement the following switching functions with two-level diode circuits. Show the schematic diagrams of the circuits. The input variables are available in both primed and unprimed forms.

(a) $T = x'y'z' + xy'z' + xy'z$
(b) $T = x'yz + x'yz' + xyz'$

5.2. Use two-level diode switching circuits to implement the following functions. Show symbolic representations of the circuits. The input variables are available in both primed and unprimed forms.

(a) $T = (a' + b' + c')(a' + b' + c)(a' + b + c)$
(b) $T = (a + b' + c)(a + b + c')(a + b + c)$

5.3. Show symbolic representations of the two-level diode switching circuits which implement the following functions. The input variables are available in both primed and unprimed forms.

(a) $T(w, x, y, z) = \prod M(0, 1, 4, 5, 6, 7, 9, 13)$
(b) $T(a, b, c, d) = \prod M(3, 7, 10, 11, 12, 13, 14, 15)$

5.4. Show symbolic representations of the two-level diode switching circuits which implement the following functions. The input variables are available in both primed and unprimed forms.

(a) $T(w, x, y, z) = \sum m(3, 6, 7, 12, 13, 14, 15)$
(b) $T(a, b, c, d) = \sum m(1, 2, 3, 5, 7, 9, 13)$

5.5. The block diagram of a serial subtractor is shown in Fig. 5.17. a_i is the ith bit (binary digit) of the minuend, e_i is the ith bit of the subtrahend, B_i is the borrow generated at the ith stage, and D_i is the ith bit of the difference. Use diode-gates to construct the *subtractor* shown in Fig. 5.17.

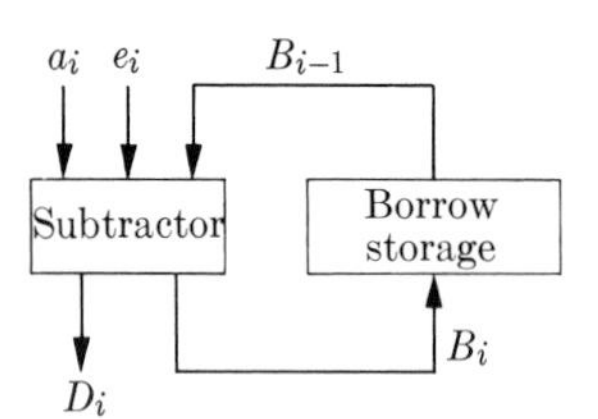

FIGURE 5.17

5.6. Two switching functions, T_1 and T_2, are specified by the following composite truth table. Use diode gates to implement them.

Input variables			Switching functions	
A	B	C	T_1	T_2
0	0	0	1	0
0	0	1	1	0
0	1	0	1	0
0	1	1	0	1
1	0	0	0	1
1	0	1	0	1
1	1	0	0	1
1	1	1	0	1

5.7. In Problem 5.6, the truth values of T_1 and T_2 are not specified when the input variables assume the following set of truth values: $A = 0$, $B = 1$, and $C = 1$. In other words, whenever the input combination $A = 0$, $B = 1$, and $C = 1$ prevails, the truth values of T_1 and T_2 can be either 1 or 0. Such an input combination is generally called a *don't-care condition.* A don't-care condition may be brought about either because a specific input combination will never occur or the truth value corresponding to that input combination is to be ignored.

Can you make use of this don't-care condition to optimize the circuits obtained for Problem 5.6?

5.8. If pulses with finite width instead of levels are to be used in the switching circuits, should you modify the circuits you designed in Problems 5.1, 5.2, 5.3, and 5.4? State the reason for your decision.

CHAPTER 6

SWITCHING FUNCTION MANIPULATION METHODS

6.1 Introduction. The first step in designing a switching system is to formulate a switching function, or set of switching functions, which incorporates the set of rules to be executed. This is presented in Chapter 3.

In Chapters 4 and 5, the implementation of a given switching function is discussed. If the switching components to be used have been predetermined, a switching function in a given form implies a specific switching circuit. For example, if diode gates are to be used to implement the switching function in Eq. (5.6), the circuit has to be that shown in Fig. 5.6; if diode gates are to be used to realize the same switching function given in a different form, as in Eq. (5.7), the circuit is that shown in Fig. 5.7.

The design of a switching system cannot be considered complete if it establishes only one circuit which can execute the specified set of rules; the designer must also try to minimize the cost and maximize the reliability of the circuit designed. To achieve this end, it must be possible to manipulate a given switching function* into different forms, because each form will bring forth a corresponding circuit. An intelligent choice can then be made.

It is certainly true that by applying all the rules of algebra, it is possible to manipulate all the switching functions no matter how complicated they may be. However, when a switching function with many variables must be manipulated, a dilemma may arise, that of not knowing where to start the manipulation process. The presentation in Section 4.4 clearly demonstrates this dilemma. Under these circumstances, it is desirable to have a systematic way of manipulating switching functions.

It is generally true that the number of literals in a given representation of a switching function gives a fairly reliable indication of the complexity of its corresponding circuit. Therefore, many manipulations are carried out in such a way as to reduce the number of literals contained in a given switching function. But the most important value of the manipulation method, presented in the following, is that this method can reveal alternative forms of representation of a given switching function with ease and speed.

Because most manipulations are done to reduce the number of literals involved, the term *simplification* is often used in place of *manipulation*.

---

* It should be stressed again that the "manipulation of a switching function" means the "manipulation of the form of representation of a switching function."

6.2 Graphical representation of switching variables and functions. One of the manipulating methods to be presented is the Veitch-Karnaugh map method,* which is based on the proper graphical representation of switching variables. Let us start with a case in which only one variable is involved.

One variable. In the domain of one switching variable, say x, the number of standard products or sums is 2, namely x and x'. Note that the following two relationships stand:

$$xx' = 0, \tag{6.1}$$

$$x + x' = 1. \tag{6.2}$$

0	x'
1	x

FIG. 6.1. A map of one switching variable.

Equation (6.1) suggests that x and x' have nothing in common. Equation (6.2) indicates that the sum of x and x' is universally true. We can represent the above interpretation with the diagram shown in Fig. 6.1. This diagram is called a Karnaugh map.

We can consider that the whole area enclosed in Fig. 6.1 is 1. This area is divided into two portions: one, labeled 0, represents x'; the other, labeled 1, represents x.

It is established that any switching function of switching variables can be expressed in terms of products or sums. Since the Karnaugh map shows all the standard products or sums, we expect that any switching function can be represented by a suitable arrangement in the Karnaugh map.

In the case of one variable, the switching function can be of the following four forms:

$$T_1(x) = x, \tag{6.3}$$

$$T_2(x) = x', \tag{6.4}$$

$$T_3(x) = x + x' = 1, \tag{6.5}$$

$$T_4(x) = xx' = 0. \tag{6.6}$$

Equations (6.3), (6.4), (6.5), and (6.6) are represented, or mapped, in Fig. 6.2(a), (b), (c), and (d), respectively.

	(a)		(b)		(c)		(d)
0	0	0	1	0	1	0	0
1	1	1	0	1	1	1	0

FIG. 6.2. Maps representing switching functions of one variable.

* KA 1 and VE 1.

Wherever the area is included in the expression, a 1 is put there; wherever the area is not included in the function, a 0 is indicated in that space.

Let us now advance to the case of two switching variables.

Two variables. In extending the above process to the domain of two variables, we must alter the Karnaugh map to take into account the four standard products or sums. From now on, the representation of standard products will be presented. The representation of standard sums will be extended later. Let the two variables be x and y; then the four standard products are xy, xy', $x'y$, and $x'y'$. They are indicated in Fig. 6.3.

It was pointed out before that standard products can be represented by binary numbers. For example, $x'y'$ can be represented by 00. Examining Fig. 6.3, we note that this representation can be obtained by taking the label on the left-hand column first and then the label directly above the area. The same is true of the three remaining areas.

Since a map can be made to indicate all the standard products, certainly a map can represent all the switching functions of two variables.

$x \backslash y$	0	1
0	$x'y'$	$x'y$
1	xy'	xy

FIG. 6.3. A Karnaugh map for two switching variables.

$x \backslash y$	0	1
0	0	1
1	1	1

FIG. 6.4. A Karnaugh map representing $T = x + y$.

EXAMPLE: Represent the function $T(x, y) = x + y$ in the Karnaugh map. The given function can be written as

$$T(x, y) = x + y = xy + xy' + x'y. \tag{6.7}$$

Equation (6.7) is represented in Fig. 6.4. The pertinent areas, areas which represent standard products included in Eq. (6.7), are labeled 1. The remaining area is labeled 0.▲

Three or four variables. This graphical representation technique can be extended to three- and four-variable cases, as shown in Figs. 6.5 and 6.6, respectively.

$x \backslash yz$	00	01	11	10
0	$x'y'z'$	$x'y'z$	$x'yz$	$x'yz'$
1	$xy'z'$	$xy'z$	xyz	xyz'

FIG. 6.5. A Karnaugh map for three switching variables.

$wx \backslash yz$	00	01	11	10
00	$w'x'$ $y'z'$	$w'x'$ $y'z$	$w'x'$ yz	$w'x'$ yz'
01	$w'x$ $y'z'$	$w'x$ $y'z$	$w'x$ yz	$w'x$ yz'
11	wx $y'z'$	wx $y'z$	wx yz	wx yz'
10	wx' $y'z'$	wx' $y'z$	wx' yz	wx' yz'

FIG. 6.6. A Karnaugh map for four switching variables.

Note that in Figs. 6.5 and 6.6, adjacent areas differ by only one variable. In Fig. 6.5, for example, the area $x'y'z'$ is adjacent to the area $x'y'z$. These two areas differ only in the variable z. Further clarification is needed, because, in Fig. 6.5, the two areas $x'y'z'$ and $x'yz'$, which are located at the opposite edges of the map, also differ only in one variable, y. The same is true of the areas $xy'z'$ and xyz'.

Observe that in Fig. 6.6, the corresponding areas along top and bottom edges also differ by only one variable. Let us now answer the question: why is the map so arranged? It is arranged so that adjacent areas differ only by one variable.* This fact will be extensively exploited in the next section.

6.3 Map method. The graphical representation technique developed in Section 6.2 leads to a systematic method for the simplification of switching functions of four variables. By "simplification of switching function" here, we mean to express a given switching function as the sum of products which contains the least number of literals, or simply minimum sum of products.

The simplification process will be illustrated by two examples.

EXAMPLE 6.1. Simplify the switching function

$$T(w, x, y, z) = x'y'z' + xy'z + w'yz + wxz + wx'y + x'yz'. \qquad (6.8)$$

This switching function can certainly be simplified by algebraic means, but that will be time-consuming and may not be successful at all.

Proceeding according to the map method, we first of all map the switching function in a Karnaugh map, as shown in Fig. 6.7. The first term, $x'y'z'$, on the right-hand side of Eq. (6.8) can be expanded into two products of four variables: $w'x'y'z'$ and $wx'y'z'$. These correspond to the

* This statement is not true for Veitch maps.

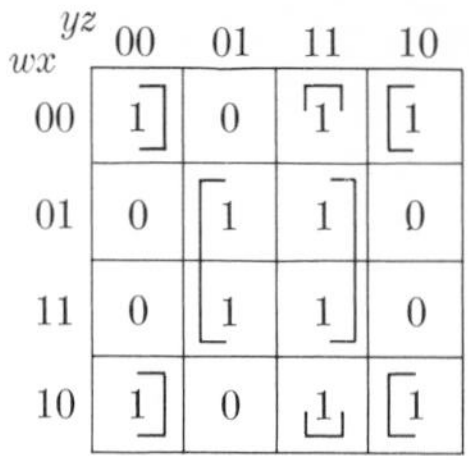

wx \ yz	00	01	11	10
00	1	0	1	1
01	0	1	1	0
11	0	1	1	0
10	1	0	1	1

FIG. 6.7. A map for the switching function in Eq. (6.8).

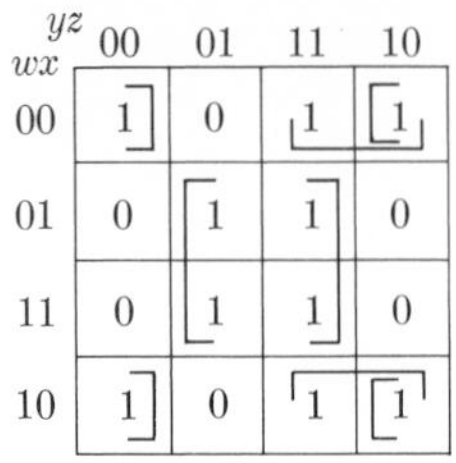

wx \ yz	00	01	11	10
00	1	0	1	1
01	0	1	1	0
11	0	1	1	0
10	1	0	1	1

FIG. 6.8. Another factoring scheme for Example 6.1.

binary notations 0000 and 1000; consequently, the relevant areas are labeled 1. We can now carry out this process for the rest of the terms on the right-hand side of Eq. (6.8).

We have completed the task of representing this switching function in a map. Now, how can we make use of the map to simplify the switching function? Note that in Fig. 6.7, areas 0101 and 1101 are adjacent to each other; 0101 stands for $w'xy'z$ and 1101 for the term $wxy'z$. From this, we see that

$$w'xy'z + wxy'z = (w' + w)xy'z = xy'z. \tag{6.9}$$

This development implies that whenever two areas included in a switching function are adjacent to each other, one switching variable can be eliminated. What has been used in Eq. (6.9) is a very simple switching algebra relationship, but this graphical representation demonstrates where it can be applied.

Now note the areas 0111 and 1111, both of which are included in the given switching function; 0111 stands for the standard product $w'xyz$, 1111 for $wxyz$. The following relationship can be established:

$$w'xyz + wxyz = xyz. \tag{6.10}$$

Equation (6.10) illustrates the same thing as Eq. (6.9), but if these two equations are combined, a very interesting development is observed:

$$xy'z + xyz = xz(y' + y) = xz. \tag{6.11}$$

The term xz of Eq. (6.11) actually can be interpreted as the sum of four products, namely $w'xy'z$, $wxy'z$, $w'xyz$, and $wxyz$. These four terms are represented in four areas which are adjacent to each other and form a rectangle. Now inspect the labels on the left-hand side for row two and row three, 01 and 11, and note that 1 is a common factor. This corresponds to x in the simplified expression. The labels on the top of the map for column two and column three are 01 and 11, and 1 is a common factor which corresponds to z in the simplified expression.

Since 0101, 1101, 0111, and 1111 are grouped into a rectangle, a term xz is found to be the simplified expression. A pair of brackets are drawn, as shown in Fig. 6.7, to show that these four areas are already factored.

Next, the areas 0000, 0010, 1000, and 1010, which occupy the four corners of the map, are also considered to be adjacent to each other, according to Section 6.2. They can be grouped together. The sum will be obtained by the same inspection process.

In row one and row four, the labels are respectively 00 and 10; 0, which stands for x', is the common factor. In column one and column four, the labels are respectively 00 and 10; 0, which stands for z', is the common factor. Therefore, the sum of these four areas is $x'z'$.

After these four areas are bracketed as shown, note that only two areas, 0011 and 1011, are left out. They are adjacent to each other. The sum of these two areas is $x'yz$. However, this is not the best combination we can make. If the four areas in column three are grouped together, a term yz will be obtained. To do this, we would have to use the two areas 0111 and 1111 twice, which we can do.

The final expression is

$$T(w, x, y, z) = xz + x'z' + yz. \tag{6.12}$$

Equation (6.12) is obtained by adopting the factoring scheme shown in Fig. 6.7.

This is not the only combination scheme possible. Using the scheme shown in Fig. 6.8, we obtain

$$T(w, x, y, z) = xz + x'z' + x'y. \tag{6.13}$$

Equations (6.12) and (6.13) are certainly equivalent. This shows that the map method displays with ease two different simplified forms of a given switching function. ▲

EXAMPLE 6.2. Simplify the switching function

$$T_{12}(w,x, y, z) = w'y' + wx' + yz' + x'z'. \tag{6.14}$$

This is the same function as Eq. (4.5). We used a long process to effect the simplification of Eq. (4.5). After re-reading that paragraph, we might ask: how do we know which way to proceed? This highlights the point that even though the rules in switching algebra can be used to simplify a switching function, it is very hard to find the right process. Now, let us examine how to proceed when we do decide to use the map method to simplify the function given. We also expect to present and illustrate the steps to be taken in employing the map method in this and the following example.

First of all, we must map the given function on a Karnaugh map. Note that although the given function is not expressed in terms of standard products, this does not present any insurmountable difficulty. One way we can solve this problem is to determine the standard products contained in each term. For example, the standard products contained in $w'y'$ can be obtained by expanding $w'y'(x + x')(z + z')$, or we can look at the map and see what areas have to be labeled 1 in order to produce a given term. For example, in order to have the term $w'y'$, the following four areas have to be labeled 1: 0000, 0001, 0100, and 0101. By using either one of these approaches, we can map the given function, as shown in Fig. 6.9.

We are now in a position to establish appropriate groupings among the 1-labeled cells so that a minimum sum of products can be obtained. We search first for cells which cannot be grouped with any other cell. If such a cell is found, its corresponding standard product should be entered in the final expression by an or-operation. In the present problem, there is none. Next we look for 1-labeled cells which can *only* be covered with groupings of two adjacent cells. If such a cell is located, the two-cell grouping which covers this cell should be made. Its corresponding product will be entered in the final expression by an or-operation.* The map in Fig. 6.9 shows that each 1-labeled cell can be covered by a two-cell grouping; however, each one can also be covered by grouping of more than two cells.

We move on to locate cells which can *only* be covered by four-cell groupings. Note that the cell 1110 can be covered by the grouping containing cells 0010, 0110, 1110, and 1010, which form a rectangle. This grouping is promptly made and its corresponding product, yz', is entered through an or-operation into the final expression, because there is no other grouping containing four or more cells which will cover the 1-labeled cell 1110.

The 1-labeled cell 0100 can be, however, covered by either one of two groupings. One grouping, called grouping A, contains the cells 0000, 0100, 0001, and 0101. The other, called grouping B, contains the cells 0000, 0100, 0010, and 0110. So far as covering the cell 0100 is concerned, either grouping is equally desirable and either one is enough. The choice has to be made by other considerations. By examining the situation at

* The reader might question the wisdom of trying to make two-cell groupings first. The reasoning behind this can be appreciated by noting in the previous statement, the presence of the word *only* and by working Problem 6.7 at the end of this chapter.

$wx \backslash yz$	00	01	11	10
00	1	1	0	1
01	1	1	0	1
11	0	0	0	1
10	1	1	1	1

Fig. 6.9. A map for Example 6.2.

$wx \backslash yz$	00	01	11	10
00	0	0	1	1
01	1	1	1	1
11	1	1	1	1
10	0	1	1	1

Fig. 6.10. A map for Example 6.3.

cell 0101, we realize that it cannot be covered by any grouping of four or more cells other than grouping A; therefore, grouping A is chosen and the product $w'y'$ is entered into the simplified expression in Eq. (6.15). The same reasoning is used to make the grouping covering cells 1000, 1001, 1011, and 1010.

Since every 1-labeled cell in the map is covered by at least one grouping, the grouping process is completed. The given switching function is simplified to

$$T_{12}(w, x, y, z) = w'y' + wx' + yz'. \blacktriangle \tag{6.15}$$

Example 6.3. Simplify the four-variable switching function

$$T(w, x, y, z) = m_2 + m_3 + m_4 + m_5 + m_6 + m_7 + m_9 + m_{10} + m_{11} + m_{12} + m_{13} + m_{14} + m_{15}. \tag{6.16}$$

Equation (6.16) is mapped in Fig. 6.10.

A subsequent search shows that there is no 1-labeled cell which can be covered only by a two-cell grouping. Note that the cell 1001 can be covered by the grouping containing cells 1101, 1111, 1001, and 1011. There is no other grouping containing four or more cells which will cover the cell 1001. The four-cell grouping is made and its corresponding product, wz, is entered into the final simplified expression in Eq. (6.17).

Even though the remaining nine 1-labeled cells can be covered by four-cell groups, no further grouping is made. The reason is that they can also be covered by eight-cell groupings. Two eight-cell groupings are then made. The final simplified expression is

$$T = x + y + wz. \blacktriangle \tag{6.17}$$

From the previous examples it can be seen that whenever two 1-labeled areas or, four 1-labeled areas, or eight 1-labeled areas, form a rectangle, one, two, or three switching variables can be eliminated through proper grouping. If six 1-labeled areas form a rectangle, a single grouping cannot be accomplished. However, four of these areas can be grouped at a time.

6.4 Variations of the map method. The approach presented in the previous section is called the *1's factoring*, because the factors are taken by grouping the appropriate 1's. In the map method, there is another approach, that of grouping the 0's.

In Fig. 6.7, the areas labeled 1 are used to represent the switching function defined by Eq. (6.8). According to previous development in Section 3.9, the negative of a switching function should contain all the standard products not included in the function itself. We can thus consider that the sum of areas labeled 0 in Fig. 6.7 represents the negative of the given switching function.

This reasoning immediately suggests that we can group the 0-labeled areas and obtain a simplified expression for the negative of the original function. We can do this by the process presented in Section 6.3. The factoring is shown in Fig. 6.11:

$$T' = xz' + x'y'z. \qquad (6.18)$$

In order to obtain the function itself, a negation operation is applied to Eq. (6.18):

$$\begin{aligned} T &= (T')' = (xz' + x'y'z)' \\ &= (x' + z)(x + y + z') \\ &= xz + x'z' + x'y. \end{aligned} \qquad (6.19)$$

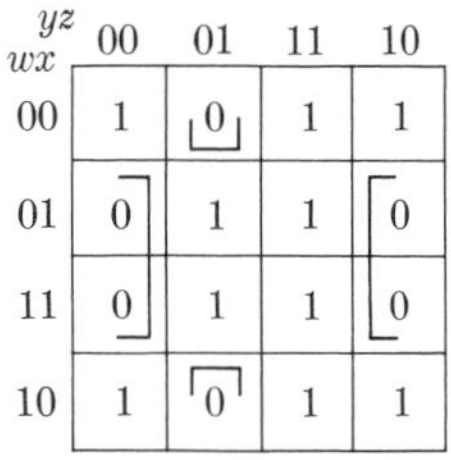

$wx \backslash yz$	00	01	11	10
00	1	0	1	1
01	0	1	1	0
11	0	1	1	0
10	1	0	1	1

FIG. 6.11. A map for Example 6.1, obtained by zero factoring.

Equation (6.19) is, of course, the same as Eq. (6.13).

Practical situations do arise. For example, in Section 9.5, it is immaterial whether certain standard products are included in the switching function or not. These terms are called the *don't-care conditions*. This flexibility can be advantageously used to simplify switching functions.

EXAMPLE 6.4. Simplify the switching function

$$T(w, x, y, z) = \sum m\ 2, 3, 4, 9, 11, \qquad (6.20)$$
$$\text{don't-care conditions: } m_5, m_6, m_{10}, m_{12}, m_{13}, \text{ or } m_{14}.$$

The graphical representation of the function is shown in Fig. 6.12. Each area corresponding to one of the standard products is labeled 1. The don't-care conditions are represented by x-marked areas on the map. Corresponding to the definition of the don't-care conditions, these x-marked areas can be grouped with the 1-marked areas, but they can also be neglected. Using the scheme of factoring shown in Fig. 6.12, we obtain

$$T(w, x, y, z) = xz' + wx'z + x'y. \qquad (6.21)$$

$wx \backslash yz$	00	01	11	10
00	0	0	1	1
01	1	x	0	x
11	x	x	0	x
10	0	1	1	x

FIG. 6.12. A map for Example 6.4.

$wx \backslash yz$	00	01	11	10
00	0	0	1	1
01	1	x	0	x
11	x	x	0	x
10	0	1	1	x

FIG. 6.13. An alternative grouping for Example 6.4.

In the above factoring, don't-care products m_6, m_{10}, m_{12}, and m_{14} are included in the factoring, because they help the simplification. This is, however, not a unique solution. A different factoring is shown in Fig. 6.13. By including the don't-care products m_5, m_{10}, m_{12}, and m_{13}, we obtain

$$T(w, x, y, z) = xy' + x'y + x'wz. \tag{6.22}$$

It is worthwhile to mention that the switching function in Eq. (6.21) is not identical with that in Eq. (6.22). Once again the map method easily shows various alternatives for a given switching function.▲

EXAMPLE 6.5. Simplify the switching function

$$T(w, x, y, z) = M_5M_6M_7M_{13}M_{14}M_{15}. \tag{6.23}$$

The previous examples in this section illustrate mainly switching functions expressed in terms of standard products. The switching function in this example can of course be converted into a form in terms of products. However, it is quite enlightening to see whether we can work on the sums directly.

First we must represent the sums on a map. Let us examine the factor M_{15}, which stands for the switching function

$$M_{15} = w + x + y + z. \tag{6.24}$$

The binary equivalent for this term is 1111, which can be adequately specified by the area 1111. Using this reasoning, we can then map the function in Eq. (6.23) as shown in Fig. 6.14.

$wx \backslash yz$	00	01	11	10
00	0	0	0	0
01	0	1	1	1
11	0	1	1	1
10	0	0	0	0

FIG. 6.14. Map for Example 6.5.

Now we are ready to commence simplification. Note that the area 1111 is adjacent to the area 1101. Since 1111 stands for $w + x + y + z$ and 1101 stands for $w + x + y' + z$, the following simplification can be effected:

$$(w + x + y + z)(w + x + y' + z) = w + x + z + yy' = w + x + z. \tag{6.25}$$

Areas 0111 and 0101, which are also adjacent with each other, indicate another possible simplification:

$$(w' + x + y + z)(w' + x + y' + z) = w' + x + z + yy' = w' + x + z. \tag{6.26}$$

Equations (6.25) and (6.26) can be further simplified:

$$(w + x + z)(w' + x + z) = ww' + x + z = x + z. \tag{6.27}$$

Equation (6.27) indicates that four areas forming a rectangle can be bracketed together to effect function simplification. This grouping is shown in Fig. 6.14. Another grouping, involving areas 0111, 1111, 0110, and 1110, can also be made to produce

$$(w' + x + y + z)(w + x + y + z)(w' + x + y + z')(w + x + y + z') = (x + y + z)(x + y + z') = x + y. \tag{6.28}$$

If we examine the left-hand labels of the areas, we see that 1 is the common factor which is responsible for the x in the simplified expression. We note also that 1, which stands for y, is the common top label for the areas involved.

The final expression is of course the product of the expressions in Eqs. (6.27) and (6.28):

$$T(w, x, y, z) = (x + z)(x + y) = x + yz. \tag{6.29}$$

This example shows that a switching function expressed in terms of standard sums can be mapped and simplified directly on its map. Once the reader is familiar with map simplification, there are many variations available.▲

6.5 Extension of the map method. The map method developed so far is applicable only to cases in which the switching function has four switching variables. Since we cannot expect that all switching functions will have at most four variables, it is natural to attempt to expand the diagram to accommodate five or more switching variables. The map method is attractive, because it indicates clearly how a given function can be simplified. The map can be used to simplify switching functions, because each area in the map represents a basic form, a standard product (or sum) and two standard products (or sums), represented by two adjacent areas, differ only in one variable. For example, in Fig. 6.11, the area 0101 represents the standard product $w'xy'z$. One of its adjacent areas, 0111, represents $w'xyz$. The switching variable y appears in the product $w'xy'z$ in primed form, while it appears in $w'xyz$ in unprimed form. These two products, of course, can be combined to eliminate the variable y. Such a pair is called a *combinable pair*.

The extension of the map from one switching variable to four variables does not present any problem; however, extension to more than four variables does. We know that a standard product (or sum) of four switching variables can be combined with any one of four other standard products (or sums) for variable elimination. Therefore, if a diagram is to be useful in showing the simplification possibilities, each area should have four adjacent areas. With four variables this is possible.

However, when there are five switching variables, a standard product can be combined with any one of five other standard products for variable elimination. If a diagram is to be useful, it has to provide five "adjacent" areas for each area to accommodate the five combinable standard products (or sums). This is where the difficulty begins.

ab \ *cde*	000	001	011	010	110	111	101	100
00	0	1	3	2	6	7	5	4
01	8	9	11	10	14	15	13	12
11	24	25	27	26	30	31	29	28
10	16	17	19	18	22	23	21	20

FIG. 6.15. A map of five variables.

In an effort to provide five "adjacent" areas for each one, the map in Fig. 6.15 is suggested. The center double line can be considered a mirror. Each area is considered adjacent not only to its four neighboring areas, but also to its mirror image. The decimal designation for a standard product (or sum) is shown in its corresponding area. The area 9 is not only adjacent to areas 1, 8, 11, 25, but also to 13, which is its mirror image. The following example will illustrate how this map can be used.

EXAMPLE 6.6. Simplify the switching function

$$T(a, b, c, d, e) = m_0 + m_3 + m_4 + m_7 + m_9 + m_{11} + m_{13} + m_{15} + m_{16} + m_{20} + m_{25} + m_{27} + m_{29} + m_{31}. \qquad (6.30)$$

$ab \backslash cde$	000	001	011	010	110	111	101	100
00	1	0	1	0	0	1	0	1
01	0	1	1	0	0	1	1	0
11	0	1	1	0	0	1	1	0
10	1	0	0	0	0	0	0	1

FIG. 6.16. A five-variable map for Example 6.6.

The given function is mapped on a five-variable map, as shown in Fig. 6.16. The areas at the four corners can be grouped together to produce $b'd'e'$. By using the mirror property, we can combine areas 3, 7, 11, and 15 to obtain $a'de$. By the same reasoning, the eight areas 9, 11, 13, 15, 25, 27, 29, and 31 can be combined to produce be. Therefore, the simplified function is

$$T(a, b, c, d, e) = be + a'de + b'd'e'. \blacktriangle \tag{6.31}$$

Six-variable maps have been proposed. If a switching function contains more than six switching variables, other simplification methods become more desirable.

6.6 Tabulation method. The map method, together with variations, can be easily applied to any switching function of four, five, or six variables. Efforts have been made to extend this approach to functions of more than six variables. Unfortunately, as the number of variables increases, too many are involved to draw an appropriate map capable of displaying all possible simplifications.

This section will present a method developed by Quine and improved by McCluskey, the *tabulation method.** This method can be used to handle switching functions of many variables, even though it is quite tedious when the number of variables is large. The tabulation method can be machine programmed, which is a great advantage when we consider the easy accessibility to computers that most designers now enjoy.

This tabulation method will be presented by the following examples.

EXAMPLE 6.7. Simplify the following switching function by using the tabulation method:

$$T(w, x, y, z) = \sum m\ 0, 2, 3, 5, 7, 8, 10, 11, 13, 15.$$

---

* MC 1, QU 1, QU 2, and QU 3.

TABLE 6.1

0	0000 ✓	0,2	00–0 ✓	0, 2, 8, 10	–0–0	A
2	0010 ✓	0,8	–000 ✓	2, 3, 10, 11	–01–	B
8	1000 ✓	2,3	001– ✓	3, 7, 11, 15	––11	C
3	0011 ✓	2,10	–010 ✓	5, 7, 13, 15	–1–1	D
5	0101 ✓	8,10	10–0 ✓			
10	1010 ✓	3,7	0–11 ✓			
7	0111 ✓	3,11	–011 ✓			
13	1101 ✓	5,7	01–1 ✓			
11	1011 ✓	5,13	–101 ✓			
15	1111 ✓	10,11	101– ✓			
		7,15	–111 ✓			
		13,15	11–1 ✓			
		11,15	1–11 ✓			

First step. Write down the binary representations of the standard products of the switching function. They are

0000, 0010, 0011, 0101, 0111,
1000, 1010, 1011, 1101, 1111.

Second step. Group these binary representations according to the number of 1's contained, as shown in Table 6.1.

Third step. It has already been stated that any two standard products which are different from each other by only one variable can be grouped together and, subsequently, that variable can be eliminated. Examining the grouping scheme in the second step, we realize that eliminations, if possible, can be accomplished only by members of adjacent groups. Adjacent groups are defined as two groups whose number of 1's differ only by one.

An exhaustive comparing process is then undertaken. Each member of a group must be compared with every member of its adjacent group. This task should be started from group 0 (a group that has no 1 at all).

0000 stands for $w'x'y'z'$, 0010 for $w'x'yz'$. In this combining process, y is eliminated. The term $w'x'z'$ can be represented by 00–0. A bar ("–") is used to denote that y is eliminated. This new term is entered in Table 6.1, while terms 0000 and 0010 are checked off, as shown in Table 6.1. This process is continued downward until every combinable pair (any two terms which can be combined to eliminate one variable) is taken into account.

The same searching and comparing process is then applied to the second column in Table 6.1. At this stage, one more restriction should be added. A term can be compared with a member of the next adjacent group only when they have bars at the same locations. The entries obtained in this process are then entered as the third column in Table 6.1.

The decimal equivalents are written on the left-hand side of each entry for identification purposes.

The elimination process should be carried on as long as it is possible. In the present example, the operation stops at the third column.

Fourth step. At this point, note that in the three columns of Table 6.1, there are checked entries and unchecked entries. Each checked entry has been taken into account by an entry in the subsequent column. Therefore, the or-combination of all unchecked entries presents a simplified version of the given function. In the present example, the given switching function is simplified to

$$T(w, x, y, z) = x'z' + x'y + yz + xz. \tag{6.32}$$

We should not, however, accept Eq. (6.32) as the final answer, because there may be redundancies in it. In order to uncover any possible redundancy, we label each unchecked entry as shown in Table 6.1 and draw the chart shown in Fig. 6.17.

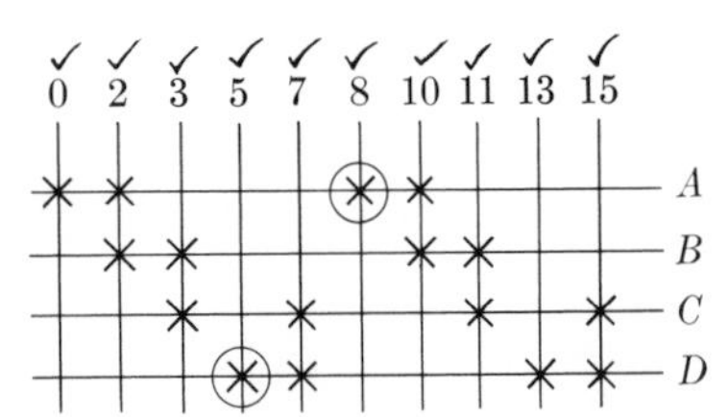

FIG. 6.17. Chart for Example 6.7.

At this stage, decimal equivalents are used. Term A is the result of combining four standard products: 0, 2, 8, and 10. At the cross-point of A and 0, a cross is placed. This cross indicates that m_0 is contained in A. At the cross-point of A and 2, a cross is again placed. The same process is continued until the decimal equivalents of term D are taken into account.

In Fig. 6.17, we find only one cross below standard product 5. This is located at the crossing point with D. We can conclude that in order to enable the final, simplified expression to contain standard product 5, term D has to be included in the final expression. A circle is added to that cross to indicate the fact; m_5 is then checked off. By examining horizontally on line D, we see three more crosses. This means that by having D in the final expression, m_7, m_{13}, and m_{15} are also taken into account. These terms are, therefore, checked off.

Next we note that on the line of standard product 8, only one cross is found. This means that term A has to be included in the final expression. A circle is added to that cross. In having A in the final expression, m_0, m_2, and m_{10} are also taken into account and crossed off.

The fact is that the designer has no alternative but to include terms A and D. This is why such terms, if any, should be located first.

Let us now examine Fig. 6.17 again. If only terms A and D are combined to form the final expression, all the products except m_3 and m_{11} will be included. In order to take into account these two products, either term B or term C can be used, but there is certainly no need for both.*

The final expression can be

$$T(w, x, y, z) = A + D + B = xz + x'y + x'z', \tag{6.33}$$

or

$$T(w, x, y, z) = A + D + C = xz + yz + x'z'. \tag{6.34}$$

It is very interesting to note that the switching function in Eq. (6.33) is the same as that in Eq. (6.13), and the switching function in Eq. (6.34) is the same as that in Eq. (6.12). We would expect this to be true, although we have used different approaches to simplify the same switching function.▲

So far as the above problem is concerned, the map method yields the final expressions much faster. It is quite true, however, that if the number of switching variables is more than six, the tabulation method is a systematic alternative.†

6.7 Discussion of the tabulation method. In the previous section, where the tabulation method is presented, the approach necessary to deal with don't-care conditions is not mentioned. Actually it is quite simple. When we use the tabulation method, since don't-care conditions are useful wherever they help to simplify a switching function, all the don't-care condition products should be treated as though they were products of the given function. In the final chart simplification, all the don't-care products should be ignored. This is justified by the reasoning that the final expression will be acceptable no matter whether or not any don't-care product is included in the final expression.

---

* Systematic approaches to display all alternatives in selecting the prime implicants can be found in PE 1, GA 1, MO 2, UR 1, and HA 4.

† For another approach, see SA 1, CH 2, DU 1, PR 1, and PY 1.

The whole process will be illustrated by the following example.

EXAMPLE 6.8. Simplify the following switching function by the tabulation method:

$$T(w, x, y, z) = \sum m\ 2, 3, 4, 9, 11,$$

don't-care conditions: $m5$, 6, 10, 12, 13, or 14.

Following the steps outlined in Section 6.6, we construct Table 6.2. Note that all the don't-care products are treated the same as those of the given function.

TABLE 6.2

2	0010 ✓	2, 3	001– ✓	2, 3, 10, 11	–01–	C
4	0100 ✓	2, 6	0–10 ✓	2, 6, 10, 14	––10	D
3	0011 ✓	2, 10	–010 ✓	4, 5, 12, 13	–10–	E
9	1001 ✓	4, 5	010– ✓	4, 6, 12, 14	–1–0	F
5	0101 ✓	4, 6	01–0 ✓			
6	0110 ✓	4, 12	–100 ✓			
10	1010 ✓	3, 11	–011 ✓			
12	1100 ✓	9, 11	10–1 A			
11	1011 ✓	9, 13	1–01 B			
13	1101 ✓	5, 13	–101 ✓			
14	1110 ✓	6, 14	–110 ✓			
		10, 11	101– ✓			
		10, 14	1–10 ✓			
		12, 13	110– ✓			
		12, 14	11–0 ✓			

In making the final simplification chart, we will ignore all the don't-care products, because it is necessary to determine only if all the standard products in the given function are included.

The simplification chart is shown in Fig. 6.18.

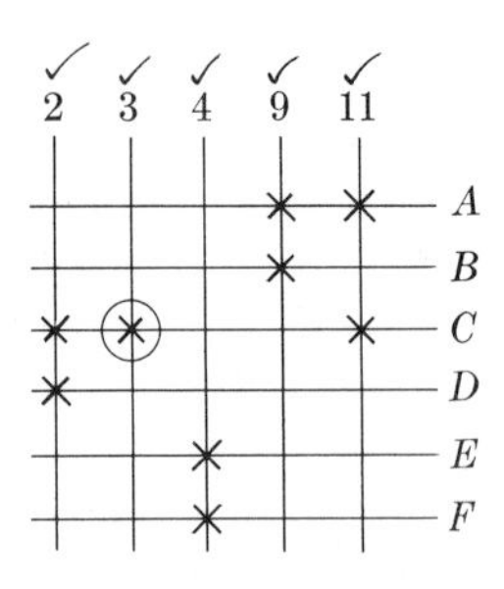

FIG. 6.18. Simplification chart for Example 6.8.

Possible expressions of the given switching function can be found by using the reasoning presented in Example 6.7. It can also be obtained by using an algebraic approach,* which is to be presented in the following.

Through the tabulation reduction just completed, we have found six products, namely A, B, C, D, E, and F. The remaining task is to select the necessary products to form the final expression of the given function. The selection has to be made in such a way that the final expression will contain no redundancy. There is no reason to believe that such a selection is unique. The algebraic approach is capable of displaying all such nonredundant forms of a switching function from the set of products found by the tabulation reduction.

A function G is generated as follows:

$$G = (C + D)(C)(E + F)(A + B)(A + C).$$

We can consider that G is a switching function of six switching variables, namely A, B, C, D, E, and F. The truth value of G is 1 when the set of products selected covers every standard product in the given function, otherwise its value is 0. The truth values of A, B, C, D, E, and F are determined by the following convention. If the product represented by A is chosen to form the final expression, the truth value of A is 1; otherwise its value is 0.

With the above understanding established, we are now in a position to see how the function G is generated. Note that G is a product of five sums. The truth value of G is 1 if and only if each one of the five sums is 1. Each sum corresponds to a column of the simplification chart in Fig. 6.18. The first sum, $C + D$, indicates the fact that either C or D can cover m_2. When either C or D, or both, is selected, m_2 will be represented and the sum $C + D$ will be 1. Since m_3 can be covered only by the product C, a term C is found in G. The sum $E + F$ is entered in G, because either E or F can be used to cover m_4. The other two sums can be interpreted in the same way.

Since G is considered to be a switching function, its form of representation can certainly be manipulated. Since

$$(C)(C + D)(C + A) = C,$$

the expression for G can be simplified to

$$G = C(A + B)(E + F) = CEA + CFA + CEB + CFB.$$

Whenever the product CEA is 1, G will be 1. The product CEA is 1 only

---

* PE 1.

when $C = 1$, $E = 1$, and $A = 1$. That is to say, if the products C, E, and A are used to form the expression of the given function, every standard product in the given function will be covered. Furthermore, this selection yields a nonredundant expression, because there is no redundancy in the product CEA. One possible form of expression of the given function is thus found to be $C + E + A$, as it is shown in Eq. (6.35). The remaining three products yield three other forms of expressions for the given function. They are given in Eqs. (6.36), (6.37), and (6.38):

$$T_1 = C + E + A = x'y + xy' + wx'z, \tag{6.35}$$

$$T_2 = C + F + A = x'y + xz' + wx'z, \tag{6.36}$$

$$T_3 = C + E + B = x'y + xy' + wy'z, \tag{6.37}$$

$$T_4 = C + F + B = x'y + xz' + wy'z. \tag{6.38}$$

Equations (6.35) and (6.36) are identical with Eqs. (6.22) and (6.21), respectively. Equations (6.37) and (6.38) can also be obtained by the map method through different groupings.▲

All the examples shown involve switching functions expressed in terms of standard products. However, the tabulation method without any significant modification can also be applied to functions expressed in terms of standard sums.

6.8 Function manipulation and circuit optimization. Two methods, the map method and the tabulation method, have been presented. It is of interest to investigate how these methods are used for circuit optimization. We will now study their application to the optimization of relay switching circuits and diode switching circuits.

To optimize a relay switching circuit, it is necessary to reduce to a minimum the number of springs needed. This corresponds to reducing to a minimum the number of literals in the given switching function. Therefore, both methods can be applied, as shown in the following example.

EXAMPLE 6.9. Use relay contacts to realize the switching function

$$T(w, x, y, z) = x'y'z' + xy'z + w'yz + wxz + wx'y + x'yz'. \tag{6.39}$$

Equation (6.39) is the same as Eq. (6.8). The task of reducing the number of literals in a given expression can be carried out by using either the map method (see Eq. 6.12) or the tabulation method (see Eq. 6.34). The final result is

$$T(w, x, y, z) = z(x + y) + x'z'. \tag{6.40}$$

The final circuit corresponding to this form is shown in Fig. 6.19. This circuit requires eight springs. The final expression in Eq. (6.40) proves that this is the absolute minimum. Because the variable x appears in both primed and unprimed forms, three springs are needed. The same can be said about z. But the variable y, which appears only in unprimed form, needs two springs. However, the circuit in Fig. 6.19 is not the only answer. Both the map method and the tabulation method show, in Eqs. (6.13) and (6.33) respectively, that another expression can be found for the given switching function. This simplified version can also be realized by a relay switching circuit of eight springs. The point to note here is that for a given problem, there may be several optimum solutions. The map method and the tabulation method are very helpful in uncovering them.▲

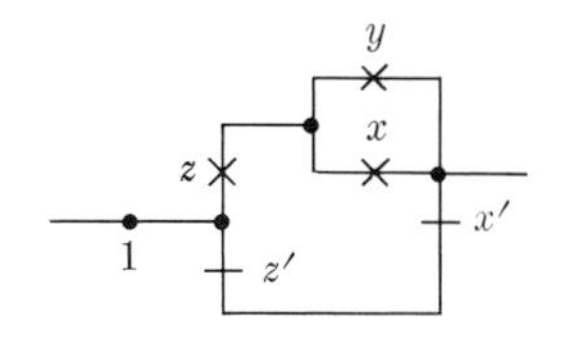

FIG. 6.19. Relay switching circuit for the switching function in Eq. (6.40).

Let us now study the optimization of a diode switching circuit. The criteria for an optimum circuit are that the circuit can, at most, have two levels, and that the number of diodes needed should be the least possible. The restriction to a two-level circuit is justified, considering the fact that a multilevel diode switching circuit introduces excessive delay and signal distortion.*

In order to have a two-level switching circuit, the corresponding switching function must be either the or-combination of products (they do not have to be standard products) or the and-combination of sums (they do not have to be standard sums). Since the number of diodes needed is equal to the sum of the number of literals and the number of terms in a given switching function, we must reduce this sum as much as possible to optimize a two-level diode switching circuit. The map method and the tabulation method are very helpful in this effort.

EXAMPLE 6.10. Use diode gates to realize the switching function in Eq. (6.39).

Equation (6.39) corresponds to a two-level switching circuit. The number of diodes needed is equal to the sum of the number of literals (18 in this problem) and the number of terms (six in this problem); therefore, we will need 24 diodes to realize the corresponding circuits.

---

* If the circuit components are such that multilevel circuits are feasible, another approach, the decomposition method, is of interest; see AS 1, AS 2, CU 1, and GI 6.

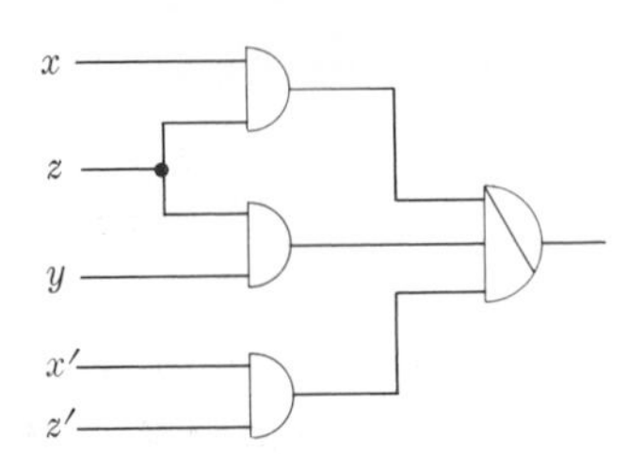

FIG. 6.20. Diode switching circuit for the switching function in Eq. (6.41).

By using either the map method or the tabulation method, we can simplify the given expression to

$$T = xz + yz + x'z'. \tag{6.41}$$

The expression in Eq. (6.40) calls for a three-level switching circuit and is, therefore, ignored. The implementation of the expression in Eq. (6.41) is shown in Fig. 6.20. This two-level circuit requires nine diodes. Following the criteria for an optimum diode switching circuit, this is the best we can do, but it is not the only good one. Both manipulation methods can display all possible alternatives.▲

Some interesting and important observations can be made by examining Eq. (6.41) again. It is an or-combination of three product terms, namely xz, yz, and $x'z'$.

We can see that when xz has a truth value of 1, the given function also has a truth value of 1. We can then say that the given function contains (or includes) xz. To put it in more general terms, the following definitions can be made.

A switching function $A(x_1, x_2, \ldots, x_n)$ is said to contain (or include) another switching function $a(x_1, x_2, \ldots, x_n)$ if $A(x_1, x_2, \ldots, x_n)$ has a truth value of 1 when $a(x_1, x_2, \ldots, x_n)$ does. Following the above definition, it is clear that yz and $x'z'$ are also contained in the given switching function.

Besides being contained in the given switching function, the three terms xz, yz, and $x'z'$ have another interesting property with respect to the given switching function. If we eliminate x in the product term xz to form a new product with the remaining literal (or literals) z, then we see that this new product is not contained in the given function, because the fact that z has a truth value of 1 does not guarantee that the given function will be 1. Instead of eliminating x, we can delete z to obtain a new term x, and then conclude that x is not contained in the given function. The same observation can be made about the product terms yz and $x'z'$. The three product terms xz, yz, and $x'z'$ are termed the *prime implicants* of the given switching function. The prime implicant of a given switching function is defined as a product term which is contained in the function, and the elimination of any literal from this product term will yield a new product which is not contained in the given function.

The introduction of the terms *contained* and *prime implicant* shed new light on the interpretation of the tabulation method and the optimization of two-level diode switching circuits.

The simplification of the switching function in Eq. (6.39) is carried out in Table 6.1. Through successive eliminations made in Table 6.1, there are four unchecked terms, namely $x'z'$, $x'y$, yz, and xz. Each one of the four product terms is a prime implicant of the given switching function. Therefore, it can be said that the tabulation elimination is actually a process of finding all the prime implicants of a given switching function. However, the final simplified form of a given switching function is not the or-combination of *all* the prime implicants. The chart elimination carried out in Fig. 6.17 determines the necessary prime implicants which should be included in the final version. In summary, the tabulation method consists of two steps: the tabulation elimination constitutes the first step, and it yields all the prime implicants of a given switching function. The second step, the chart elimination, selects among all the prime implicants the necessary ones which form the final simplified expression.

Next let us investigate the optimization of two-level diode switching circuits. It has already been established that in order to realize a given switching function with two-level diode switching circuits, this function has to be expressed either as the sum of products or as the product of sums. Now it can be further asserted that in order to obtain an optimum two-level diode switching circuit for a given switching function, this function must be manipulated to be the sum of prime implicants. To validate this statement, let us suppose that an optimum two-level diode switching circuit is obtained from an expression which is the sum of products, but one of the products is not a prime implicant. That immediately means one or more literals can be eliminated from that term. That, in turn, indicates the possibility that one or more diodes can be saved from the original circuit. This, of course, contradicts the claim that the original circuit is an optimum one; i.e., in order to implement a given switching function with an optimum two-level diode switching circuit, the given function must be manipulated to be the sum of some (or all) of its prime implicants.* That is why the given function in Eq. (6.39) is manipulated by either the map method or the tabulation method to be the sum of three of its four prime implicants, as shown in Eq. (6.41).

* MC 2, pp. 67–88.

6.9 Optimization by computer. The criteria for optimum relay and diode switching circuits have been presented. They are relatively simple, but they do not reflect all the considerations that have to be taken. It is true that the number of springs needed in a relay switching circuit dictates to a certain extent its cost; but the cost of construction, the switching speed, its reliability, and other factors must also be considered. Similarly, simply counting the number of diodes needed in a two-level diode switching circuit is not an adequate test. We need to judge a switching circuit by more reliable standards.

Another difficulty previously mentioned is that when the number of switching variables involved is large, the switching circuit becomes quite cumbersome and tedious to manipulate into different forms so that an optimum one can be chosen.

In order to carry out necessary, but tedious, manipulations in a speedy fashion and to judge each circuit by a more critical standard, efforts have been made and proved to be successful in programming the switching circuit optimization problems into high-speed computers.* The basic approach employed is, however, the tabulation method.

PROBLEMS

In the statements of the following problems, "to simplify a switching function" means to express the given switching function as the minimum sum of products if the function is originally expressed as sum of products, or as the minimum product of sums if the function is originally given as product of sums.

6.1. Use the map method to simplify the following switching functions.

(a) $T(w, x, y) = \sum m(0, 1, 6, 7)$
(b) $T(w, x, y) = \sum m(0, 2, 4, 6)$
(c) $T(w, x, y) = \sum m(0, 1, 3, 4, 5, 7)$

6.2. Use the map method to simplify the following switching functions.

(a) $T(a, b, c) = \sum m(2, 3, 4, 5)$
(b) $T(A, B, C) = \sum m(1, 3, 5, 7)$
(c) $T(A, B, C) = \sum m(1, 2, 3, 5, 6, 7)$

6.3. Simplify the following switching functions.

(a) $T(a, b, c, d) = \sum m(0, 4, 10, 14)$
(b) $T(a, b, c, d) = \sum m(0, 1, 4, 5, 12, 13)$

6.4. Simplify the following switching functions.

(a) $f(w, x, y, z) = \sum m(2, 6, 8, 12)$
(b) $f(w, x, y, z) = \sum m(2, 3, 6, 7, 14, 15)$

---

* BA 1, BA 2, and MC 2, pp. 89–102.

6.5. Simplify the switching function

$$T(w, x, y, z) = w'x' + y'z' + w'y + w'z'.$$

6.6. Simplify the switching function

$$T(a, b, c, d) = cd' + ab' + ac' + ad'.$$

6.7. Simplify the following switching functions.

(a) $T(a, b, c, d) = \sum m(1, 2, 3, 4, 5, 7, 9, 15)$
(b) $T(w, x, y, z) = \sum m(0, 5, 8, 9, 11, 12, 13, 14)$

6.8. It is pointed out in Section 6.4 that the simplification procedure can be carried out by grouping the areas labeled 0. Apply this approach to Problems 6.1(c) and 6.3(b). Discuss whether there is any advantage in doing this in each case.

6.9. It is pointed out in Section 6.4 that the simplification procedure can be carried out by grouping the areas labeled 0. Apply this approach to Problems 6.2(b), 6.2(c), and 6.4(b). Discuss whether there is any advantage in doing this in each case.

6.10. Simplify the following switching functions and indicate those don't-care standard products that have been included.

(a) $T(a, b, c, d) = \sum m(0, 1, 2, 3, 5)$
don't-care conditions: $m(4, 6, 7, 12, 13, \text{ or } 14)$
(b) $T(a, b, c, d) = \sum m(2, 6, 10, 11, 14)$
don't-care conditions: $m(5, 7, 9, 13, \text{ or } 15)$

6.11. Simplify the following switching functions and indicate those don't-care standard products that have been used.

(a) $T(w, x, y, z) = \sum m(3, 5, 7, 11, 15)$
don't-care conditions: $m(1, 4, 6, 9, 13)$
(b) $T(w, x, y, z) = \sum m(0, 4, 5, 8, 12)$
don't-care conditions: $m(1, 3, 9, 12, \text{ or } 15)$

6.12. Simplify the following five-variable function by the map method:

$$T = \sum m(1, 3, 9, 13, 26, 27, 30, 31).$$

6.13. Simplify the following five-variable function by the map method:

$$T = \sum m(0, 4, 25, 29, 18, 19, 22, 23).$$

6.14. Use the map method to simplify the switching function

$$T(a, b, c, d) = \prod M(1, 3, 7, 9, 11, 15).$$

6.15. Use the map method to simplify the switching function

$$T(w, x, y, z) = \prod M(0, 2, 3, 4, 6, 10, 11).$$

6.16. Simplify the switching function given in Problem 6.12 by the tabulation method.

6.17. Simplify the switching function given in Problem 6.13 by the tabulation method.

6.18. Simplify the following switching functions of six switching variables.

(a) $T(a, b, c, d, e, f) = \sum m(3, 7, 12, 14, 15, 19, 23, 27, 28, 29, 31, 35, 39, 44, 45, 46, 48, 49, 50, 52, 53, 55, 56, 57, 59, 60, 62, 63)$

don't-care conditions: $m(0, 11, 13, 23, 30, 32, 43, 47, 51, 54, 61)$

(b) $T(w, x, y, z, u, v) = \sum m(7, 15, 23, 31, 48, 50, 51, 53, 54, 56, 57, 59, 60, 61, 62)$

don't-care conditions: $m(1, 2, 49, 52, 55, 58, 63)$

[*Note:* Approach this problem in two ways: (1) Devise a six-variable map and use the map method. (2) Use the tabulation method.]

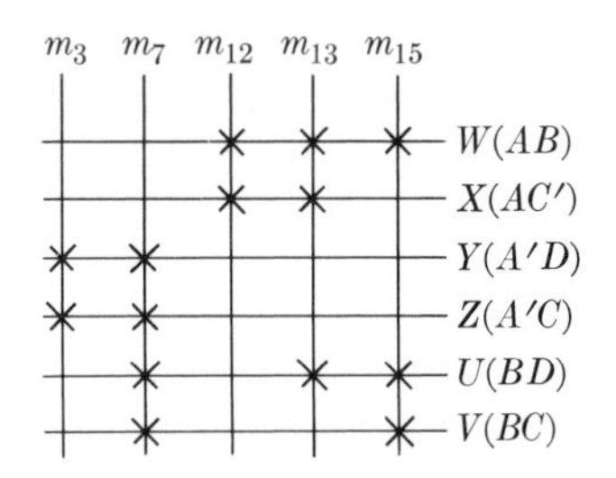

FIGURE 6.21

6.19. A switching function of four variables, A, B, C, and D, is to be simplified by the tabulation method. A chart (Fig. 6.21) is established. The prime implicant AB is represented by W, AC' by X, $A'D$ by Y, and so on.

Determine all possible forms which contain the least number of literals of its final expression. For each form, indicate the don't-care standard products included, if any.

CHAPTER 7

CIRCUIT REALIZATION III: TRANSISTOR GATES

7.1 Introduction. There are two major shortcomings in using diode switching gates to implement a given switching function. The first is the signal deterioration, which is caused by the presence of forward resistance in the diode and the interaction between stages. The second is that diode gates cannot perform the negation operation. Transistor switching gates possess the ability to amplify and to invert. Therefore, transistors are indispensable components in electronic switching circuits.

There are two complementary types of transistors, npn and pnp, available. As in electron tube circuits, transistor circuits can have three basic configurations. To show the switching capability of a transistor, the common-emitter or the grounded-emitter configuration of an npn transistor is shown in Fig. 7.1.

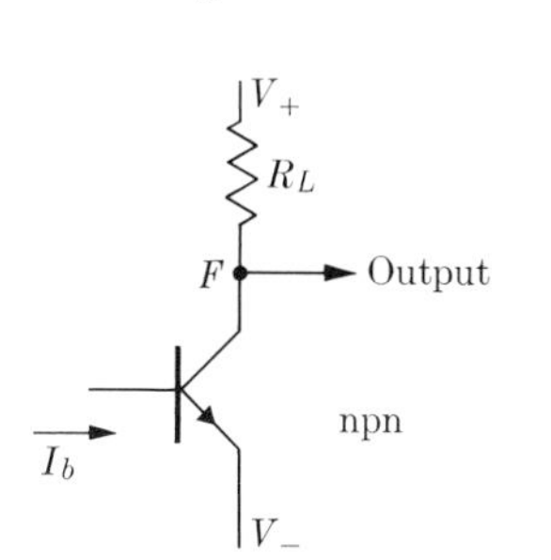

FIG. 7.1. A common-emitter configuration for an npn transistor.

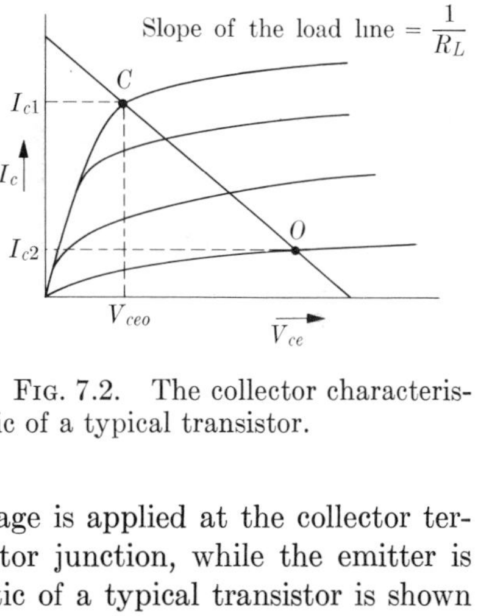

FIG. 7.2. The collector characteristic of a typical transistor.

In an npn transistor, a positive voltage is applied at the collector terminal in order to back-bias the collector junction, while the emitter is held at V_-. The collector characteristic of a typical transistor is shown in Fig. 7.2. Since the load resistance R_L is given, and the assumption is made that the junction resistance is negligible compared with R_L, the slope of the load line can be determined.

The collector characteristic shows that the operating point of the circuit depends on the voltage level at the base, or the base current, I_b. If I_b is sufficiently large, the operating point of the transistor will be located at C. At this point, the voltage drop across the emitter and the collector is small. However, the collector current is large. We can thus conclude that the transistor offers a very small resistance, or the *switch is closed.* If the voltage level of the base is at V_-, the base current will be very small and the operating point will be located at O. By examining the collector characteristic, we see that the voltage drop across the emitter and the collector is large, and the collector current is small. This situation can be interpreted to mean that the transistor offers a very large resistance, or the *switch is open.*

The above development serves one purpose, i.e., it shows that transistors can be considered as switches in their operation in switching circuits.

Let us now examine the voltage level at the collector terminal. When the base current I_b is large and positive, the transistor switch is closed. The voltage at the collector terminal F can be expressed as

$$V_{Fo} = V_+ - I_{c1}R_L = V_{ceo}. \tag{7.1}$$

Since V_{ceo} is small, the output voltage, the voltage level at the collector terminal, is very small. In fact, it is approximately the same voltage level as that of the emitter, V_-. The magnitude of V_{ceo} serves as an indication of the switching quality of the transistor.

When the voltage level at the base is at V_-, the transistor switch is open; the voltage at the collector terminal is

$$V_{F1} = V_+ - I_{c2}R_L = V_{ce1}. \tag{7.2}$$

Since I_{c2} is very small, the voltage level at the collector terminal can be considered as at V_+. The switching quality of a transistor is also indicated by the magnitude of I_{c2}.

It is obvious now that a transistor so arranged exhibits a very interesting *inversion* property. By inversion, it is meant that the transistor output is always the opposite of the input, i.e., when the input at the base is at V_-, the output is at V_+, and when the input at the base is at V_+, the output is at V_-.*

7.2 Direct-coupled transistor gates. The transistor as a switching element is introduced in the previous section. Direct-coupled transistors can be used to execute the three switching operations defined. To initiate the study, we will examine two configurations, shown in Figs. 7.3 and 7.4.

In the circuit in Fig. 7.3, the voltage levels, or the signals, at bases a and b are represented by a and b, respectively. The output, which is the voltage level at the collector terminal, is represented by f.

It is assumed here that one of the two voltage levels, V_+ or V_-, will be applied at the base. However, as yet neither level has been assigned

---

* Further discussion on transistors used in switching can be found in MI 1 and AN 1.

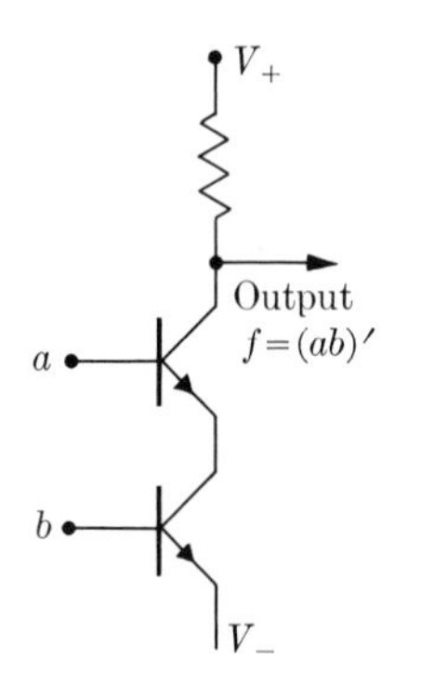

Fig. 7.3. A direct-coupled transistor nand-gate.

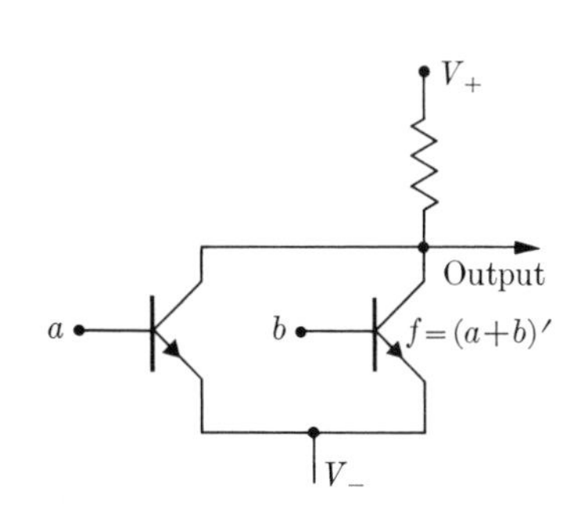

Fig. 7.4. A direct-coupled transistor nor-gate.

the truth value of 1. There are four input conditions possible. Corresponding to each input condition, the output will be *approximately* either V_+ or V_-. The complete picture is shown in Table 7.1.

Table 7.1 can be explained very easily. In the circuit given, the two transistors will not be conducting at the same time until V_+ is applied at both a and b. That is to say, the voltage level at the collector terminal will be V_+ until both bases assume voltage levels of V_+.

Table 7.1

a	V_-	V_-	V_+	V_+
b	V_-	V_+	V_-	V_+
f	V_+	V_+	V_+	V_-

Table 7.2

a	0	0	1	1
b	0	1	0	1
f	1	1	1	0

What operation does the gate shown in Fig. 7.3 perform? This depends on which voltage level represents the truth value of 1. In the first assignment scheme, which specifies the convention used in this book, the voltage level V_+ represents the truth value of 1, and V_- the truth value of 0. Under this assignment, Table 7.1 can be redrawn to yield Table 7.2.

Table 7.2 shows that the functional relationship between the inputs and the output can be expressed by

$$f = (ab)'. \tag{7.3}$$

Equation (7.3) suggests that the inputs a and b are first processed by an and-gate. The output of the and-gate is subsequently negated. The circuit in Fig. 7.3 is called a not-and-gate (from here on, it will be abbreviated as nand-gate). The symbolic representation for a transistor

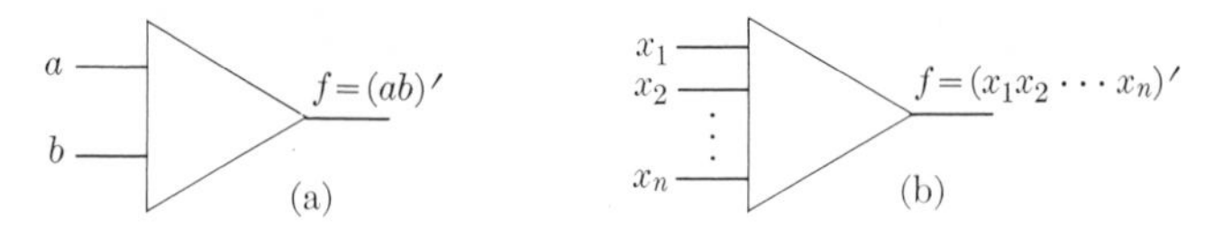

FIG. 7.5. Symbolic representation of transistor nand-gates.

nand-gate is shown in Fig. 7.5. In the circuit in Fig. 7.3, two transistors are connected in series, and two input variables can be accommodated. If more input variables are involved, the necessary modification of the circuit is very obvious. The symbolic representation of an n-input transistor nand-gate is shown in Fig. 7.5(b).

In the second assignment scheme, the voltage level V_- represents the truth value of 1, and V_+ the truth value of 0. Under this assignment, Table 7.1 can be redrawn to yield Table 7.3. By examining Table 7.3, we can establish a functional relationship between the inputs a and b and the output f:

TABLE 7.3

a	1	1	0	0
b	1	0	1	0
f	0	0	0	1

$$f = (a + b)'. \tag{7.4}$$

Equation (7.4) indicates that the inputs a and b are first gated by an or-gate. The output of the or-gate is subsequently negated. The circuit in Fig. 7.3 is then called the not-or-gate. However, since the first assignment scheme is adopted in this book, the configuration shown in Fig. 7.3 is to be considered a nand-gate. A nand-gate with only one input is actually a not-gate.

The same analysis can be made for the circuit in Fig. 7.4. It can be easily shown that if voltage level V_+ represents the truth value of 1 and V_- the truth value of 0, the inputs a and b to that circuit are first processed by an or-gate, and the output of the or-gate is subsequently negated. Therefore, the circuit in Fig. 7.4 can be considered as a not-or-gate (from here on, it will be abbreviated as nor-gate). The symbolic representations of a transistor two-input nor-gate and a transistor n-input nor-gate are shown in Fig. 7.6(a) and 7.6(b), respectively. A nor-gate with only one input is actually a not-gate.

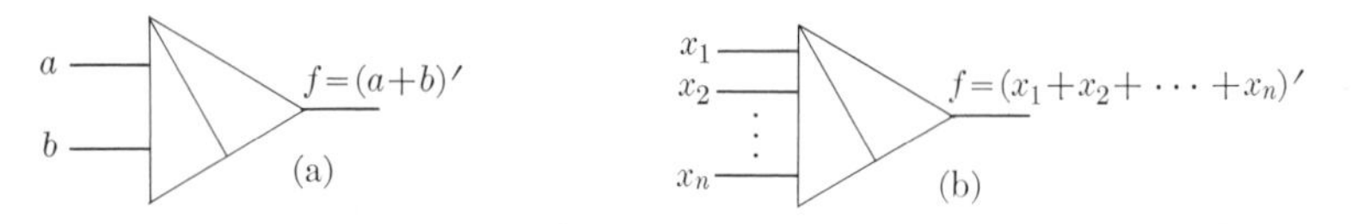

FIG. 7.6. Symbolic representation of transistor nor-gates.

In summary, two basic configurations of direct-coupled transistor gates are introduced to perform the not-and-operation and the not-or-operation. This is equivalent to saying that all three switching operations defined can be performed by direct-coupled transistor gates.

7.3 Switching function implementation with direct-coupled transistor gates. In using direct-coupled transistor gates to implement a given switching function, the designer is generally confronted with two new considerations. First of all, a direct-coupled transistor gate does not perform just an and-operation or an or-operation; it executes not-and-operation or not-or-operation. Secondly, the optimization criteria for a direct-coupled transistor switching circuit have not yet been clearly defined. The number of transistors needed serves as an approximate indication of the component cost. Besides this consideration, the construction cost, the reliability, the delay involved, the loading of each gate, and other factors must also be weighed.

To illustrate the procedures involved, an example is given.

EXAMPLE 7.1. Use direct-coupled transistor gates to implement a comparator for two binary digits.

One of the basic operations of a computer is to compare two numbers. This is essential not because of the fact that computations involve comparison operations, but because of the fact that the comparison operation is an indispensable tool for the programmer.

The comparison switching circuit is also used extensively in control systems. Occasionally, a certain variable of the system is to be held within certain limits. Comparison logic circuits are thus needed to detect whether any limit is reached or not.

In the present problem, only two binary digits A and B are to be compared. A truth table is constructed as shown in Table 7.4.

The switching function T_1 for $A > B$ can then be written as

$$T_1 = AB'. \tag{7.5}$$

TABLE 7.4

Input		Output		
A	B	$A > B$	$A = B$	$A < B$
0	0	0	1	0
0	1	0	0	1
1	0	1	0	0
1	1	0	1	0

The switching function T_2 for $A = B$ is

$$T_2 = A'B' + AB. \tag{7.6}$$

The switching function T_3 for $A < B$ is

$$T_3 = A'B. \tag{7.7}$$

The switching functions T_1, T_2, and T_3 are to be realized.

The first task in carrying out the circuit realization is to identify the available inputs. This point is not mentioned in the discussion of diode switching circuits, because diode gates are not capable of performing inversion, and all the inputs needed are assumed available. In the present problem, it is assumed that both A and B are available in unprimed forms.

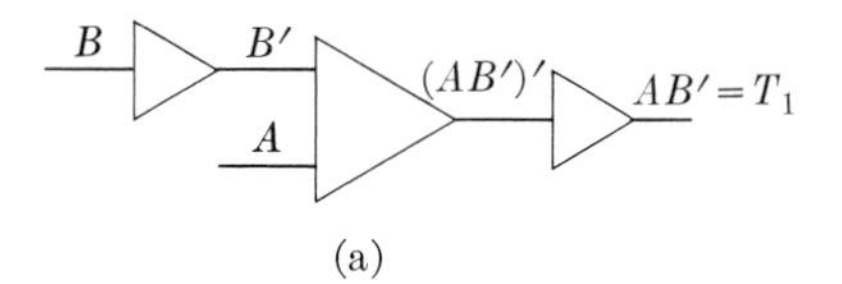

(a)

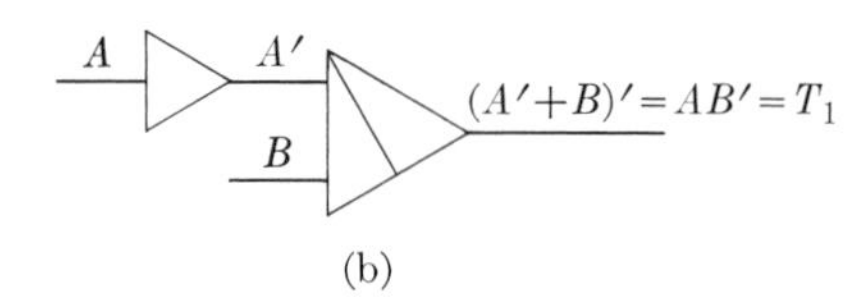

(b)

FIG. 7.7. Direct-coupled transistor switching circuit implementing T_1 of Eq. (7.5).

T_1 is to be realized first. A three-level implementation is shown in Fig. 7.7(a). The reasoning we use to arrive at this circuit is very straightforward. It can be summarized as follows. Since the term AB' is wanted, it is logical to send A and B' through an and-gate. However, two additional gates are needed. One inverter is used to produce B' from the available B, and the other to invert the output of the nand-gate to obtain the term AB'. The final inverter is used strictly to cancel the effect of the not-operation by the nand gate. Instead of using an additional inverter to cancel the undesirable effect of negation, we can anticipate this negation and obtain the circuit shown in Fig. 7.7(b). The development in arriving at this circuit is as follows. Start from the output terminal at the right-hand side. At the output we expect the final result to be AB'. Knowing that a direct-coupled transistor gate always performs a negation before it finally releases the output, we can rewrite $AB' = (A' + B)'$. What this indicates is that if A' and B are sent to a nor-gate, its output will be AB'. This explains the appearance of the two-input nor-gate in Fig. 7.7(b). In order to provide A' for the nor-gate, an inverter is used to invert the available A. The circuit in Fig. 7.7(a) is a three-level one, because the signal is processed successively by three gates and needs four transistors. The circuit in Fig. 7.7(b) is a two-level one and needs only three transistors. Generally speaking, each level will introduce a certain amount of delay; therefore, the circuit in Fig. 7.7(b) is better than that in Fig. 7.7(a). This claim is true if the available inputs are A and B. If instead, the available inputs are A and B', the best circuit is that in Fig. 7.8, which is actually the circuit in Fig. 7.7(a) with one inverter omitted.

The realization of T_3 of Eq. (7.7) can be approached the same way. The result is shown in Fig. 7.9.

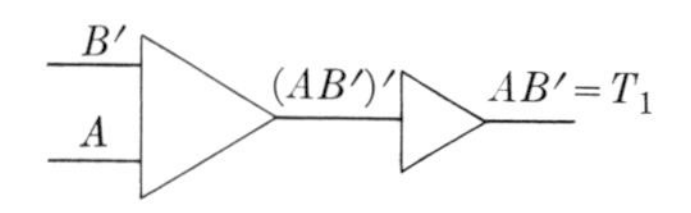

FIG. 7.8. Direct-coupled transistor switching circuit implementing T_1 of Eq. (7.5) if the available inputs are A and B'.

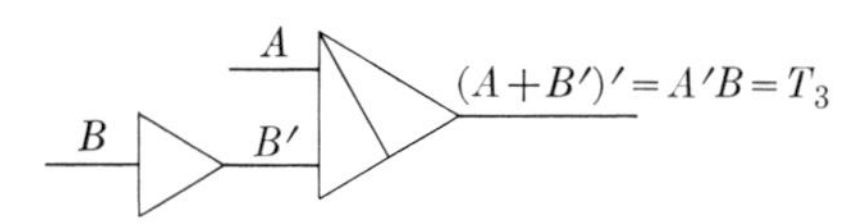

FIG. 7.9. Direct-coupled transistor switching circuit implementing T_3 of Eq. (7.7).

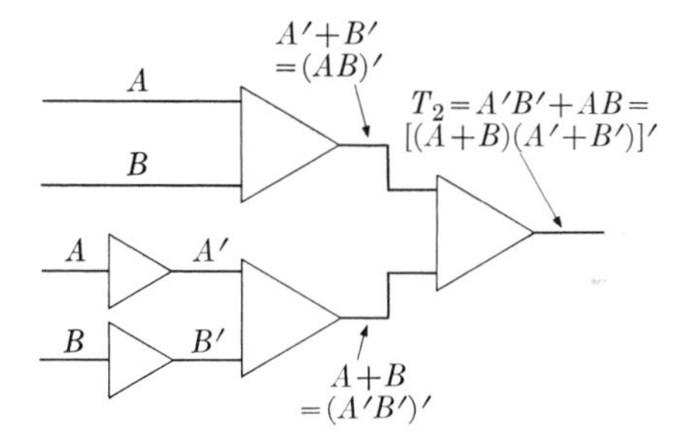

FIG. 7.10. Direct-coupled transistor switching circuit implementing T_2 of Eq. (7.6).

The implementation of T_2 of Eq. (7.6) is shown in Fig. 7.10. The evaluation of the circuit starts from the output terminal. The output is rewritten as

$$T_2 = A'B' + AB = [(A + B)(A' + B')]'. \tag{7.8}$$

Equation (7.8) suggests the use of a nand-gate, as shown. The rest can be explained in the same way. The circuit is a three-level one which needs eight transistors.

We can rewrite the right-hand side of Eq. (7.8) as

$$T_2 = (AB' + A'B)' = (T_1 + T_3)'. \tag{7.9}$$

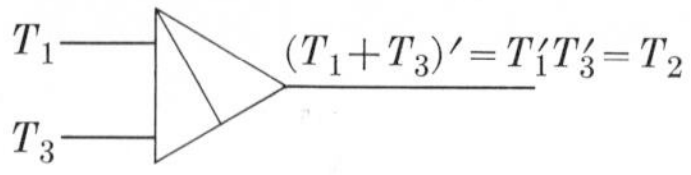

T_1

T_3

$(T_1+T_3)'=T_1'T_3'=T_2$

FIG. 7.11. An alternative realization of T_2 of Eq. (7.6).

This immediately suggests that the implementation of T_2 can make use of the outputs of the circuits already realized. The circuit is shown in Fig. 7.11.▲

7.4 Diode-transistor gate. In previous sections of this chapter, we have demonstrated that transistors can be properly used to realize a given switching function. In Chapter 5, it is shown that diodes can be used to form and-gates and or-gates. In employing diode gates, the designer is always concerned with the inevitable signal deterioration. Furthermore, the diode gates cannot perform the not-operation. Direct-coupled transistor gates are capable of executing all three switching operations, but they are generally more costly and act more slowly than the diode gates.

It is, therefore, conceivable to attempt to use both transistors and diodes in switching gates. Their simultaneous use is shown in Fig. 7.12. By examining the schematic diagrams in Fig. 7.12(a) and 7.12(c), we see

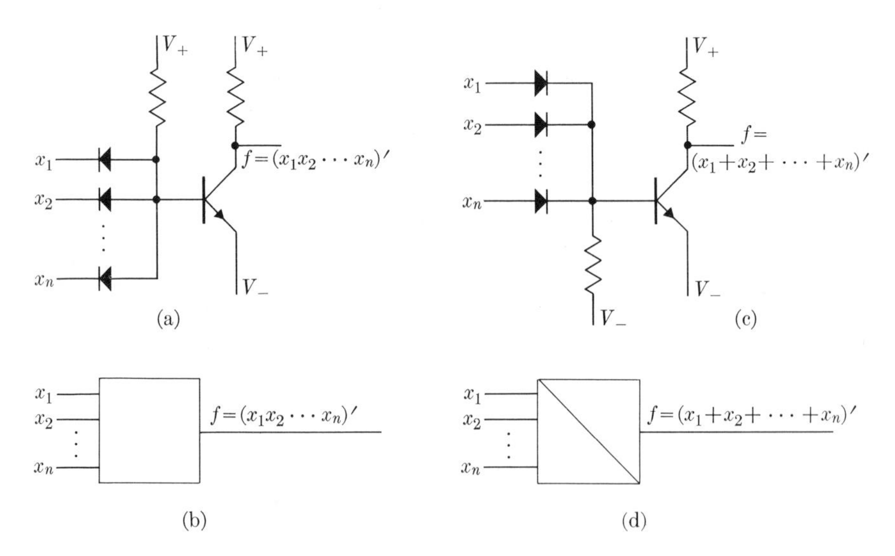

FIG. 7.12. (a) The schematic diagram of a diode-transistor nand-gate. (b) The symbolic representation of a diode-transistor nand-gate. (c) The schematic diagram of a diode-transistor nor-gate. (d) The symbolic representation of a diode-transistor nor-gate.

that these are actually the cascading of diode gates with transistor inverters. Therefore, their operations are obvious. The diode-transistor gates offer somewhat of a compromise between diode gates and transistor gates. The symbolic representations of diode-transistor gates are shown in Fig. 7.12(b) and 7.12(d).

It is very interesting to explore certain variations from the diode-transistor logic gates. In certain cases, the diodes in the circuits in Fig. 7.12(a) and Fig. 7.12(c) can be replaced by resistors.* This is a welcome variation, because, in general, a resistor is cheaper than a diode. However, it does bring in other considerations in circuit design; for example, the interaction between inputs. Such gates with resistors and transistors are called resistor-transistor gates.

7.5 Switching function implementation with diode-transistor gates. It is now time to use the diode-transistor gates developed in the previous section to implement switching functions. The following example will demonstrate the general approach.

EXAMPLE 7.2. Implement the following switching function of four variables by transistor gates:

$$T(w, x, y, z) = \sum m\ 1, 2, 3, 4, 5, 6, 7, 10, 11, 12, 13, 14, \text{and } 15. \quad (7.10)$$

This switching function can be realized by diode-transistor gates without simplification. However, it should be emphasized that the designer should always be alert for possible simplification in the switching function. As has been stated before, this simplification process will reduce cost and at the same time enhance the reliability of the system realized.

Since the given switching function contains four switching variables, the map method can be used, as shown in Fig. 7.13. The switching function is simplified to

$$T = x + y + w'z. \quad (7.11)$$

It is assumed at this stage that the inputs for x, y, w, and z are available in unprimed form.

Following the reasoning used in implementing a given switching function with direct-coupled transistor gates, we can pro-

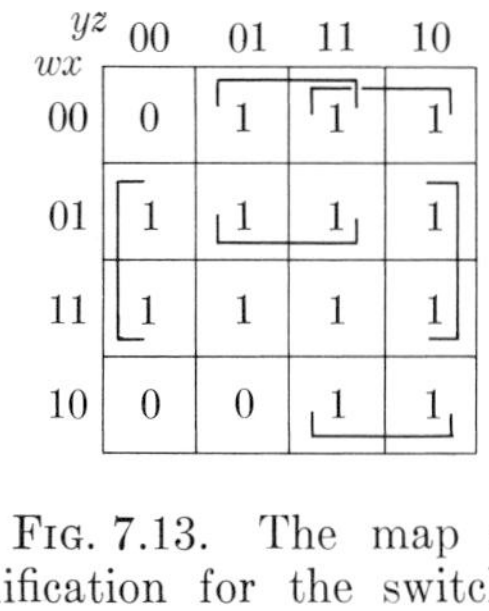

$wx \backslash yz$	00	01	11	10
00	0	1	1	1
01	1	1	1	1
11	1	1	1	1
10	0	0	1	1

FIG. 7.13. The map simplification for the switching function in Eq. (7.10).

* CH 1.

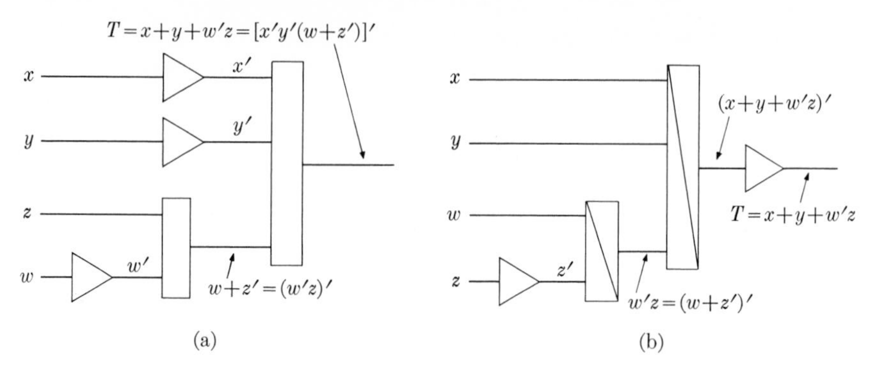

FIG. 7.14. The two alternative circuits to implement the switching function in Eq. (7.11).

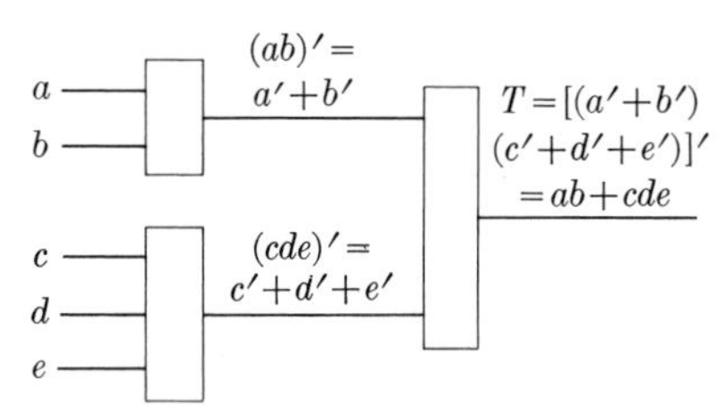

FIG. 7.15. The implementation of the switching function in Eq. (7.13).

TABLE 7.5

24	11000 ✓	24, 25	1100– ✓	24, 25, 26, 27	110–– ✓	
25	11001 ✓	24, 26	110–0 ✓	24, 25, 28, 29	11–0– ✓	
26	11010 ✓	24, 28	11–00 ✓	24, 26, 28, 30	11––0 ✓	
28	11100 ✓	25, 27	110–1 ✓	25, 27, 29, 31	11––1 ✓	
7	00111 ✓	25, 29	11–01 ✓	26, 27, 30, 31	11–1– ✓	
15	01111 ✓	26, 27	1101– ✓	28, 29, 30, 31	111–– ✓	
23	10111 ✓	26, 30	11–10 ✓	7, 15, 23, 31	––111	*B*
27	11011 ✓	28, 29	1110– ✓			
29	11101 ✓	28, 30	111–0 ✓			
30	11110 ✓	7, 15	0–111 ✓			
31	11111 ✓	7, 23	–0111 ✓			
		15, 31	–1111 ✓			
		23, 31	1–111 ✓			
		27, 31	11–11 ✓			
		29, 31	111–1 ✓			
		30, 31	1111– ✓			
24, 25, 26, 27, 28, 29, 30, 31			11–––		*A*	

duce the two circuits shown in Fig. 7.14 for the implementation of the switching function in Eq. (7.11). The circuit in Fig. 7.14(a) is a three-level one which needs five transistors and five diodes. The circuit in Fig. 7.14(b) is a four-level one which requires four transistors and five diodes.▲

EXAMPLE 7.3. Realize the following switching function of five variables with diode-transistor gates:

$$T(a, b, c, d, e) = \sum m\ 7, 15, 23, 24, 25, 26, 27, 28, 29, 30, \text{ and } 31. \quad (7.12)$$

This switching function can of course be realized as it is, but it is profitable to simplify the function first. The tabulation method is used. The steps are outlined in Table 7.5.

According to the defined process, we should draw a chart to determine whether term A or term B or both should be included in the final function, but in the present case, we can do this by inspection. Since standard products 7 and 15 are contained only in term B, A and B should both be included. The simplified switching function can be expressed as

$$T = ab + cde. \quad (7.13)$$

It is assumed that all the switching variables a, b, c, d, and e are available in unprimed form.

One scheme for implementation with diode-transistor gates is shown in Fig. 7.15.

PROBLEMS

7.1. Implement the following switching functions with direct-coupled transistors and at most two resistors. The inputs are available only in the unprimed form. Specify the voltage level that represents 1. Show the schematic diagrams of the circuits.

(a) $T = a(b + c) + d$ (b) $T = abe + cde$
(c) $T = xy(z + w) + xz + v$ (d) $T = xw + yz + uv$

7.2. Implement the following switching functions with direct-coupled transistors and only one resistor. The inputs are available in both primed and unprimed forms. Specify the voltage level that represents 1. Show the schematic diagram of the circuits.

(a) $T = d(a' + bc)$
(b) $T = (a + b + e')(c + d' + e')$
(c) $T = u(x + y' + z'w')(x + z')$
(d) $T = (x + w)(y' + z')(u + v)$

7.3. The notion of the nor-gate is introduced in this chapter. This kind of gate has a certain very attractive practical importance. Each gate is capable of setting the voltage or current level. Interconnections between successive gates can be freely made.

By using nor-gates alone, one can implement any given function for a combinational switching circuit. Prove this statement.*

[*Hint:* It has already been established that and-gates, or-gates, and not-gates can be used to implement a given switching function. One, therefore, has to show that using nor-gates alone, all these three operations can be performed.]

7.4. Use only nor-gates to implement the switching functions given in Problem 7.1. Show both the schematic and symbolic diagrams of the circuits.

7.5. Implement the switching functions given in Problem 7.2 with nor-gates alone. Show the symbolic diagrams of these circuits.

7.6. In Problem 7.3, the advantages of using nor-gates are presented. The same things can be attributed to nand-gates. Prove that any given function of a combinational switching circuit can be implemented with nand-gates alone.

7.7. Use nand-gates alone to implement the switching functions given in Problem 7.1. Show both the schematic and symbolic diagrams of the circuits.

7.8. Implement the switching functions given in Problem 7.2 with nand-gates alone. Show the symbolic diagrams of these circuits.

7.9. Use direct-coupled transistor gates to implement the following switching functions. It is assumed that the switching variables involved are available in the unprimed form. Optimize the circuits so that the number of transistors used is a minimum.

(a) $T = a'b'c + a'bc' + ab'c' + abc$
(b) $f = a'bc + ab'c + abc' + abc$

7.10. Use direct-coupled transistor gates to implement the following switching functions. It is assumed that the switching variables involved are available in the primed form. Optimize the circuits so that the number of transistors used is a minimum.

(a) $T = abc' + ab'c + a'bc + a'b'c'$
(b) $f = ab'c' + a'bc' + a'b'c + a'b'c'$

7.11. The adder circuit which has been discussed so far can be summarized by the diagram in Fig. 7.16, where a_i is the ith bit of the addend, b_i is the ith bit of the augend, and c_i is the carry produced in the ith stage.

The circuit shown in Fig. 7.16 is termed a *full adder*. This name comes from the fact that all three relevant inputs are processed in one unit.

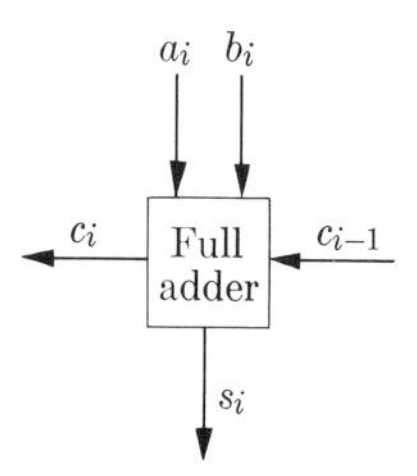

FIGURE 7.16

* Discussion of nor logic can be found in EA 1 and SH 4.

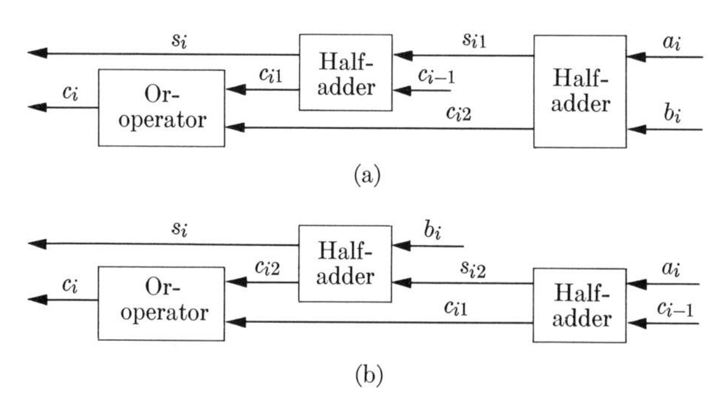

FIGURE 7.17

Another popular variation in designing an adder circuit is to treat two inputs at a time. This leads immediately to the two schemes shown in Fig. 7.17.

In your opinion, which one is better? One point is very clear; that is, so far as addition is concerned, the two serve the same purpose. You should look into the speed with which a possible carry is propagated through stages.

Use direct-coupled transistor gates to implement the complete unit. Label the inputs and outputs to each subcircuit clearly.*

7.12. The subtractor of a digital computer is mentioned in Problem 3.5. The scheme presented can be represented as in Fig. 7.18, where a_i is the ith bit of the minuend, b_i is the ith bit of the subtrahend, and e_i is the borrow made by the ith stage.

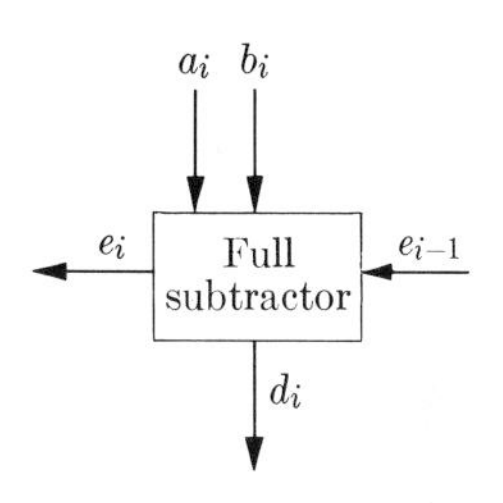

FIGURE 7.18

The circuit shown in Fig. 7.18 is called a *full subtractor,* since it takes care of all three relevant inputs in one unit.

There is, however, another common variation in designing a binary subtractor. The two popular schemes are shown in Fig. 7.19(a) and (b).

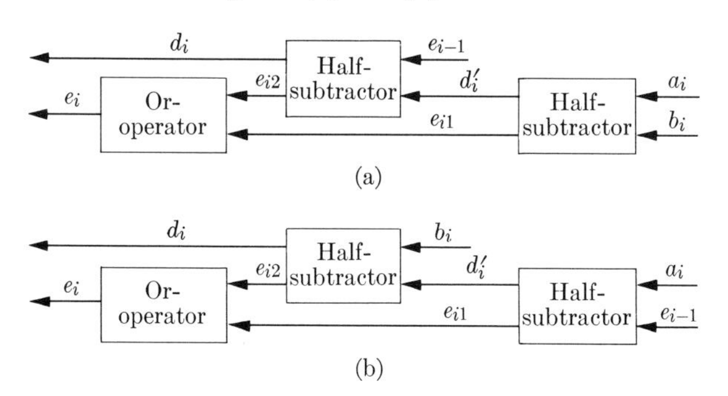

FIGURE 7.19

* RI 1, GI 4, HE 2, MA 2, PH 1, RE 1, SC 1, and UN 3.

If one examines these two schemes, he can see that both serve the purpose. However, if one looks into the speed of borrow propagation, he will see that one is better. Which one? State your justifications.

Use direct-coupled transistor gates to implement the complete unit. Label the inputs and outputs to each subcircuit clearly.

7.13. Use diode-transistor gates to implement the following switching functions. Show the schematic diagram of each circuit. Label the inputs clearly.

(a) $T(a, b, c, d) = m_1 + m_5 + m_7 + m_9$

don't-care conditions: $m_0, m_4, m_{11}, m_{13}, m_{15}$

(b) $T(a, b, c, d) = m_5 + m_6 + m_{12} + m_{15}$

don't-care conditions: m_0, m_3, m_{10}, m_{11}

(c) $T(a, b, c, d) = M_4 M_5 M_7 M_{15}$

don't-care conditions: $M_3, M_6, M_8, M_{11}, M_{13}$

CHAPTER 8

CIRCUIT REALIZATION IV: CORE GATES

8.1 Introduction. Solid-state switching devices are used extensively in switching systems. However, other high-speed switching components are being investigated and applied. Among them, *magnetic cores* have some attractive features which deserve our attention. A magnetic core is generally reliable, light, durable, small in size, and consumes power only when it is being switched. In this era of space exploration, switching systems are expected to function properly not only on earth, but also in space. The characteristics of a magnetic core show remarkable independence of environmental changes. It has been conclusively proved that while radiation has a deteriorating effect on solid-state switching devices, it does not destroy the usefulness of magnetic cores.

Magnetic cores were initially employed in switching systems as memory units. In this chapter, the fundamental switching properties of a magnetic core will be discussed first. Then the implementation of combinational switching functions with magnetic cores will be presented.

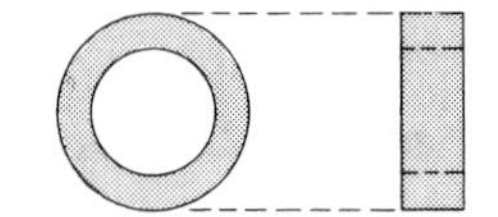

FIG. 8.1. A magnetic core.

8.2 Magnetic core circuits. The magnetic core to be discussed in this chapter is shown in Fig. 8.1. It is made either by wrapping ultra-thin ferromagnetic metallic tape on toroidal bobbins of stainless steel, or by molding sintered ceramic ferrite into a toroid. The distinct feature of a switching core is that the relationship between its magnetic flux, ϕ, and the applied magnetomotive force, F, can be expressed by a nearly square loop, as shown in Fig. 8.2. This characteristic has a direct bearing on its usefulness as a switching component.

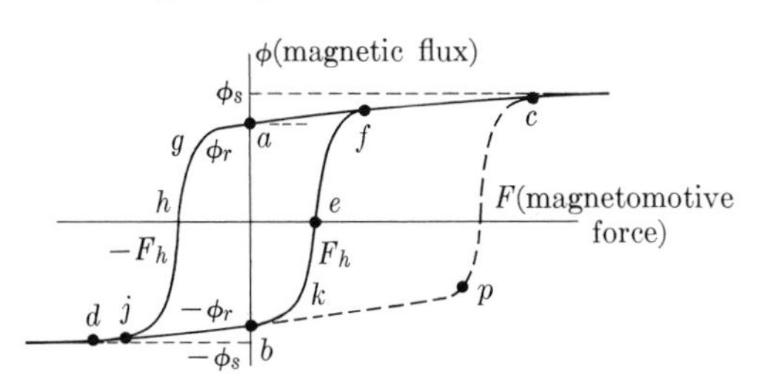

FIG. 8.2. The ϕ-F characteristic of a magnetic switching core.

To illustrate the fundamental considerations involved in a core switching circuit, a magnetic core with three windings is shown in Fig. 8.3. The dotted ends denote the terminals into which a positive current can be sent to establish the presence of clockwise magnetic flux in the core.

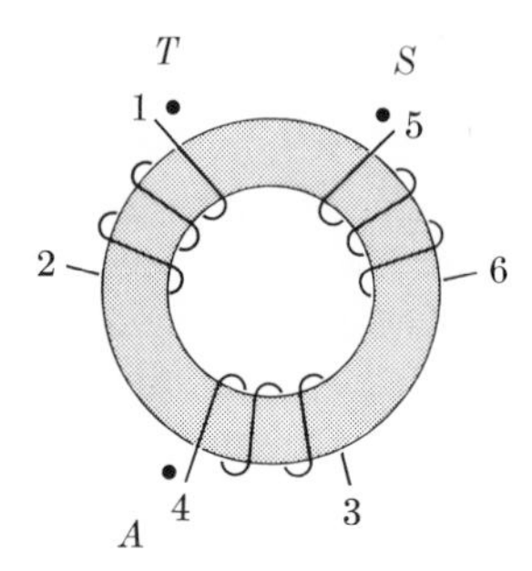

FIG. 8.3. A magnetic core with an input winding T and an advance winding A.

To understand how this circuit works, we must understand how switching variables are represented in windings. A pulse occurring at a specific instant, with adequate amplitude and duration, is used to indicate that the truth value of a certain switching variable is 1. The fact that no pulse occurs at a specified instant indicates that the truth value of a certain switching variable is 0. The pulse can be either positive or negative. It is assumed in the subsequent presentation that all pulses are positive.

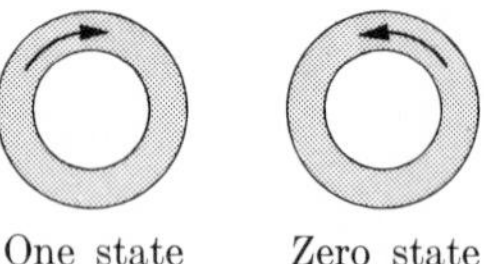

FIG. 8.4. The two states of a magnetic core.

How is the truth value of a switching variable or a switching function represented in a magnetic core? Figure 8.4 illustrates that the magnetic flux in a core can be either in the clockwise direction, which is used to represent the truth value of 1, or in the counterclockwise direction, which is used to represent the truth value of 0. When the flux in a core is in the clockwise direction, the core is said to be set. When the magnetic flux in a core is in the counterclockwise direction, the core is said to be reset.

Now we are in a position to examine the operation of the simple core circuit in Fig. 8.3. Generally, each operation is completed by two steps, or two phases, the input phase and then the advance phase. At the start of the input phase, the core is assumed to be already reset. Pulses representing input variables are sent through appropriate input windings. Their composite magnetomotive force (mmf) will set the core or leave it in the reset state. In the setup shown in Fig. 8.3, only one winding, T, is considered to be an input winding. The A winding and the S winding are used for other purposes. There is no restriction whatever on the number of input windings one magnetic core can have; it can have as many input windings as is physically feasible.

At the start of the input phase, if the input switching variable has a truth value of 1, a pulse is sent to the T winding through the dotted end. When the resultant current pulse flows through the N_T turns of the T winding, an mmf is applied to the core. Following the convention concerning the dotted end, we see that this force tries to establish clockwise magnetic flux in the core. Whether it can succeed or not depends on its magnitude and the ϕ-F characteristic of the core. For ease of design and operation reliability, we would like to have a clear-cut threshold concerning the applied mmf. When the applied mmf is larger than the threshold, a definite amount of magnetic flux is established. On the other hand, if the applied mmf is less than the threshold, the magnetic state of the core should remain unchanged. This requirement immediately suggests that it is highly desirable to have the two segments, *kef* and *jhg*, be two vertical straight lines, as shown in Fig. 8.2. It is then evident that the threshold is F_h.

If the pulse sent through winding T establishes an mmf which does exceed the threshold F_h, clockwise magnetic flux is then present in the core. For example, the state of the core may be represented by point c in Fig. 8.2. Experimental results show that the larger the mmf, the faster the resultant flux is established. As soon as the applied mmf disappears, the core flux is reduced slightly to ϕ_r and stays in this condition indefinitely so long as no disturbance is applied. The core is set, or the core is in the 1-state. If, at the start of the input phase, the input switching variable has a truth value of 0, no pulse is sent to the T winding. Therefore, the core remains reset or in the 0-state. The input phase is completed as soon as the core is set or reset, according to the applied mmf.

The advance phase follows the input phase. In this phase, the output of the core circuit is produced, and the core is reset for the next operation. The advance phase is always executed by sending a pulse into the advance winding, A, through the undotted end. Following the convention established in this section, the resultant mmf is so oriented that it tries to establish counterclockwise magnetic flux in the core. If this mmf is less than $-F_h$, a counterclockwise magnetic flux will be established.

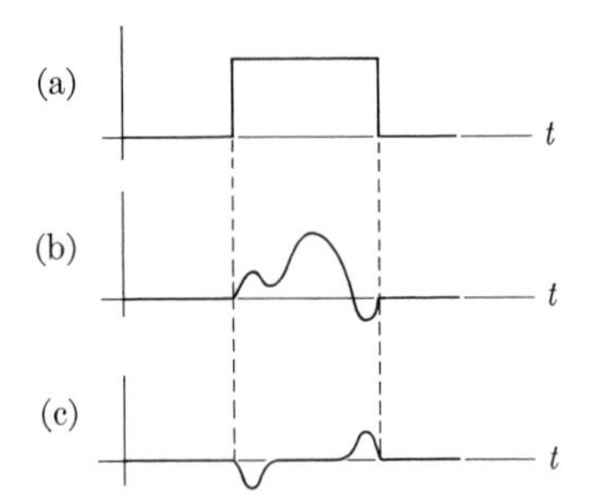

FIG. 8.5. The waveform of the induced voltage in S winding. (a) Advance pulse. (b) Induced voltage in S winding when the core is switched. (c) Induced voltage in S winding when the core is not switched.

The state of the core can be represented by a point, say d, in Fig. 8.2. When the advance pulse disappears, the state of the core will be indicated by point b. The core is said to be reset, or in the 0-state.

By sending a pulse properly through the advance winding A, the core is reset and ready for the next operation. This justifies the previous assumption that at the start of each operation the core is already reset.

However, we have not indicated how the output is to be produced. The existence of winding S on the core is for the purpose of producing an adequate output. If the core is set during the input phase when the advance pulse, shown in Fig. 8.5(a), is properly applied, the core will be switching back to the 0-state. The magnetic flux in the core will change from ϕ_r to $-\phi_r$. This flux change will induce a voltage in the S winding. The polarity of this voltage can be determined from Lenz law. The waveform of the induced voltage, shown in Fig. 8.5(b), can be explained in the following way. The first small peak is due to the flux decrease from point a to point g (Fig. 8.2). The main peak is due to the flux change from point g to point j. The small negative peak is due to the increase in flux from point j to point b. The two small peaks are certainly not desirable. The only way to reduce them or to eliminate them is to make the segments $cfag$ and $djbk$ horizontal, or nearly horizontal, lines.

If the core stays reset during the input phase, the resetting advance pulse only drives the core into saturation. When the advance pulse disappears, the state of the core will be back at point b. The induced waveform is shown in Fig. 8.5(c). The presence of the two small peaks is due to the fact that the segment djb in Fig. 8.2 is not quite horizontal. Therefore, by properly using the induced voltage in the S winding during the advance phase, we can sense how the core was set during the input phase and produce an output.

What has been presented above shows that when the core flux changes, an electromotive force is induced in the S winding. We can see that this happens not only during the advance phase, but also during the input phase. The induced voltage during the input phase is to be ignored.

To summarize this section, magnetic cores are introduced,* and a simple core circuit is studied. No attempt, however, has been made to show how switching cores can be properly used to implement switching functions. Before introducing this subject, a set of notations concerning core switching circuits must be explained.

8.3 Mirror notation. In the previous section, dot notations are used to describe a core circuit. This representation scheme is widely adopted, but there is another scheme which has proved to be very simple and useful. It is the *mirror notation*,† which displays clearly the relationship between the inducing and the induced voltages.

To state the conventions used in the mirror notation, we redraw the core circuit in Fig. 8.3. The result is shown in Fig. 8.6(b). The circuit shown originally in Fig. 8.3 is repeated in Fig. 8.6(a) for reference.

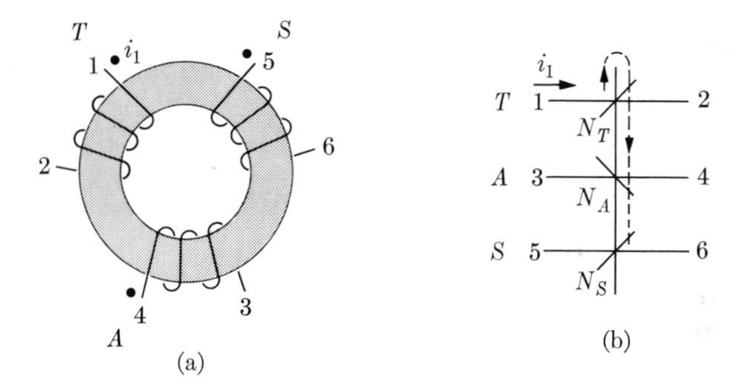

FIG. 8.6. Illustration of the mirror notation for a core circuit.

The magnetic core itself is represented by a vertical bar. If there is more than one core in a circuit, a number or a literal can be placed at the top of the bar. In the present circuit, since there is only one core, there is no need for this.

The winding leads are represented by horizontal line segments which intersect the vertical bar at right angles. For example, winding T has two leads, 1 and 2; they are represented respectively by the left endpoint and the right endpoint of the horizontal line segment. We are entirely at

* ME 1
† For the origin of the mirror notation, see KA 2.

liberty to place lead 1 at either the left-hand side or the right-hand side of the vertical bar.

If a current flows through a lead into a winding, it is represented by an arrow with its head toward the vertical bar and placed immediately above the corresponding horizontal line segment. For example, in Fig. 8.6(a), current i_1 flows into winding T through lead 1. An arrow, labeled i_1, with its head toward the vertical bar, is placed immediately above the line segment 12.

The clockwise magnetic flux in a core is represented by an arrow pointing upward beside the vertical bar. The counterclockwise magnetic flux in a core is denoted by an arrow pointing downward.

Each winding itself is represented by a short line segment which passes through the intersection of the vertical bar and the horizontal line segment representing its two leads. This short line segment makes an angle of 45° with both the horizontal and the vertical. One question immediately comes to mind. This short line segment can be slanted from right to left or from left to right. This freedom allows us to denote the direction of the winding. For example, in the circuit in Fig. 8.6, current i_1, flowing into winding T from lead 1, will try to establish magnetic flux in the clockwise direction. This statement is, of course, substantiated by the direction of the winding. In this situation, the short line segment representing T is slanted from right to left, because, if we consider this short line segment as a mirror, the arrow representing current i_1 moves from left to right and will be subsequently reflected upward. Using the same reasoning, we can place two other short line segments to represent windings A and S, as shown in Fig. 8.6(b). If we are interested in knowing the induced electromotive forces in the windings T, A, and S when the clockwise magnetic flux is being established by i_1, we can move the upward-pointing arrow, which indicates the clockwise magnetic flux, along the vertical bar, round the top of the bar, and continue downward, as shown in Fig. 8.6(b). When this downward-moving arrow meets the T winding "mirror," it is reflected toward lead 1, which indicates that an electromagnetic force is induced in winding T which opposes i_1. This of course states the physical fact. When the downward-moving arrow meets the A winding mirror, it is reflected toward lead 4. This means that an induced voltage is present in winding A which tends to send current out from lead 4. Such a current in winding A would oppose the establishment of the clockwise flux, as it should.

Finally, the number of turns in each winding is indicated by a number placed immediately below its corresponding horizontal lead line.

The circuit in Fig. 8.6(a) is completely described by the mirror representation in Fig. 8.6(b).

If not otherwise stated, the input current flows from left to right.

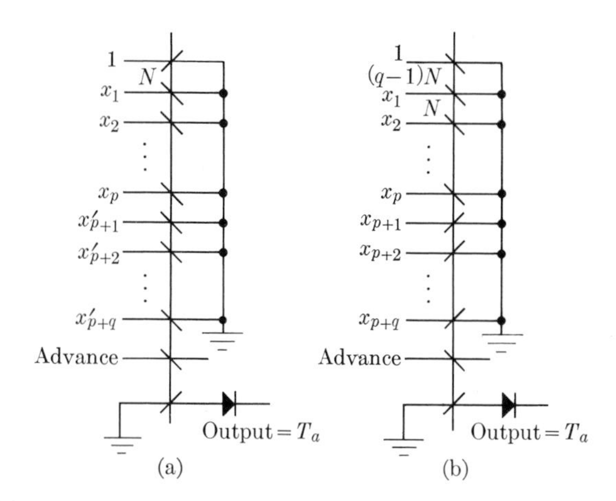

FIG. 8.7. Symbolic diagrams for magnetic core and-gate.

8.4 Primitive synthesis of switching functions by magnetic cores.* We know that the switching function of a combinational switching circuit can be expressed either as the sum of products or as the product of sums. It is also known that the sum is the result of an or-operation, and the product is the result of an and-operation. It is, therefore, logical that we should first study how an and-operation or an or-operation is performed by core switching circuits.

To establish a core switching circuit which is capable of performing and-operations, we have only to try to implement the switching function

$$T_a = x_1'x_2'x_3' \cdots x_p'x_{p+1}x_{p+2} \cdots x_{p+q}. \tag{8.1}$$

The circuit in Fig. 8.7(a) produces the switching function in Eq. (8.1). It is understood that the number of turns in each winding is equal to an integer N. It is also understood that the input, represented by 1, takes the form of a current pulse and is the same for each winding. Furthermore, the amplitude of each single input, I, and the number of turns of any winding, N, will generate enough mmf to switch the core. Note that one winding always receives an input of 1. This winding is termed the *unit winding.*

The switching operation, as mentioned in Section 8.2, is completed in two phases. At the start of the input phase, a current pulse is sent to the unit winding. This generates an mmf which tries to establish a clockwise flux in the core, or to switch the core to the set state. This attempt will be successful only if none of the other windings on the core receives any current pulse. If any winding does receive a current pulse,

* MI 2 and KA 2.

the resultant mmf will definitely leave the core in the reset state. In other words, in order to have the core in the set state, the following set of conditions must be met:

$$\begin{aligned} x_1 &= 0 \\ x_2 &= 0 \\ &\vdots \\ x_p &= 0 \\ x_{p+1} &= 1 \\ x_{p+2} &= 1 \\ &\vdots \\ x_{p+q} &= 1. \end{aligned} \tag{8.2}$$

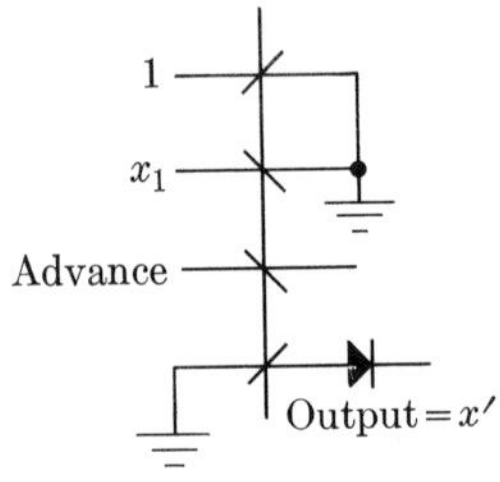

FIG. 8.8. A magnetic core not-gate.

The conditions listed in Eq. (8.2) guarantee that T_a in Eq. (8.1) is equal to 1. During the input phase, inputs are received by the core, and the truth value of the product is stored in the core. This completes the input phase.

During the subsequent advance phase, an output is produced by sensing the core and the core is reset for the next operation. At the start of the advance phase, a current pulse is sent through the advance winding. An mmf is generated to reset the core. If the core is already reset at the completion of the input phase, that is to say $T_a = 0$, the induced voltage in the output winding is negligible. If the core is set at the completion of the input phase, $T_a = 1$, there will be an induced voltage appearing at the output terminal. In either case, the core is reset at the completion of the advance phase. Note that there is a diode attached to the output terminal. Its presence will be explained later.

It is very interesting to note that if we eliminate $x_2, x_3, \ldots, x_p, x'_{p+1}, \ldots, x'_{p+q}$ windings from the circuit in Fig. 8.7(a), we obtain a not-gate for x_1. The resultant circuit is shown in Fig. 8.8.

Some of the required inputs to the and-circuit in Fig. 8.7(a) are primed and some are unprimed. If the available inputs are all in unprimed form, the circuit in Fig. 8.7(b) can be used. All the assumptions made for the circuit of Fig. 8.7(a) still hold, except that the unit winding has $(q - 1)N$ turns instead of N turns.

To establish a core switching circuit that is capable of performing an or-operation, we have only to try to implement the switching function

$$T_b = x'_1 + x'_2 + \cdots + x'_p + x_{p+1} + x_{p+2} + \cdots + x_{p+q}. \tag{8.3}$$

Two alternative circuits are shown in Fig. 8.9. The required inputs of the circuit in Fig. 8.9(a) consist of both primed and unprimed forms, while the required inputs of the circuit in Fig. 8.9(b) are only of the unprimed form. The number of turns of each winding in the former circuit

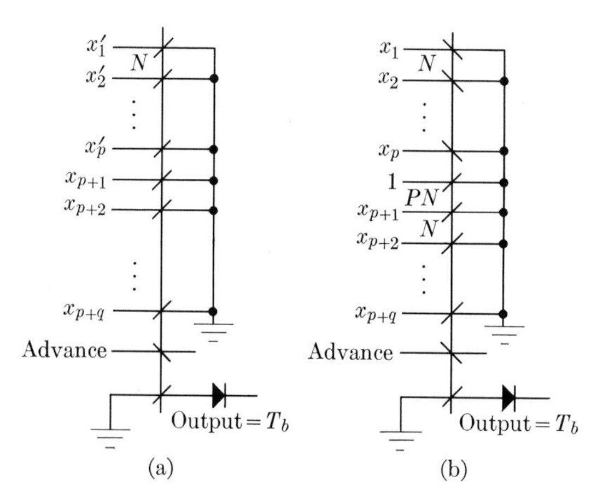

FIG. 8.9. Symbolic diagrams for magnetic core or-gates.

is equal to N, and it is also true for the latter circuit except that the unit winding has PN turns. It is assumed that the mmf generated by sending a current pulse through any winding is strong enough to switch the core.

It can be easily seen that if $x_1' = 1$, or $x_2' = 1, \ldots,$ or $x_{p+1} = 1$, or $x_{p+2} = 1, \ldots,$ the resultant mmf will set the core and subsequently an output will be produced during the advance phase. The presence of the diode in the output winding will be explained later.

The previous presentation shows that core circuits can be used to perform the and-operation, the or-operation, and the not-operation. With this background, we can proceed to investigate how a switching function can be implemented with magnetic core switching circuits.

EXAMPLE 8.1. Use magnetic cores to implement the switching function

$$T = a'b'c' + ab'c' + abc'. \tag{8.4}$$

Since the given function is expressed as the sum of products, it certainly can be realized with magnetic core and- and or-circuits. Generally speaking, we can use three and-circuits to generate the three products and send their outputs to an or-circuit to produce the given function. However, we can easily see that simplification of the given switching function should be attempted, because the elimination of one product means the elimination of one and-circuit, and the elimination of one literal means at least the saving of one winding. The given function is thus simplified to

$$T = b'c' + ac'. \tag{8.5}$$

The simplified version of the given function is implemented with the circuit in Fig. 8.10. It consists of two and-circuits and one or-circuit. It

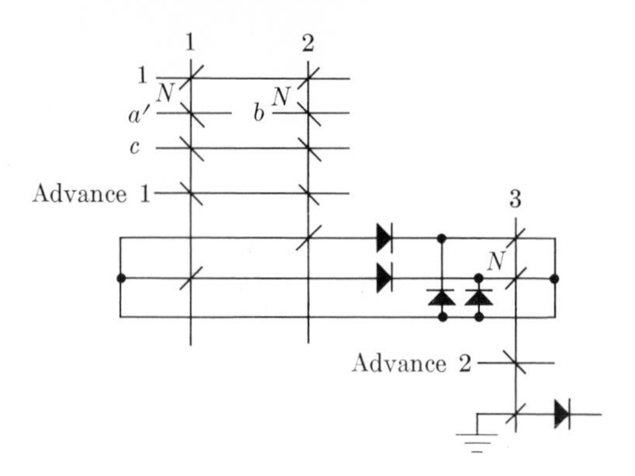

FIG. 8.10. Diagram for the implementation of the switching function of Eq. (8.5).

was stated that the operation of a switching circuit which has only one magnetic core is completed in two phases, the input phase and the advance phase. The circuit in Fig. 8.10 has two levels, because the output of one core circuit is the input to the other.

During the input phase, cores 1 and 2 are set or stay reset according to their respective input values. If any core is being set, the induced voltage in the output winding would try to send a false signal to core 3. To prevent this from happening, a diode is attached to the output winding of each core.

During the advance phase for cores 1 and 2, appropriate outputs are generated in the output windings of cores 1 and 2 and sent to the input windings of core 3. Therefore, the advance phase for cores 1 and 2 is the input phase for core 3. Core 3 is set, or stays reset, according to its inputs.

During the advance phase for core 3, an output, indicating the value of the given switching function, is produced. If core 3 is set during its input phase (the advance phase for cores 1 and 2), the resetting of the core during its advance phase will induce voltages in its input windings. These induced voltages have the tendency to set cores 1 and 2. To prevent the occurrence of this undesirable feedback, two additional diodes are added, as shown in Fig. 8.10. They provide paths to guide the currents away from the two output windings of cores 1 and 2.

This circuit needs two cores with five windings each (two five-winding cores) and one core with four windings. If we write the given switching function as $T = c'(b' + a)$, we see that another two-core circuit can be obtained.

Since the output of the circuit in Fig. 8.10 is generated through transformer action, it is called a *T-type* circuit. This is, however, not the only way to extract an output from a core switching circuit. Another approach is shown in the circuit of Fig. 8.11.

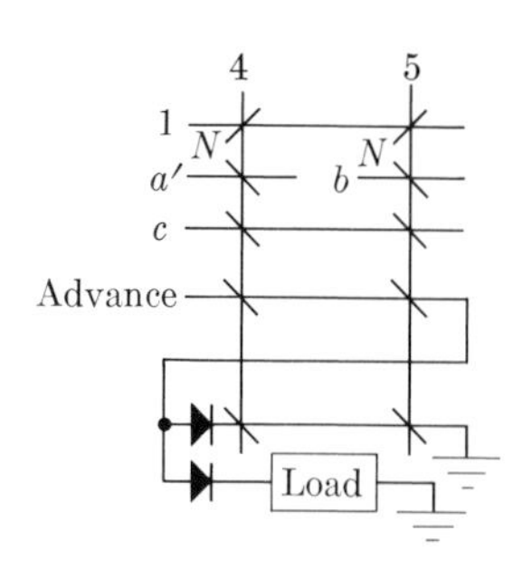

FIG. 8.11. An alternative circuit for the implementation of the switching function of Eq. (8.5.)

It can be seen that core 4 of Fig. 8.11 is the same as core 1 of Fig. 8.10, except that the direction of the output winding of core 4 is opposite to that of core 1. The same comments can be made about core 2 in Fig. 8.10 and core 5 in Fig. 8.11.

Each operation of the circuit in Fig. 8.11 is completed in two phases. During the input phase, core 4 and core 5 are either set or remain reset by their respective inputs. During the advance phase, a pulse is sent through the advance winding of cores 4 and 5. If either core 4 or core 5 or both is set during the input phase, an induced electromotive force will be present during the advance phase in core 4 or core 5 or both to back-bias its attached diode. Consequently, the advance pulse will be flowing into the load. This means the output is 1. If neither core 4 nor core 5 is set during the input phase, no appreciable induced electromotive force will be present during the advance phase. To put it another way, the impedance offered by the output windings of cores 4 and 5 will be very small. In this situation, the advance pulse will be flowing through these two output windings. The load is entirely bypassed. This indicates that the output is 0.

The circuit in Fig. 8.11 needs only two five-winding cores to perform the two and-operations. The needed or-operation is actually carried out by the way the output windings, the advance windings, and the load are connected. This circuit is also faster than that shown in Fig. 8.10, because each operation is completed in two phases.

Since the output of such a circuit is provided by the advance pulse itself, it is sometimes called an *A-type* circuit.▲

EXAMPLE 8.2 Use magnetic cores to implement the switching function

$$T = ab' + a'b. \tag{8.6}$$

The input variables are available only in unprimed forms.

A T-type implementation is shown in Fig. 8.12. The and-circuits provided by core 1 and core 2 are patterned after the circuit in Fig. 8.7(b). The or-circuit provided by core 3 is patterned after the circuit in Fig. 8.9(b).

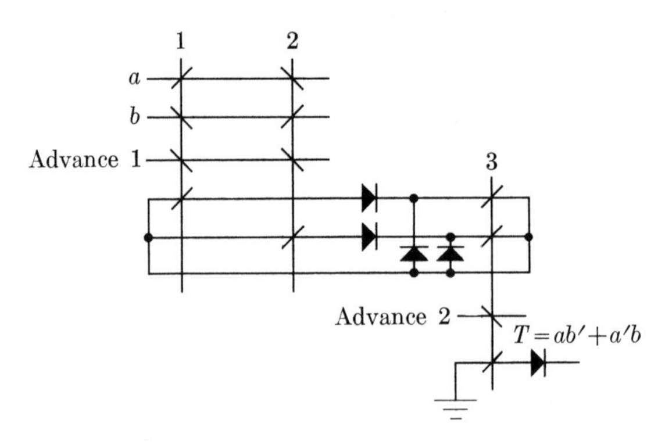

FIG. 8.12. Circuit for the implementation of the switching function of Eq. (8.6).

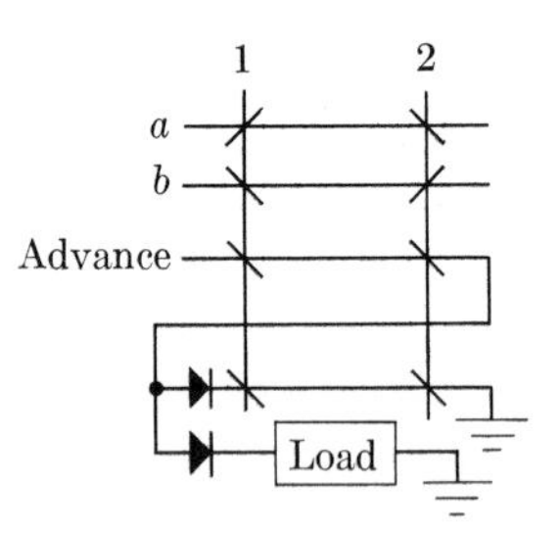

FIG. 8.13. An alternative circuit for the implementation of the switching function of Eq. (8.6).

An A-type implementation of the given switching function is shown in Fig. 8.13. The operation of this circuit is quite obvious. The implementations shown in Figs. 8.12 and 8.13 are and-or in nature. The outputs of the and-gate are used as the inputs to the or-gate. This is true because the given switching function is expressed, in Eq. (8.6), as the sum of products. If the same function is expressed as the product of sums,

$$T = (a + b)(a' + b'), \tag{8.7}$$

implementations which are or-and in nature can be obtained.

A T-type circuit is shown in Fig. 8.14. The or-circuit provided by cores 1 and 2 is patterned according to the basic circuit in Fig. 8.9(b), while the and-circuit provided by core 3 is patterned according to the basic circuit in Fig. 8.7(b).

An A-type implementation is shown in Fig. 8.15. No further explanation is needed for the or-circuits provided by cores 1 and 2. The final and-operation is executed, however, by connecting the two output windings of cores 1 and 2 in parallel. By arranging it this way, the advance pulse will be allowed to flow into the load only when $a + b$ is 1 and $a' + b'$ is also 1. It is now interesting to note that in the circuit in Fig. 8.13, the final or-operation is executed by connecting the output windings in series.▲

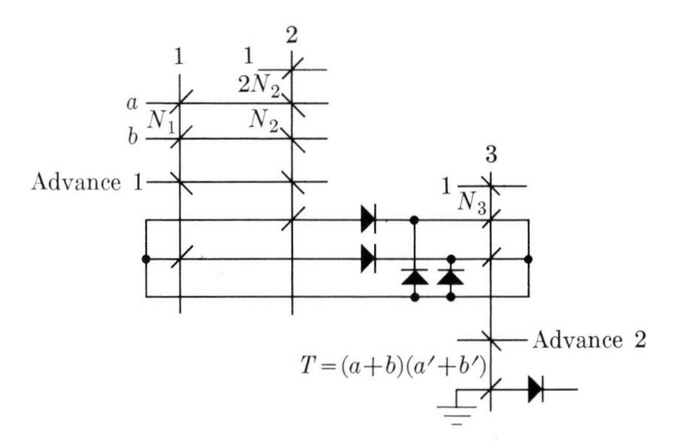

FIG. 8.14. Another alternative circuit for the implementation of the switching function of Eq. (8.6).

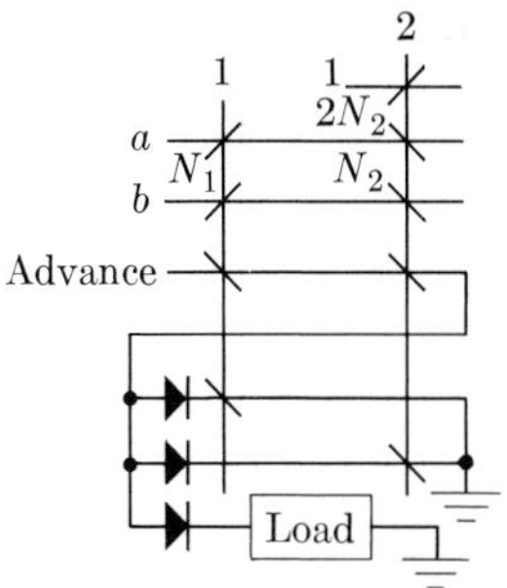

FIG. 8.15. Another alternative circuit for the implementation of the switching function of Eq. (8.6).

Both and-or and or-and core switching circuits are studied in this section. Their ability to implement combinational switching functions is well demonstrated. This section derives its title from the fact that no attempt except the simplification of the switching function has been made to optimize a circuit. Optimization will be discussed in Section 8.5.

8.5 Core circuit optimization. As is true in any optimization problem, the optimization of magnetic core switching circuits involves many conflicting considerations. The optimization procedure introduced below centers around the idea of reducing to a minimum the number of cores needed. This is by no means the only criterion used in practice. Generally speaking, a circuit with the least number of cores is often proven to be acceptable.

The presentation of the optimization procedure is made by two examples. A formal discussion will be given in the following section.

EXAMPLE 8.3. Implement the following switching function with an optimum magnetic core switching circuit:

$$T = a'b'c' + ab'c' + abc'. \tag{8.8}$$

All variables are available in the unprimed form. This function is the same as that given in Eq. (8.4). Two primitive implementations are shown in Figs. 8.10 and 8.11, using three cores and two cores, respectively. An attempt is launched here to see if one core is sufficient to implement the given function.

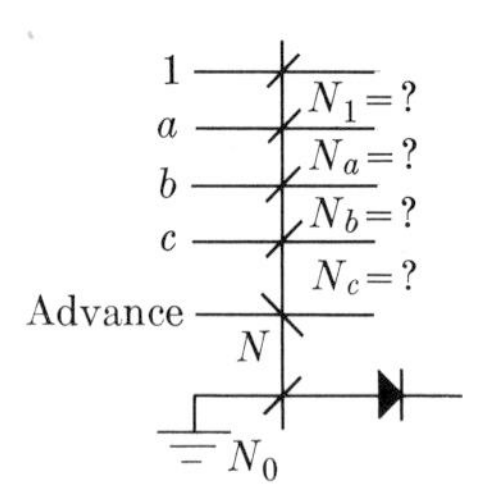

FIG. 8.16. Illustrating the unknowns in the optimization of magnetic core switching circuits.

Suppose one magnetic core is enough. How many turns and what direction should each winding have in order to implement the given switching function? This situation is illustrated in Fig. 8.16. The problem now is translated into one of identifying N_1, N_a, N_b, and N_c, each of which can be either positive or negative. If any number is found to be negative, then the direction of its corresponding winding is opposite to that shown in Fig. 8.16.

In order to present the problem more concretely, we express the composite mmf on the core during the input phase as

$$\text{Composite mmf} = N_1 I + aN_a I + bN_b I + cN_c I, \tag{8.9}$$

where I is the amplitude of the current pulse.

According to Eq. (8.8), if the input combination is (0, 0, 0), the corresponding value of the given function should be 1. If this input combination is applied to the core during the input phase, the core should be set. In order to set the core under this input combination, we must make sure that the composite mmf exceeds the threshold F_h for setting the core. This requirement is expressed in the inequality (8.10a). Each one of the remaining input combinations brings about an inequality, shown in (8.10):

$$N_1 I > F_h, \tag{8.10a}$$
$$(N_c + N_1)I < F_h, \tag{8.10b}$$
$$(N_b + N_1)I < F_h, \tag{8.10c}$$
$$(N_b + N_c + N_1)I < F_h, \tag{8.10d}$$
$$(N_a + N_1)I > F_h, \tag{8.10e}$$
$$(N_a + N_c + N_1)I < F_h, \tag{8.10f}$$
$$(N_a + N_b + N_1)I > F_h, \tag{8.10g}$$
$$(N_a + N_b + N_c + N_1)I < F_h. \tag{8.10h}$$

The problem is essentially to select a set of values for N_1, N_a, N_b, and N_c to satisfy simultaneously the eight inequalities in (8.10). By the same reasoning, in the case of n input variables,* there are 2^n input combinations and consequently there are 2^n inequalities generated. In this situation, a set of $n + 1$ values have to be chosen to satisfy the 2^n inequalities simultaneously.

One thing should be understood at this point. It is not always possible to implement an arbitrarily given switching function with just one magnetic core. By manipulating the inequalities (8.10), we expect to either conclude that one core is not enough or arrive at a set of values for N_1, N_a, N_b, and N_c.

From (8.10a) and (8.10b), we obtain

$$N_1 I > F_h > (N_c + N_1)I,$$

or

$$N_c < 0.\dagger \tag{8.11}$$

From (8.10a) and (8.10c), we arrive at

$$N_b < 0. \tag{8.12}$$

The combination of (8.10f) and (8.10g) yields

$$N_a + N_c + N_1 < N_a + N_b + N_1,$$

or

$$N_c < N_b. \tag{8.13}$$

From (8.10g) and (8.10c), we have

$$N_a > 0. \tag{8.14}$$

The above process serves two purposes. We want to see if any contradictory requirements are made on N_1, N_a, N_b, and N_c by the inequalities (8.10). If they do exist, we can conclude that the given function cannot be implemented with one core. Since there are no contradictory requirements found in the present problem, we can use the derived inequalities (8.11), (8.12), (8.13), and (8.14) as guide lines to assign values for N_1, N_a, N_b, and N_c.

In order to satisfy (8.10a), N_1 is set to be N, where NI is sufficiently larger than F_h. Using (8.11), (8.12), (8.13), and (8.14) as guide lines, we tentatively set N_a, N_b, and N_c to be N, $-N$, and $-2N$, respectively. This selection has to satisfy each one of the eight inequalities in (8.10).

---

* It is assumed that none of the n variables can be eliminated.

† I can be reasonably assumed to be positive.

Since it does, we can consider $N_1 = N$, $N_a = N$, $N_b = -N$, and $N_c = -2N$ as one acceptable solution. The resultant circuit is shown in Fig. 8.17. It can be easily seen that this solution is by no means the only one available.▲

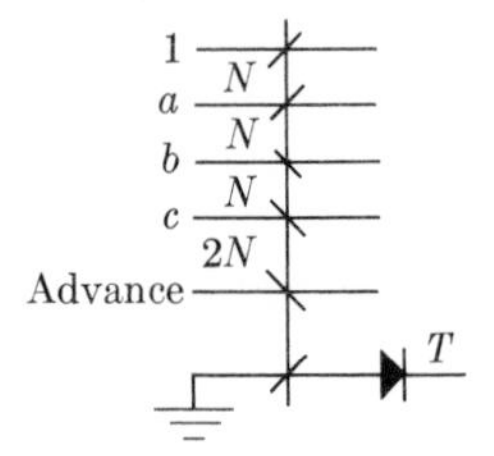

FIG. 8.17. The resultant circuit for Example 8.3.

EXAMPLE 8.4. Implement the following switching function with an optimum magnetic core switching circuit:

$$T = ab' + a'b. \tag{8.15}$$

All variables are available in the unprimed form.

This function is the same as that in Eq. (8.6). Two primitive realizations are shown in Figs. 8.12 and 8.13.

Following the procedure adopted in the previous example, we obtain the following set of four inequalities:

$$N_1 I < F_h, \tag{8.16a}$$
$$(N_b + N_1)I > F_h, \tag{8.16b}$$
$$(N_a + N_1)I > F_h, \tag{8.16c}$$
$$(N_a + N_b + N_1)I < F_h. \tag{8.16d}$$

Combining (8.16b) and (8.16c), we have

$$(N_a + N_b + 2N_1)I > 2F_h. \tag{8.17}$$

The inequalities (8.16d) and (8.17) indicate that

$$N_1 I > F_h. \tag{8.18}$$

It can be seen from (8.16a) and (8.18) that contradictory requirements have been made on N_1. It can therefore be concluded that the switching function in Eq. (8.15) cannot be realized by one core. A two-core circuit has already been shown in Fig. 8.13.▲

What has been presented above is a crude cut-and-try process. More systematic and efficient approaches, which concern more than just reducing the number of cores employed, have been proposed.*

* MI 2, EI 1, and GA 3.

8.6 Threshold switching. In the previous sections of this chapter, the design of magnetic core switching circuits is presented. It is, however, appropriate to point out that the magnetic core switching circuit is only a representative, a worthy one indeed, of a versatile switching component, the threshold switching device.

The schematic diagram of a threshold switching device is shown in Fig. 8.18.

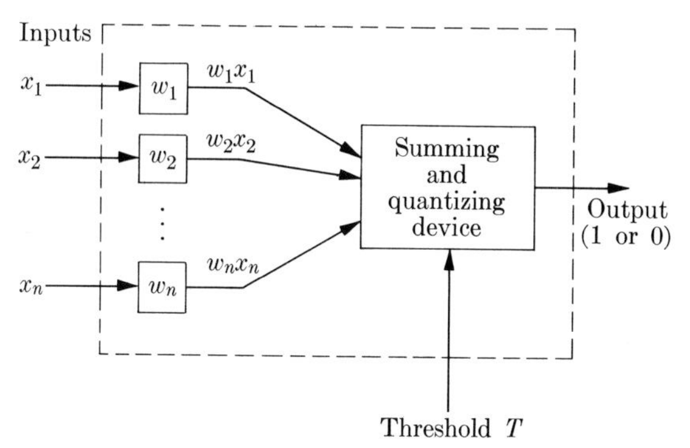

FIG. 8.18. Schematic diagram of a threshold switching device.

The inputs are $x_1, x_2, \ldots, x_n$. The weighting factors w_i and the threshold T are considered to be either continuous or discrete, either positive or negative real variables.

The quantized output of the threshold switching is 1 if

$$T + \sum_{i=1}^{n} x_i w_i > 0, \tag{8.19}$$

and 0 if

$$T + \sum_{i=1}^{n} x_i w_i < 0. \tag{8.20}$$

It will be shown that the optimization problem discussed in the previous section is actually a special case of the following questions. How does one determine whether a given switching function can be implemented with just one threshold switching device? How does one determine the weighting factors and the threshold if a given function is found to be realizable with just one such device? These questions are of practical and theoretical importance.

Let us re-examine Example 8.4. When the given switching function, Eq. (8.15), is to be 1, we require that

$$N_1 I + N_a I \cdot a + N_b I \cdot b > F_h. \tag{8.21}$$

The inequality (8.21) can be rewritten as

$$(N_1 I - F_h) + N_a I \cdot a + N_b I \cdot b > 0. \tag{8.22}$$

When the given switching function is to be 0, another inequality is obtained:

$$(N_1 I - F_h) + N_a I \cdot a + N_b I \cdot b < 0. \tag{8.23}$$

The inequalities (8.22) and (8.23) can be rewritten by making certain obvious substitutions:

$$T + w_a a + w_b b > 0, \tag{8.24}$$

$$T + w_a a + w_b b < 0. \tag{8.25}$$

If we compare the expressions in (8.24) and (8.25) to those in (8.19) and (8.20), we can see easily that a magnetic core with appropriate windings is a threshold switching device.

To give a geometrical interpretation of the problems stated above, another scheme of representing the function in Eq. (8.15) is shown in Fig. 8.19.

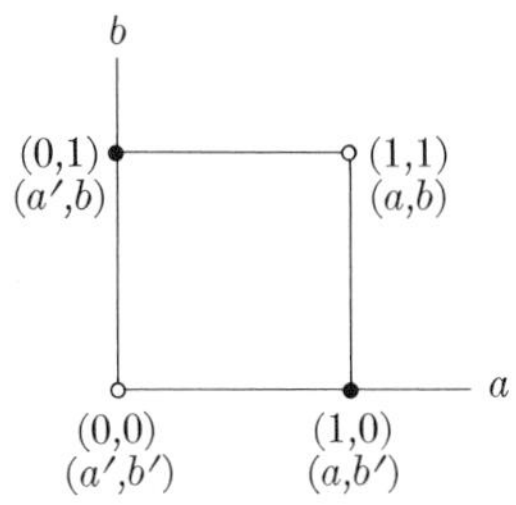

FIG. 8.19. The representation of $T = ab' + a'b$.

There are four vertices on the unit square. Each one is used to represent a standard product. Since the standard products ab' and $a'b$ are contained in the given function, two solid dots are placed on their corresponding vertices. These vertices are called *true* vertices. The remaining two vertices represent two standard products which are not contained in T; they are termed *false* vertices.

The dividing line between the two inequalities (8.24) and (8.25) can be expressed as

$$T + w_a a + w_b b = 0. \tag{8.26}$$

The expression in Eq. (8.26) represents a straight line in the (a, b)-plane. The original problem can therefore be interpreted as follows.

Can a straight line be drawn on the (a, b)-plane so that it divides the unit square into two regions, while one contains all the true vertices of the given function and the other all the false vertices of the given function?

By examining the situation in Fig. 8.19, we see clearly that it is impossible to draw such a straight line, and, therefore, the given switching function cannot be realized by just one threshold switching device. This, of course, confirms the finding made in Example 8.4. The extension of this geometrical interpretation to functions of more than two variables is left as an exercise.*

Threshold switching devices are also extensively used in pattern recognition systems and perception-like automata.†

PROBLEMS

8.1 Implement the following switching functions with T-type core circuits. The inputs are available in their unprimed form.

(a) $T = a'b'c + ab'c + abc$
(b) $T = a'b'c' + a'bc' + abc$

8.2. Implement the following switching functions with A-type core circuits. The inputs are available in their primed form.

(a) $T = a'bc + ab'c + abc$
(b) $T = a'b'c + ab'c' + abc'$

8.3. Implement the switching functions given in Problem 6.3 with core switching circuits. Specify the inputs required and explain why A- or T-type circuits are used.

8.4. Implement the switching functions given in Problem 6.4 with core switching circuits. Specify the inputs required and explain why A- or T-type circuits are used.

8.5. Optimize the circuits obtained in Problem 8.1 in the sense that the number of cores used is the least possible.

8.6. Optimize the circuits obtained in Problem 8.2 in the sense that the number of cores used is the least possible.

8.7. Redraw the schematic diagrams of the magnetic core and-gate shown in Fig. 8.7 into that shown in Fig. 8.18. Identify the weighting factors and the threshold.

8.8. Redraw the schematic diagrams of the magnetic core or-gate shown in Fig. 8.9 into that shown in Fig. 8.18. Identify the weighting factors and the threshold.

---

* Further reading on this topic, which concerns the linear separability of switching functions, can be found in CH 3, CO 2, MC 5, MI 2, PA 2, and SI 3.

† RO 1, KE 2, and MA 1.

8.9. Try to present another switching gate which can be considered as a threshold switching device.

8.10. By mapping a switching function of three variables on a unit cube, give a geometrical interpretation to the results obtained in Example 8.3.

8.11. Use the geometrical interpretation presented to find out how many different switching functions of two variables can be realized by just one threshold switching device. (*Ans.* 14)

8.12. Use the geometrical interpretation presented to find out how many different switching functions of three variables can be realized by just one threshold switching device. (*Ans.* 104)

CHAPTER 9

MULTITERMINAL NETWORKS

9.1 Introduction. Up to this point we have been mainly concerned with the design of single-output combinational switching circuits with n inputs, as shown in Fig. 9.1. Situations do occur in which a set of input variables determines not just one switching action, but many switching actions. To accomplish this, a multiterminal switching circuit is needed, as shown in Fig. 9.2. Each output represents one switching action to be taken. The design of a multiterminal network can be accomplished by finding one single-output combinational switching circuit for each of the m outputs required. This is certainly feasible. However, by designing one circuit with m outputs, we can effect certain optimization which is not possible if we design m circuits separately.

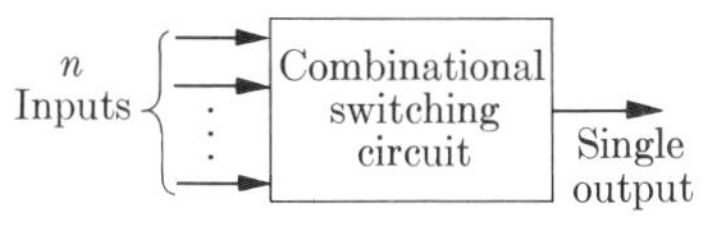

FIG. 9.1. Block diagram of a single-output combinational switching circuit.

n
Inputs
Combinational
switching
circuit
m
Outputs

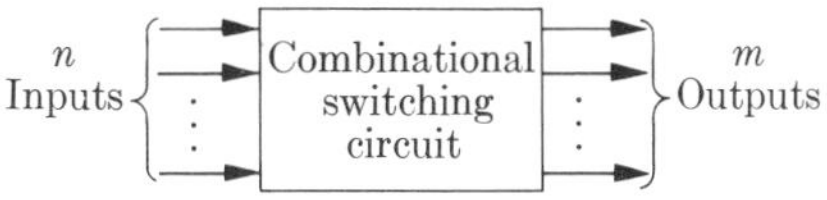

FIG. 9.2. Block diagram of a multiterminal switching circuit.

The above discussion claims that whenever a set of input variables determines many switching actions, a multiterminal network is required. This does not cover the whole story.

In Section 5.5, a selecting switching circuit is introduced. In such a circuit, a specific set of input variables determines only one corresponding specific output. There are as many possible sets of input variables as there are outputs, say m. The diagram in Fig. 5.11 shows the result when it is treated as a problem of designing m independent single-output switching circuits. But, if we approach the problem as the design of a multiterminal network, we obtain the circuit in Fig. 5.12. This shows that even though a set of input variables determines only a single switching action, it is sometimes profitable to employ the multiterminal network approach. Another dramatic example of this category is the telephone switching system.

A telephone switching system provides a communicating path between the calling and the called stations. The most primitive scheme provides a specific path between every pair of stations. The case of six stations is shown in Fig. 9.3. But problems arise. As the number of stations in-

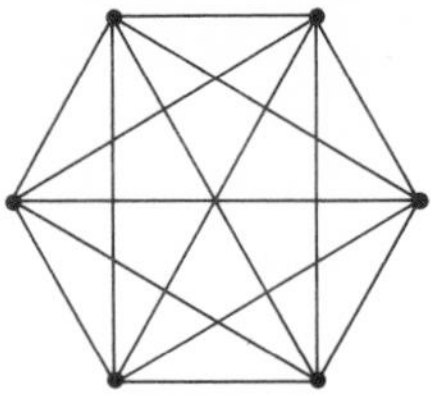

FIG. 9.3. Illustrating a primitive six-station telephone switching system.

creases, the cost increases; one station does not necessarily need to call every other station, and there is no necessity to be connected all the time to every other station, because the connection is not used constantly. To overcome these problems, a multiterminal switching network was provided which can establish a path between any two stations whenever requested, as shown in Fig. 9.4. Each telephone can be considered as either a calling or a called station.

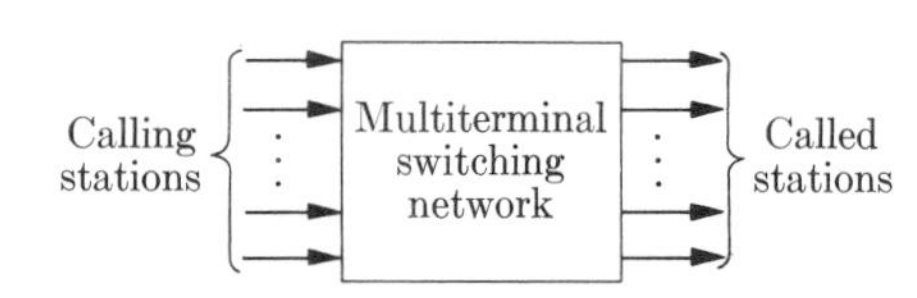

FIGURE 9.4.

9.2 Tree networks. Any switching function can be expressed in terms of standard products. To optimize a relay switching circuit, it is generally a good policy to employ as many transfer contacts as possible. It certainly is an interesting, perhaps profitable, venture to see if a switching network made only of transfer contacts can implement all possible standard products. If it does, then by properly connecting relevant terminals, we can realize any given switching function.

A multiterminal network using only transfer contacts is shown in Fig. 9.5(a). Each one of the four output terminals provides one of the four standard products of two switching variables. Such a network is called

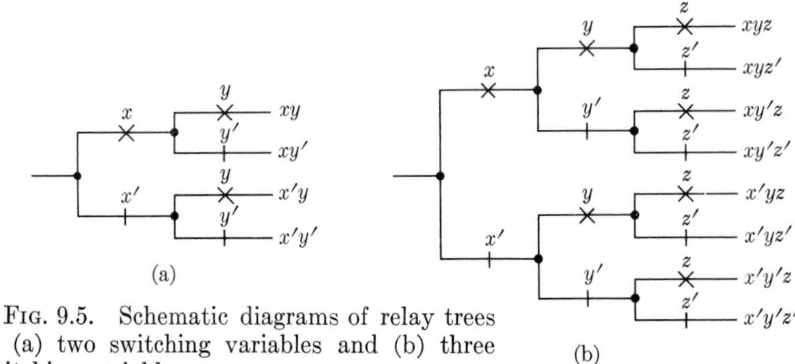

FIG. 9.5. Schematic diagrams of relay trees of (a) two switching variables and (b) three switching variables.

a *tree network*. Figure 9.5(b) shows a tree network for three switching variables. With this development, we have succeeded in showing that a switching network made only of transfer contacts can implement all possible standard products.

Since a relay tree is made with transfer contacts and makes all standard products available, it is very interesting and profitable to obtain a single-output or multiterminal switching network by "trimming a tree." The following examples will show the considerations involved.

EXAMPLE 9.1. Implement the carry circuit of a binary adder with relays.

The switching function of the carry circuit of a binary adder has been developed and is shown in Eq. (3.7). It is repeated below:

$$c_i = a_ib_ic'_{i-1} + a_ib'_ic_{i-1} + a'_ib_ic_{i-1} + a_ib_ic_{i-1}. \tag{9.1}$$

Since the function in Eq. (9.1) has three switching variables, we propose to start with a relay tree of three variables, as shown in Fig. 9.6(a). This tree provides eight terminals, each representing one standard product. Since the product term $a_ib_ic_{i-1}$ appears in Eq. (9.1), the top terminal in Fig. 9.6(a) is connected to endpoint B. The next terminal, which corresponds to the standard product $a_ib_ic'_{i-1}$, is connected to endpoint B by the same reasoning. Two other terminals are likewise connected to endpoint B as shown. The lamp and battery are used to detect whether there is a connection established between points A and B. There-

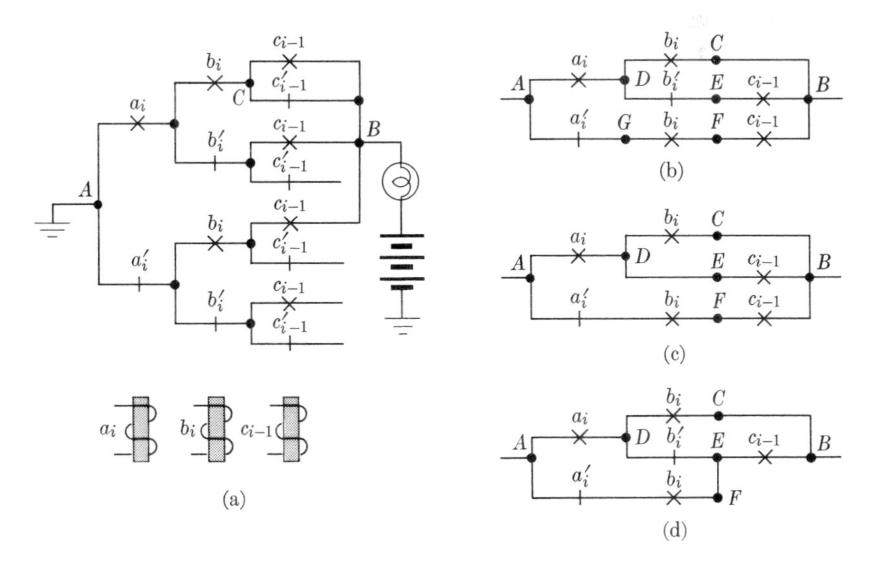

FIG. 9.6. Different implementation schemes for Example 9.1.

fore, whenever the lamp is lit, the carry has a value of 1. The complete preliminary design is shown in Fig. 9.6(a).

Now the "trimming of the tree" begins. By "trimming a tree" here, we do not intend to add any ornaments to the original circuit, instead we try to eliminate anything unnecessary from it. The terminals which are not connected to endpoint B can be erased, and so can their associated branches. Note that normally open contact c_{i-1} and normally closed contact c'_{i-1} both connect points B and C. This means that points B and C are always connected, and that the c_{i-1} transfer contact, which provides the c_{i-1} and the c'_{i-1} contacts, can be eliminated. The resultant circuit is shown in Fig. 9.6(b). However, the trimming does not stop here.

Inspecting the branches DCB and DEB, we note that the b'_i contact between D and E is quite unnecessary. After its elimination, the simplified circuit, which requires 11 springs, is shown in Fig. 9.6(c). We might be tempted to connect points E and F in Fig. 9.6(c) by a short circuit because we see the possibility of saving one c_{i-1} contact. However, if we did this, we would create a *sneak path* $AFEDCB$, which is characterized by the switching function a'_ib_i. This is equivalent to saying that a new product, a'_ib_i, is added to the original switching function. Therefore, points E and F cannot be short-circuited. As a matter of fact, the threat of creating sneak paths is the main road-block to optimizing most relay switching circuits.

Sneak paths can be easily created in relay switching circuits, because relay contacts are bilateral in nature, since the ground can be transmitted by a pair of contacts in both directions.

It is clear that points E and F in Fig. 9.6(c) cannot be short-circuited because of creating an unacceptable sneak path. If we try to short-circuit points E and F in Fig. 9.6(b), it might seem that a sneak path $AGFEDCB$ would also be created. However, this is not the case, because its switching function is $a'_ib_ib'_ib_i = 0$. The switching function between A and B has not been altered. By short-circuiting points E and F, we can save one c_{i-1} contact. Furthermore, since E and F are to be considered as one point, a transfer contact can be used to provide the b'_i and b_i contacts needed. The resultant circuit is shown in Fig. 9.6(d). This circuit requires only 10 springs.▲

EXAMPLE 9.2. Implement the following two switching functions with a three-terminal relay network:

$$T_{12} = AB + CD, \tag{9.2}$$

$$T_{13} = (A' + B')(C' + D'). \tag{9.3}$$

This example requires the design of the three-terminal network whose block diagram is shown in Fig. 9.7. It is immediately clear that the given

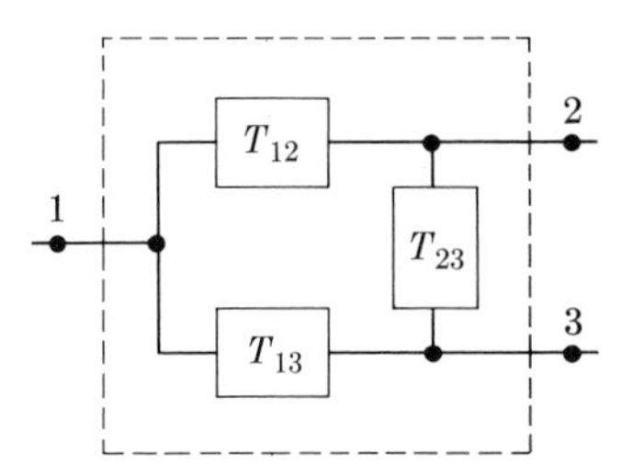

FIG. 9.7. Block diagram of the three-terminal relay network to be designed in Example 9.2.

problem has not been completely specified. It is true that if two separate circuits are to be designed for the two switching functions in Eqs. (9.2) and (9.3), there is no need to specify the switching function between terminals 2 and 3. However, if one single circuit with three terminals is to be designed, the switching function between terminals 2 and 3 has to be carefully chosen.

Let us assume that $A = 1$, $B = 1$, $C = 0$, and $D = 0$. From Eq. (9.2), we know that $T_{12} = 1$; therefore, terminals 1 and 2 would be short-circuited under this input combination. Assuming these same values for Eq. (9.3), $T_{13} = 0$. Consequently, terminals 1 and 3 should not be connected under this input combination. In this circumstance, what should T_{23} be? It must be equal to 0, because if it is equal to 1, then terminals 2 and 3 are short-circuited and consequently terminal 3 can be reached from terminal 1 via terminal 2. This violates the specification.

The above discussion reveals that if T_{12} and T_{13} do not have the same value under an input combination, T_{23} has to be zero. If T_{12} and T_{13} are equal, T_{23} can be either 1 or 0. This is one of the sources of don't-care conditions mentioned in Chapter 6 on manipulation of switching functions.

In this example, T_{12} and T_{13} are negative to each other; therefore

$$T_{23} = 0. \tag{9.4}$$

Once the problem is completely specified, we would like to follow a systematic approach to obtain an optimum circuit. Unfortunately there is no such approach available for a general set of T_{12}, T_{13}, and T_{23}.

Since T_{12} and T_{13} are negative to each other, we can use a tree network as a starting basis. If T_{12} and T_{13} are not negative to each other, a tree network cannot be used. (Why?)

Figure 9.8(a) delineates a four-variable tree. The terminals representing standard products which are contained by T_{12} are connected to form terminal 2. The remaining terminals are connected to form terminal 3.

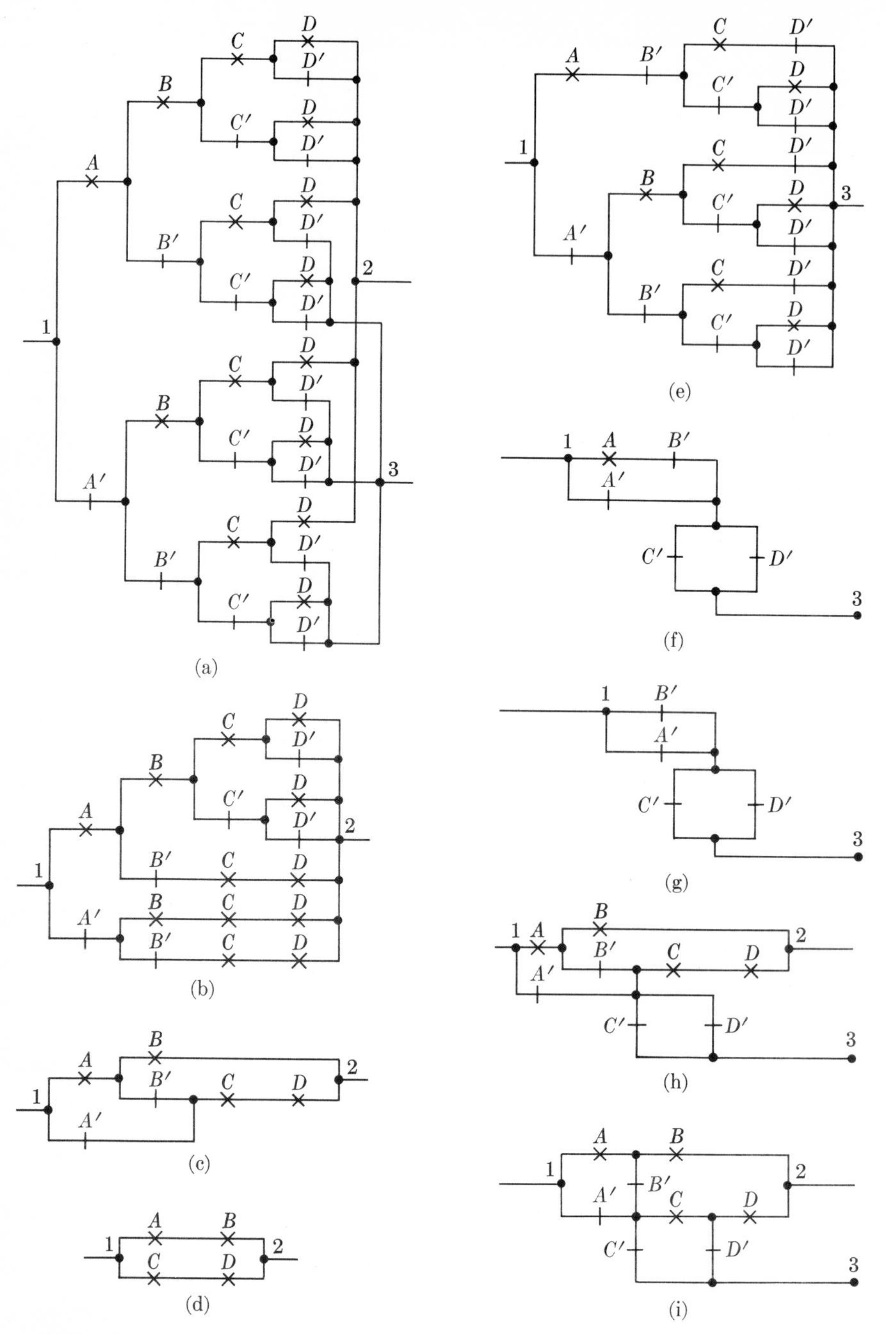

FIG. 9.8. Schematic diagrams showing the implementation of the three-terminal network of Example 9.2.

Simplification is carried out by the two circuits separately. In Fig. 9.8(b), the portion which implements the switching function T_{12} is isolated from the original circuit. This operation exposes possible simplifications. The simplified circuit is shown in Fig. 9.8(c). When we examine the given switching function T_{12} directly, we see that if T_{12} *alone* is to be implemented, the circuit in Fig. 9.8(c) is certainly not the simplest. Why should we stop at the circuit in Fig. 9.8(c), when we can implement T_{12} by the circuit in Fig. 9.8(d)? The reason is, we are concerned not only with implementing T_{12} alone, but also T_{13}. By leaving the circuit between terminals 1 and 2 as shown in Fig. 9.8(c), we have provided room for integration with the portion needed to implement T_{13}. When the resultant circuits are evaluated, it will be clear that the circuit in Fig. 9.8(c) leads to a better implementation.

In Fig. 9.8(e), the portion which implements the switching function T_{13} is taken from the original circuit. This circuit can be immediately simplified to that in Fig. 9.8(f). If the switching function T_{13} is to be implemented alone, the circuit should be further simplified to that shown in Fig. 9.8(g). But if we examine the circuits in Fig. 9.8(c) and 9.8(f) together, we see that these two can be advantageously combined, as shown in Fig. 9.8(h). This circuit can be redrawn as shown in Fig. 9.8(i). This final circuit is implemented with four transfer contacts, or 12 springs.

Let us now consider what will happen if T_{12} and T_{13} are implemented by two separate circuits. The results will be those shown in Fig. 9.8(d) and 9.8(g). Sixteen springs will then be needed. This indicates the advantage of multiterminal networks.▲

Example 9.2 demonstrates the approach that can be used to implement a given switching function and its negative with a three-terminal relay network. The general problem of synthesizing a multiterminal contactor network has not been completely solved.*

9.3 General synthesis of multiterminal networks with unilateral switching components. The previous section reveals that the synthesis of a contactor multiterminal network is essentially a cut-and-try process. This difficulty stems from the bilateral nature of contactors, whereas in other switching components that have been presented, this bilateral characteristic does not exist. Fortunately, a systematic approach to synthesis is possible. The approach to be presented is actually a slight modification of the tabulation method introduced in Chapter 6.

---

* References on tree networks: WA 1, SH 2, and BU 1. References on multiterminal contactor networks: RO 2, PO 1. An extensive list of references can be found in the papers CA 3 and LE 2.

EXAMPLE 9.3. Implement the following set of three switching functions (a) with diode gates, and (b) with direct-coupled transistor gates:

$$T_1(a, b, c, d) = m_{11} + m_{12} + m_{13} + m_{14} + m_{15}, \tag{9.5}$$

$$T_2(a, b, c, d) = m_3 + m_7 + m_{11} + m_{12} + m_{13} + m_{14} + m_{15}, \tag{9.6}$$

$$T_3(a, b, c, d) = m_3 + m_7 + m_{12} + m_{13} + m_{14} + m_{15}. \tag{9.7}$$

These three switching functions indicate the fact that a set of four input variables initiates three switching actions. These three functions can, of course, be implemented separately. In that case, the map method and the tabulation method can be applied to each one of the three functions. However, much is to be gained by manipulating the three at the same time.

The first step in using the modified tabulation method is to identify the prime implicants: those which are included in one function only, those which are contained in two functions, and those which are contained by all three functions specified. Table 9.1 is constructed for this purpose.

TABLE 9.1

3–$\check{T}_2\check{T}_3$	0011	3,7–$\check{T}_2T_3$	0–11	3,7,11,15–T_2	– –11
12–$\check{T}_1\check{T}_2\check{T}_3$	1100	3,11–$\check{T}_2$	–011	12,13,14,15–$T_1T_2T_3$	11– –
7–$\check{T}_2\check{T}_3$	0111	12,13–$\check{T}_1\check{T}_2\check{T}_3$	110–		
11–$\check{T}_1\check{T}_2$	1011	12,14–$\check{T}_1\check{T}_2\check{T}_3$	11–0		
13–$\check{T}_1\check{T}_2\check{T}_3$	1101	7,15–$\check{T}_2T_3$	–111		
14–$\check{T}_1\check{T}_2\check{T}_3$	1110	11,15–$T_1\check{T}_2$	1–11		
15–$\check{T}_1\check{T}_2\check{T}_3$	1111	13,15–$\check{T}_1\check{T}_2\check{T}_3$	11–1		
		14,15–$\check{T}_1\check{T}_2\check{T}_3$	111–		

Each standard product is not only designated by its decimal notation, but also by the switching functions within which it is contained: 3–T_2T_3 denotes that the standard product $a'b'cd$ is contained in functions T_2 and T_3; 13–$T_1T_2T_3$ denotes that the term $abc'd$ is contained in functions T_1, T_2, and T_3. As in the manipulation of a single switching function, m_3 and m_{12} are placed in one group because they both have two 1's in their binary notations. By the same reasoning, m_7, m_{11}, m_{13}, and m_{14} are grouped together.

The simplification process is carried out by comparing one member of a group to every member of its adjacent group: $3\text{–}T_2T_3$ and $7\text{–}T_2T_3$ are combined into a new term $3,7\text{–}T_2T_3$. This notation indicates that the combination of m_3 and m_7, which is $a'cd$, is contained in both T_2 and T_3. A check mark is placed on top of T_2 in $3\text{–}T_2T_3$ to indicate that "m_3 contained in T_2" is represented by the new term $3,7\text{–}T_2T_3$. A check mark is also placed on top of T_3 in $3\text{–}T_2T_3$ for the same reason. Check marks are also placed on T_2 and T_3 of $7\text{–}T_2T_3$. When $3\text{–}T_2T_3$ is compared with $11\text{–}T_1T_2$, a new term, $b'cd$, is formed which is indicated as $3,11\text{–}T_2$, when T_2 appears in both $3\text{–}T_2T_3$ and $11\text{–}T_1T_2$. This new term is contained only in T_2. Therefore, a check mark is placed on top of T_2 in $11\text{–}T_1T_2$. T_1 is later checked off when $11\text{–}T_1T_2$ is combined with $15\text{–}T_1T_2T_3$ to form $11,15\text{–}T_1T_2$. This process is continued until no further combination of terms can be made.

The combination process yields five prime implicants; for example, the prime implicant $a'cd$ is denoted by $3,7\text{–}T_3$. This means that this term is the prime implicant of T_3 only. The next task is to select the necessary prime implicants to form the specified functions. This is carried out by making a chart, as shown in Fig. 9.9.

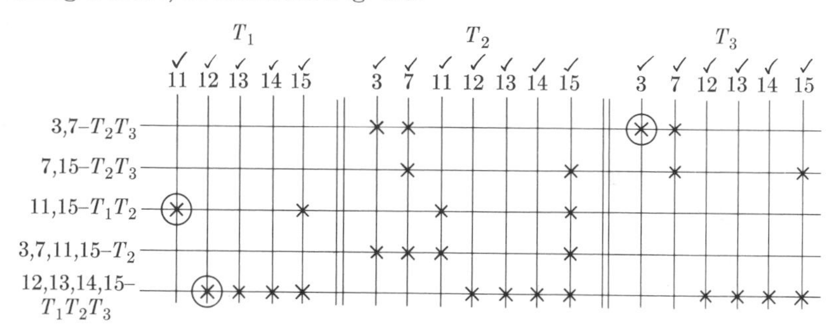

FIGURE 9.9

Figure 9.9 bears a strong resemblance to Fig. 6.17, in which the prime implicants of a single function are selected. For example, a cross is placed at the intersection of the line under $T_1\text{–}11$ and the line representing $11,15\text{–}T_1T_2$, because $11\text{–}T_1$ is contained in $11,15\text{–}T_1T_2$. The chart is completed by the same process.

When we examine the column under $11\text{–}T_1$, we note that there is only one cross to be found. This means that the prime implicant $11,15\text{–}T_1T_2$ must be included in function T_1. The inclusion of $11,15\text{–}T_1T_2$ in T_1 also means that $15\text{–}T_1$ is represented. Check marks are placed on $11\text{–}T_1$ and $15\text{–}T_1$. The notation $11,15\text{–}T_1T_2$ of this prime implicant also suggests that this term can represent $11\text{–}T_2$ and $15\text{–}T_2$. However, the decision whether or not to include $11,15\text{–}T_1T_2$ in T_2 is postponed because we do not know at this time whether or not the inclusion of 11 15–T_1T_2 in T_2 is the best way to cover 11–T_2 and 15–T_2.

There is also only one cross on the column under 12–T_1. This immediately suggests that the prime implicant 12,13,14,15–$T_1T_2T_3$ has to be included in T_1. Its inclusion also checks off 13–T_1 and 14–T_1. Its notation suggests that this term can be used to check off m_{12}, m_{13}, m_{14}, and m_{15} in T_2 and T_3. This time the decision to include 12,13,14,15–$T_1T_2T_3$ in T_2 and T_3 can be easily made, because its inclusion is the only way to check off m_{12} in T_2 and m_{12} in T_3. The formal inclusion of 12,13,14,15–$T_1T_2T_3$ in T_2 and T_3 enables us to check off 12,13,14,15–T_2 and 12,13,14,15–T_3.

In continuing our search for a column in which only one cross can be found, we reach the column under 3–T_3. This indicates that the prime implicant 3,7–T_2T_3 has to be included in T_3. Its inclusion in T_3 checks off 3–T_3 and 7–T_3. It is also clear that the inclusion of 3,7–T_2T_3 in T_2 checks off 3–T_2 and 7–T_2. However, since this is not the only way to cover these terms, the decision to check them off has to be made later.

At this point, T_1 and T_3 have already been completely specified as shown in the following:

$$T_1 = acd + ab, \tag{9.8}$$

$$T_3 = a'cd + ab. \tag{9.9}$$

We note that T_2 has three standard products, m_3, m_7, and m_{11}, which have not been checked off. There are two ways to cover these three terms: one is to include the prime implicant 3,7,11,15–T_2 in T_2, and the other is to include the two prime implicants 3,7–T_2T_3 and 11,15–T_1T_2 in T_2. In other words, we can have

$$T_2 = ab + cd, \tag{9.10}$$

or

$$T_2 = ab + a'cd + acd. \tag{9.11}$$

If we are interested in implementing only T_2, Eq. (9.10) is definitely better. However, note that whether they are used in T_2 or not, $a'cd$ and acd have to be generated to implement T_1 and T_3. This consideration makes Eq. (9.11) more desirable. This modified tabulation method not only finds prime implicants for each function, but also shows the best selection when the implementation of a complete set of switching functions is attempted.

The implementation of the expressions in Eqs. (9.8), (9.9), and (9.11) with diode gates is shown in Fig. 9.10. This two-level switching circuit requires 15 diodes. If each function were implemented separately, the total requirement would be 20 diodes.

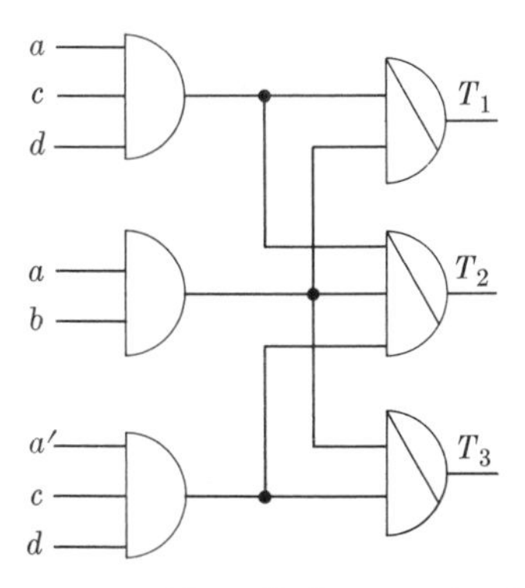

FIG. 9.10. The diode gate implementation for Example 9.3.

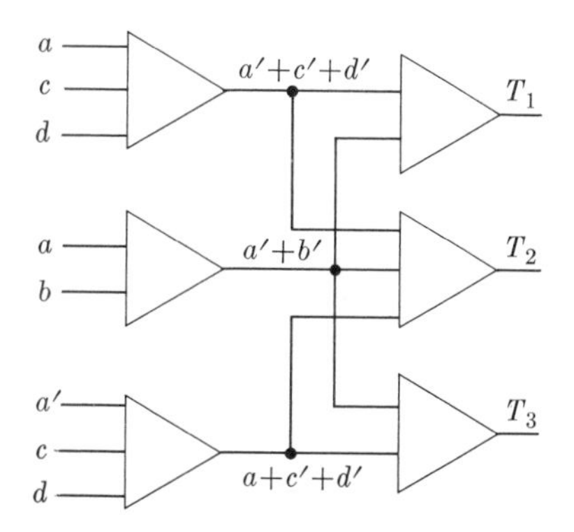

FIG. 9.11. The direct-coupled transistor gate implementation for Example 9.3.

Direct-coupled transistor gates are used to realize the three expressions shown in Fig. 9.11.▲

Note in this example that the sneak path problem does not exist, because the switching components used are unilateral.

The modified tabulation method introduced here can also be machine programmed.*

9.4 Coding in switching systems for computation. Coding is a very important and practical problem in the design of switching systems. It has been pointed out that the most economic and reliable switching components are binary in nature. Computers made up of binary switching components can handle numbers expressed in the binary system. However, the scientific and business data which most computers are called upon to process are expressed in the decimal system. There are two alternatives available. One is to express data in binary systems and process them in a computer which follows the binary arithmetic rules. The other is to code data with binary digits and process them in a computer which follows decimal arithmetic rules.

In adopting the second approach, we are inevitably confronted with the problem of coding decimal digits. There are two considerations which are of utmost importance: the mechanization of the coding scheme, and its error-detecting and error-correcting capabilities.† In designing a decimal computer, the code to be used has to be determined first. Once the coding scheme has been adopted, the computer circuits can then be de-

* BA 2 and MC 6.
† HA 1 and SL 1.

signed. The code used has a direct influence on the complexity of the resultant system. It is therefore imperative that the mechanization problem be considered when different coding schemes are being considered.

In a large computing system, many components are used. The possibility of producing erroneous results because of malfunction of certain components definitely exists. It is certainly desirable that the code adopted possess error-detecting and, if possible, error-correcting capabilities.

There are ten decimal digits, 0 to 9, to be taken care of. To represent these ten decimal digits, at least four bits (binary digits) are required. The number of permutations possible for four bits is 16, because for each position, there can be two choices.

We can look further to see how many coding schemes we can have. For the first decimal digit, say 0, we can assign any one of the 16 permutations. For the next decimal digit, say 1, we can use any one of the remaining 15. The total number of coding schemes for four bits is, therefore, $16!/6!$.

Among the coding schemes available, there is one type called the *weighted code*. From the binary digits in the weighted code, we can determine the decimal digit it represents. There are many kinds of weighted decimal codes. A very popular one, the BCD (binary-coded-decimal)code or the 8421 code, is shown in Table 9.2.

TABLE 9.2

THE BCD OR 8421 CODE

Decimal digit	Code			
	w	x	y	z
0	0	0	0	0
1	0	0	0	1
2	0	0	1	0
3	0	0	1	1
4	0	1	0	0
5	0	1	0	1
6	0	1	1	0
7	0	1	1	1
8	1	0	0	0
9	1	0	0	1

The reason that this code is called the 8421 code can be seen when we convert each four-bit combination into its corresponding decimal digit. Weights of 8, 4, 2, and 1 can be assigned to the w-, x-, y-, and z-bits, respectively.

At this point, we want to know what the corresponding arithmetic unit of the computer will be if this code scheme is adopted. There are many considerations involved, but a fair judgment can be made after designing an adder according to this coding scheme.*

The problem of designing a decimal adder using the BCD code is clarified by the block diagram in Fig. 9.12. There are nine input variables sent into the block. A set of four bits, a_1, b_1, c_1, and d_1, represents one decimal digit of the augend. Another set of four bits, a_2, b_2, c_2, and d_2, stands for the corresponding decimal digit of the addend. The remaining input variable is the carry forwarded to this stage from the addition of previous digits. This is essentially a problem of designing a five-terminal network with nine inputs. Four of the outputs form a code which represents the sum decimal digit. The remaining output is used to indicate whether or not there is any carry to be forwarded to the next addition.

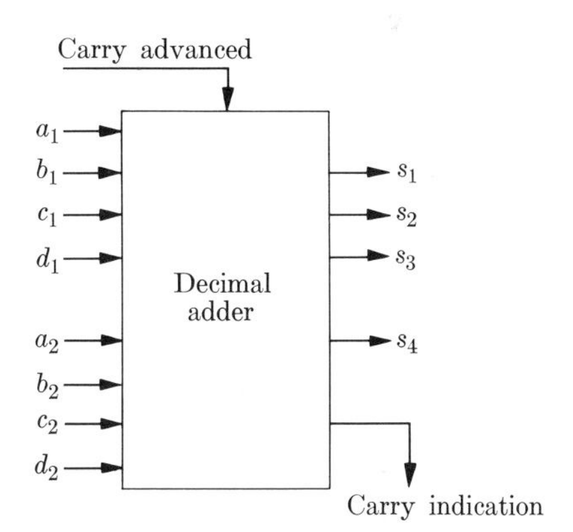

FIG. 9.12. Block diagram illustrating the problem of designing a decimal adder using the BCD code.

To carry out this design problem, we can establish a set of five switching functions expressing the five outputs. When we try to simplify and realize this set of switching functions, we see immediately that we are confronted with a tedious problem. Since there are nine input variables, the number of entries in the truth table is 512.

There are, of course, certain simplifications that can be made.

Two methods of simplification are as follows. First, a computer can be used to carry out the simplification of the switching variables by means of the tabulation method.† Second, the iterative approach, which is discussed in the next chapter, can be applied. The mechanization of the decimal adder using the BCD code is also discussed in Chapter 10.

It is clear that the BCD code (Table 9.2) does not possess any error-detecting feature.

---

* RI 1.

† BA 2.

Among the nonweighted codes, the excess-3 code shown in Table 9.3 is widely adopted for computer use.

The reason that this coding scheme is termed the excess-3 code can be seen from the code for decimal a which in excess-3 code is the same as decimal $3 + a$ in BCD code. When the mechanization of an arithmetic unit using excess-3 code is investigated its advantages will be clearly appreciated.*

TABLE 9.3

EXCESS-3 CODE

Decimal digit	Code w	x	y	z
0	0	0	1	1
1	0	1	0	0
2	0	1	0	1
3	0	1	1	0
4	0	1	1	1
5	1	0	0	0
6	1	0	0	1
7	1	0	1	0
8	1	0	1	1
9	1	1	0	0

TABLE 9.4

A TRUTH TABLE FOR EXAMPLE 9.4

Decimal digit	BCD code w	x	y	z	Excess-3 code A	B	C	D
0	0	0	0	0	0	0	1	1
1	0	0	0	1	0	1	0	0
2	0	0	1	0	0	1	0	1
3	0	0	1	1	0	1	1	0
4	0	1	0	0	0	1	1	1
5	0	1	0	1	1	0	0	0
6	0	1	1	0	1	0	0	1
7	0	1	1	1	1	0	1	0
8	1	0	0	0	1	0	1	1
9	1	0	0	1	1	1	0	0

9.5 Translating circuits: another example for the design of a multi-terminal network. Translating circuits are used to convert a quantity expressed in one code to another code. These circuits are extremely useful in communication between different switching systems.

EXAMPLE 9.4. Design a diode translating circuit which converts the BCD code into excess-3 code.

A truth table relating the two codes is first constructed, as shown in Table 9.4.

The input variables in this problem are w, x, y, and z. The output variables are A, B, C, and D. The digit A will have a value of 1 when one of the following input conditions is true: 0101, 0110, 0111, 1000, or 1001. This relationship can be expressed by

$$A(w, x, y, z) = \sum m5,6,7,8,9. \tag{9.12}$$

* RI 1 and KE 1.

Using the same reasoning, we can derive

$$B(w, x, y, z) = \sum m1,2,3,4,9, \tag{9.13}$$

$$C(w, x, y, z) = \sum m0,3,4,7,8, \tag{9.14}$$

$$D(w, x, y, z) = \sum m0,2,4,6,8. \tag{9.15}$$

The above four equations are not a complete description of the problem. In the BCD code there are six permutations, namely 1010, 1011, 1100, 1101, 1110, and 1111, to which no meaning has been attached. That means these six input conditions will never appear as inputs. Under these circumstances, it really does not matter what output will be produced if any one of these six combinations is considered as an input. These, therefore, will constitute six don't-care conditions:

$$\text{Don't-care conditions: } m \text{ 10, 11, 12, 13, 14, or 15.} \tag{9.16}$$

Before the realization process, we should try to manipulate Eqs. (9.12), (9.13), (9.14), and (9.15). In the process of simplification, we should take advantage of the don't-care conditions in Eq. (9.16). The modified tabulation method is used to do the manipulation, as shown in Table 9.5 and Fig. 9.13.

Table 9.5 is made by following the procedures established in Section 9.3. However, it should be pointed out that each standard product which represents one don't-care condition is treated as if it were included in all four functions. In this way we can take the best advantage of the availability of the don't-care conditions.

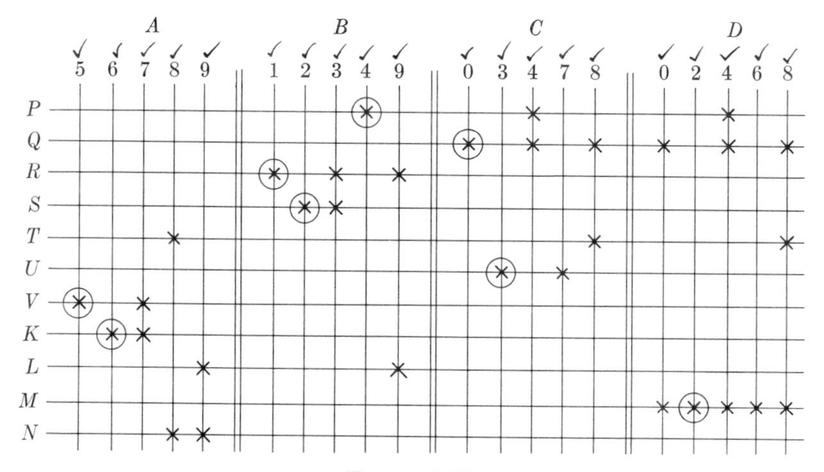

FIGURE 9.13

TABLE 9.5

0–CD	0000	0, 2–D	00–0		0, 2, 4, 6–D	0––0		0, 2, 4, 6, 8, 10, 12, 14–D	–––0	M
1–B	0001	0, 4–CD	0–00		0, 2, 8, 10–D	–0–0				
2–BD	0010	0, 8–CD	–000		0, 4, 8, 12–CD	––00	Q	8, 9, 10, 11, 12, 13, 14, 15–A	1–––	N
4–BCD	0100	1, 3–B	00–1		1, 3, 9, 11–B	–0–1	R			
8–ACD	1000	1, 9–B	–001		2, 3, 10, 11–B	–01–	S			
3–BC	0011	2, 3–B	001–		2, 6, 10, 14–D	––10				
5–A	0101	2, 6–D	0–10		4, 6, 12, 14–D	–1–0				
6–AD	0110	2, 10–BD	–010		8, 9, 10, 11–A	10––				
9–AB	1001	4, 6–D	01–0		8, 9, 12, 13–A	1–0–				
10–ABCD	1010	4, 12–BCD	–100	P	8, 10, 12, 14–ACD	1––0	T			
12–ABCD	1100	8, 9–A	100–		3, 7, 11, 15–C	––11	U			
7–AC	0111	8, 10–ACD	10–0		5, 7, 13, 15–A	–1–1	V			
11–ABCD	1011	8, 12–ACD	1–00		6, 7, 14, 15–A	–11–	K			
13–ABCD	1101	3, 7–C	0–11		9, 11, 13, 15–AB	1––1	L			
14–ABCD	1110	3, 11–BC	–011		10, 11, 14, 15–ABCD	1–1–				
15–ABCD	1111	5, 7–A	01–1		12, 13, 14, 15–ABCD	11––				
		5, 13–A	–101							
		6, 7–A	011–							
		6, 14–AD	–110							
		9, 11–AB	10–1							
		9, 13–AB	1–01							
		10, 11–ABCD	101–							
		10, 14–ABCD	1–10							
		12, 13–ABCD	110–							
		12, 14–ABCD	11–0							
		15, 7–AC	–111							
		11, 15–ABCD	1–11							
		13, 15–ABCD	11–1							
		14, 15–ABCD	111–							

A capital letter is attached for identification purposes to a prime implicant once it is found.

The selection of necessary prime implicants for each function is shown in Fig. 9.13.

The don't-care products are not entered as columns in Fig. 9.13, because their eventual inclusion in, or exclusion from, the final set of expressions is of no concern to the designer. The simplified functions are

$$A = V + K + N = w + xy + xz, \tag{9.17}$$

$$B = R + S + P = x'z + x'y + xy'z', \tag{9.18}$$

$$C = U + Q = yz + y'z', \tag{9.19}$$

$$D = M = z'. \tag{9.20}$$

After the vast searching process shown in Table 9.5 and Fig. 9.13, we might be disappointed to obtain the set of simplified expressions in Eqs. (9.17), (9.18), (9.19), and (9.20), because we could not find in these expressions prime implicants that are common to two functions. As a matter of fact, these final expressions can be obtained very easily by using the map method. Then, we may ask, why was the tabulation method used?

There are two reasons. First, the tabulation method can be applied to functions of many variables. Second, the tabulation method offers a systematic approach for locating common prime implicants between functions. The designer should always be on the alert for the common prime implicants between functions. The fact that in this problem none was found does not mean we should not have looked for them in the first place.

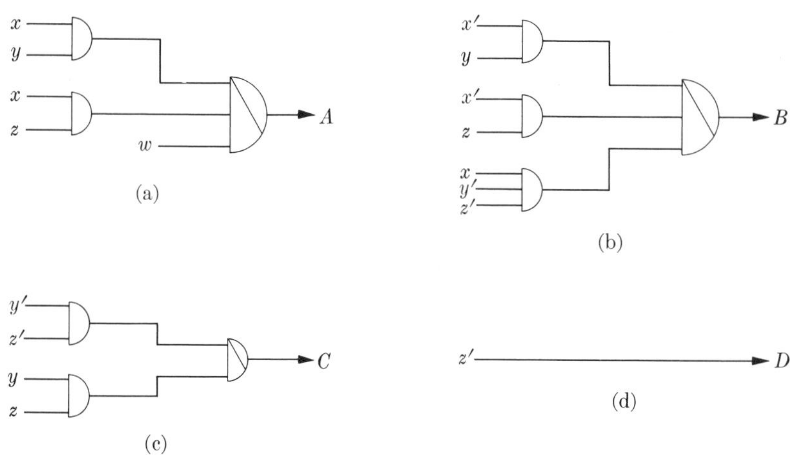

FIG. 9.14. The diode circuit implementation for Example 9.4.

The diode circuits implementing the functions in Eqs. (9.17), (9.18), (9.19), and (9.20) are shown in Fig. 9.14(a), (b), (c), and (d), respectively. ▲

EXAMPLE 9.5. Design a diode translating circuit which converts the BCD code into decimal digits.

Such a translating circuit is widely used in the output device of a computer so that the numerical results are printed in decimal digits rather than in coded form.

The design of such a circuit is essentially a problem of synthesizing a ten-terminal network which has four inputs. Table 9.2 can be considered as the truth table, with the left-hand column as the outputs. A set of

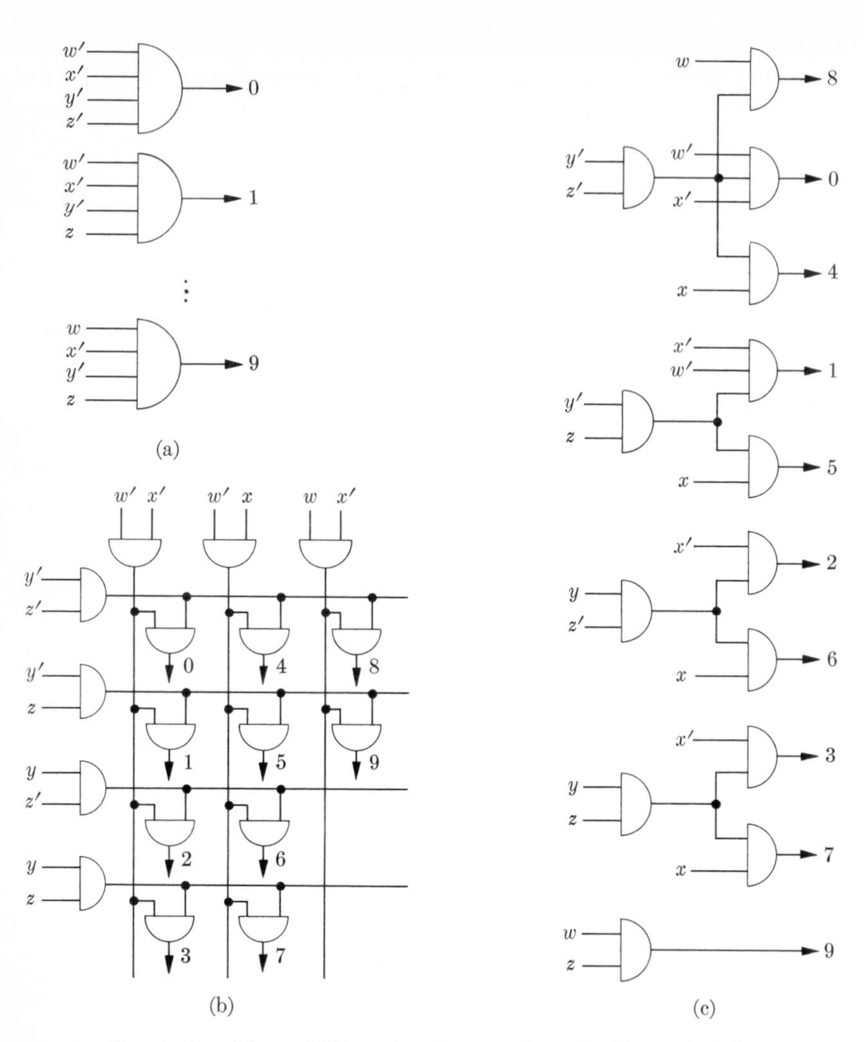

FIG. 9.15. Three different implementations for Example 9.5.

switching functions can be established:

$$
\begin{aligned}
0(w, x, y, z) &= m_0, \\
1(w, x, y, z) &= m_1, \\
&\vdots \\
9(w, x, y, z) &= m_9.
\end{aligned}
\tag{9.21}
$$

A single-level circuit which requires 40 diodes is shown in Fig. 9.15(a). A two-level matrix configuration can be used. The resultant circuit, shown in Fig. 9.15(b), needs 34 diodes.

If we consider Table 9.2 as a truth table, we see immediately that this truth table is not complete, because there are four input variables and therefore sixteen entries. The missing six actually constitute the don't-care conditions:

Don't-care conditions: m_{10}, m_{11}, m_{12}, m_{13}, m_{14}, or m_{15}.

In the design of the circuits in Fig. 9.15(a) and 9.15(b), these don't-care conditions are not used. In trying to take advantage of the presence of the don't-care conditions, we should normally use the modified tabulation method. However, in the present problem, the map method is more attractive, because each switching function in Eq. (9.21) consists of a standard product only. It is obvious from the outset that there is no common prime implicant to be found. By using the map method, we find the simplified switching functions

$$\begin{aligned}
0(w, x, y, z) &= w'x'y'z', \\
1(w, x, y, z) &= w'x'y'z, \\
2(w, x, y, z) &= x'yz', \\
3(w, x, y, z) &= x'yz, \\
4(w, x, y, z) &= xy'z', \\
5(w, x, y, z) &= xy'z, \\
6(w, x, y, z) &= xyz', \\
7(w, x, y, z) &= xyz, \\
8(w, x, y, z) &= wy'z', \\
9(w, x, y, z) &= wz.
\end{aligned} \tag{9.22}$$

The implementation of the switching functions in Eq. (9.22) is shown in Fig. 9.15(c). This circuit requires only 30 diodes.▲

9.6 Coding in switching systems for control. Codes employed to represent decimal digits are discussed in this section. Such codes are devised to yield the simplest mechanization and to possess error-detecting and error-correcting capabilities. However, in applying a switching system for "control" purposes, we have to process quantities expressed in both decimal systems and analogous entities. For example, if a digital computer is used to control the position of a shaft, the information concerning the angular position of the shaft has to be constantly and automatically fed into the computer. This means that the angular position of the shaft has to be coded.

In coding an analogous quantity, our first concern is that the codes can be easily generated. For example, let us return to the coding of the angular position of a shaft. The circumference of the shaft is to be divided into many regions, and each region is represented by a set of binary

TABLE 9.6

THE FOUR-BIT CYCLIC CODE

0	0	0	0	1	1	0	0
0	0	0	1	1	1	0	1
0	0	1	1	1	1	1	1
0	0	1	0	1	1	1	0
0	1	1	0	1	0	1	0
0	1	1	1	1	0	1	1
0	1	0	1	1	0	0	1
0	1	0	0	1	0	0	0

digits. Different regions are represented by different sets of binary digits, usually of equal length. It is certainly desirable that two sets of binary digits which represent two adjacent regions differ in only one bit. This feature facilitates the automatic generation of the representing sets of binary digits. Such a code is called a *cyclic code** and also the Gray code. A four-bit Gray code is shown in Table 9.6.

It can be seen that two adjacent sets differ in only one bit.

PROBLEMS

9.1. Implement the following set of switching functions with relays. T_{12} is the switching function between terminals 1 and 2, and T_{13} is the switching function between terminals 1 and 3.

(a) $T_{12} = (a + c')(b + d')$, $T_{13} = a'c + b'd$
(b) $T_{12} = abcd'$, $T_{13} = a' + b' + c' + d$

9.2. Implement the following sets of switching functions with relays.

(a) $T_{12}(w, x, y, z) = m_0 + m_3 + m_5 + m_6 + m_9 + m_{10} + m_{12} + m_{15}$,
$T_{13}(w, x, y, z) = m_1 + m_2 + m_4 + m_7 + m_8 + m_{11} + m_{13} + m_{14}$

(b) $T_{12}(w, x, y, z) = m_0 + m_5 + m_7 + m_8 + m_{13} + m_{15}$,
$T_{13}(w, x, y, z) = m_1 + m_2 + m_3 + m_4 + m_6 + m_9 + m_{10} + m_{11} + m_{12} + m_{14}$

9.3. A relay tree of three switching variables is shown in Fig. 9.5(b). Note that relay x has one transfer contact, relay y has two, and relay z has four. It is generally desirable to distribute an equal number of transfer contacts to every relay. Try your best to distribute transfer contacts as equally as possible among the three relays.

---

* OB 1. For discussions on applications of Gray code in arithmetic operations, see FO 1 and LU 1.

9.4. A relay tree of four switching variables is shown in Fig. 9.8(a). Relays A, B, C, and D have 1, 2, 4, and 8 transfer contacts, respectively. Try to distribute transfer contacts as equally as possible among the four relays.

9.5. Implement the following set of switching functions with relays:

$$T_{12}(a, b, c, d) = m_0 + m_1 + m_2 + m_3 + m_5 + m_9 + m_{13},$$
$$T_{13}(a, b, c, d) = m_1 + m_5 + m_9 + m_{13} + m_{14} + m_{15},$$

where T_{12} is the switching function between terminals 1 and 2 and T_{13} is the switching function between terminals 1 and 3.

9.6. Implement the following set of three switching functions (a) with diode gates, and (b) with direct-coupled transistor gates.

$$T_1(A, B, C, D) = m_0 + m_6 + m_7 + m_8,$$
$$T_2(A, B, C, D) = m_0 + m_1 + m_6 + m_7 + m_8 + m_9,$$
$$T_3(A, B, C, D) = m_1 + m_6 + m_7 + m_9.$$

9.7. Implement the following set of four switching functions (a) with diode gates and, (b) with direct-coupled transistor gates.

$$T_1(w, x, y, z) = m_1 + m_5 + m_9 + m_{12} + m_{13} + m_{14} + m_{15},$$
$$T_2(w, x, y, z) = m_3 + m_7 + m_{11} + m_{12} + m_{13} + m_{14} + m_{15},$$
$$T_3(w, x, y, z) = m_3 + m_4 + m_5 + m_6 + m_7 + m_{11} + m_{12} + m_{13} + m_{14} + m_{15},$$
$$T_4(w, x, y, z) = m_3 + m_7 + m_8 + m_9 + m_{10} + m_{11} + m_{12} + m_{13} + m_{14} + m_{15}.$$

9.8. Implement the following set of three switching functions (a) with diode gates, and (b) with direct-coupled transistor gates.

$$T_1(A, B, C, D, E) = m_6 + m_{14} + m_{15} + m_{24} + m_{25} + m_{28} + m_{30} + m_{31},$$
don't-care conditions: $m_0, m_3, m_7, m_{22}, m_{23}, m_{26}, m_{27}, m_{29}$;

$$T_2(A, B, C, D, E) = m_5 + m_{13} + m_{21} + m_{24} + m_{25} + m_{28} + m_{29} + m_{31},$$
don't-care conditions: $m_0, m_1, m_3, m_9, m_{17}, m_{26}, m_{27}, m_{30}$;

$$T_3(A, B, C, D, E) = m_{13} + m_{17} + m_{22} + m_{25} + m_{29} + m_{31},$$
don't-care conditions: $m_0, m_1, m_3, m_5, m_9, m_{21}, m_{23}, m_{30}$.

9.9. Propose a weighted code for decimal digits. Each code will consist of four binary digits. Indicate the weight of each binary digit.

9.10. Propose a weighted code for decimal digits. Each code will consist of five binary digits and each code will have only two 1's. Indicate the weight of each binary digit.

9.11. Design and implement a diode translating circuit which converts the excess-3 code into the BCD code.

CHAPTER 10

CASCADED NETWORKS*

10.1 Introduction. The approaches to implementing or realizing switching circuits with relays, diodes, transistors, or cores have been presented. There seems to be no restriction on the number of switching variables that can be handled. For each well-defined problem, a truth table can always be constructed, and subsequently a set of switching functions can be reached for implementation. This is the general approach for a given problem. However, if the number of input switching variables is large, the number of entries in the truth table increases rapidly. To illustrate this point, let us examine the design of a parallel-mode binary adder.

The modes of operation are defined in Section 3.3. The block diagram of a strictly parallel binary adder is shown in Fig. 3.1. If the binary numbers to be added in parallel are of four digits each, namely $a_3a_2a_1a_0$ and $b_3b_2b_1b_0$, there are then four separate circuits, N_0, N_1, N_2, and N_3, to be designed. Let us pursue the design of N_3, whose block diagram is shown in Fig. 10.1.

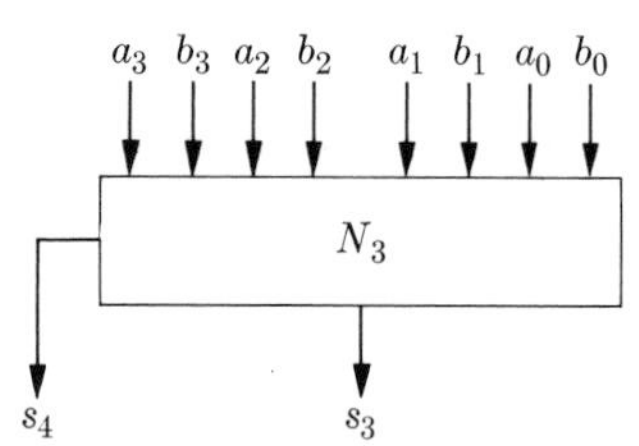

FIG. 10.1. Block diagram of a unit in a strictly parallel adder.

Note that the number of input switching variables is eight. The number of entries in the truth table, which is equal to the number of possible input conditions, or the number of possible standard products, is $2^8 = 256$. Even though it is feasible to construct a truth table, it would be cumbersome indeed. Even if construction of the truth table were completed, the switching functions thus derived would present a formidable task to the designer who tried to implement them with acceptable switching circuits. It is for this reason that the cascaded network approach has to be investigated.

---

* Also termed *iterative* networks.

The difficulty encountered in using the straightforward approach is due to the large number of input variables. We are thus led to investigate the possibility of cascading several subcircuits to form the system desired. By this process, the number of input variables for each subcircuit would be small enough to be efficiently handled. A revised block diagram of the parallel adder is shown in Fig. 10.2. If we examine this diagram from right to left, we see that the two least significant digits are processed by the circuit N_0 which produces s_0 and c_0, the carry to be forwarded to the next stage, and so on.

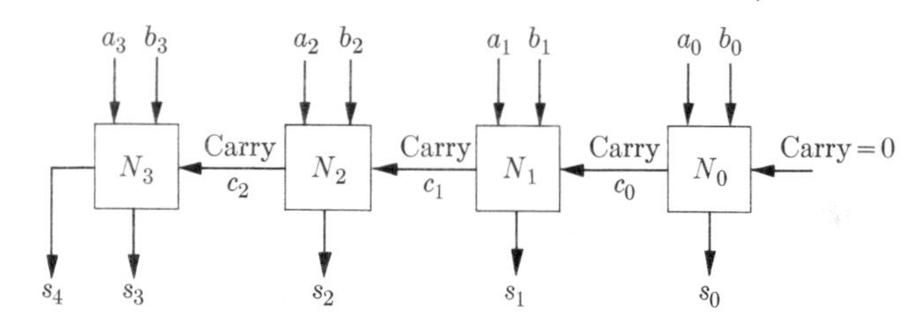

FIG. 10.2. Revised block diagram for a four-digit parallel adder.

The adder formed by following the scheme shown in Fig. 10.2 does not act so fast as the strictly parallel adder, because N_1 uses one of the outputs of N_0 as its input. By cascading, we obtain a simpler adder circuit, but a slower one.

It is interesting to note that the subcircuits N_0, N_1, N_2, and N_3 are identical, each having three input variables and two output variables. By cascading the subcircuits, we have transformed the original cumbersome circuit into four identical circuits, each of which has only three input variables and two output variables. Because the resultant circuit is obtained by cascading identical subcircuits, such a network is called a *cascaded network*, or an *iterative network*. Each one of these subcircuits is called a *typical cell*. This chapter will be devoted to the discussion of problems which can be solved by cascading typical cells.

10.2 Circuits for error detection. The first step in designing a cascaded network is to identify the typical cell; in other words, to distribute the input variables and output variables to a number of typical cells. The next task is to design the typical cell.

When designing the typical cell, we have only to deal with the assigned inputs and produce the assigned outputs. There is a vital point which has not been discussed in the design of cascaded networks. This is the problem of interconnection between the typical cells. The communication between typical cells of a cascaded network is provided by certain inputs and outputs of each cell. Some of the outputs of a cell are considered as a part of the final result of the whole circuit, but at the same time, certain outputs of one cell are used as inputs for other cells. This constitutes the cascading effects of the cells and brings up the problem of *state identification.* In the adder circuit in Fig. 10.2, each typical cell has two outputs; one is used to provide one digit in the sum and the other is used to transmit the carry to the next cell, thus providing communication between cells.

The discussion up to this point might seem a bit vague, especially since the term *state* has not been defined yet. The following example is expected to clear these points.

EXAMPLE 10.1. Given a sequence of n binary digits, design a switching circuit (a) with relay gates, and (b) with direct-coupled transistor gates, which can indicate whether the number of 1's contained in this sequence is even or odd.

It should be mentioned at the outset that this is not a trivial problem; on the contrary, it is of practical importance.

In a modern switching system (for instance a data processing machine), numerous components are used. Even though painstaking efforts are made to improve the reliability of the system, it is still probable that some component will not function properly. This will in turn introduce error into the output. It is, therefore, desirable to install an automatic checking process in the system.

One of the most extensively employed schemes is called the *parity check.** In a system using the parity-check scheme, all the coded messages contain either an odd number of 1's or an even number of 1's. At any stage of the process, we can examine or count the number of 1's contained in the message to see whether they have remained odd or even. If the number of 1's in a message is even, it is termed an *even-parity* check. If the number of 1's in a message is odd, it is termed an *odd-parity* check.

But note that there is still a source of undetected error here: in a message of n binary digits, if only an odd number of digits has erred, the parity-checking scheme will be able to detect the error. But, if an even number of digits go wrong, this check will not discover it. Nevertheless, this checking scheme is still favored because of the following two reasons: first, the most common error that can happen in a modern switching system is of a one bit nature; secondly, this scheme is relatively easy to implement.

To establish the parity-check scheme in a switching system, we have to pay attention to the coding scheme to be adopted. If a computer designer decides to use the BCD code, he can see from Table 9.2 that the number of 1's contained in each message is not always even or odd. In order

* GA 2, PE 3, and CA 4.

TABLE 10.1

Decimal digit	Parity bit	Code
0	1	0000
1	0	0001
2	0	0010
3	1	0011
4	0	0100
5	1	0101
6	1	0110
7	0	0111
8	0	1000
9	1	1001

to have a parity check, we have to introduce a parity bit (binary digit) into each message to make the number of 1's contained be either always even or always odd. The value which the parity bit assumes in each message depends on the number of 1's contained in that message and also on the specific parity scheme adopted. Suppose an odd-parity checking scheme is used; the BCD code has to be modified to the form shown in Table 10.1.

Sometimes the odd-parity check is more desirable than the even-parity check, because, in using the odd-parity check, each message contains at least one 1. This is a welcome feature in communication systems. Even though four binary digits are enough to code the ten decimal digits, five are used in Table 10.1. The extra one is introduced for error-detection purposes.

Now let us return to the original problem. The total number of input variables is n, namely $a_{n-1}, a_{n-2}, \ldots, a_1, a_0$. The number of output variables is two: one stands for the case in which the number of 1's contained is even, and the other for odd. Instead of designing a network of n inputs, we can use the cascading scheme and distribute one input to each one of the n typical cells.

The scheme of interconnection of the n identical cells, or blocks, is shown in Fig. 10.3. The sign "$\Rightarrow$" is used to show the interrelationships between cells. The necessity for having the interconnections is intuitively

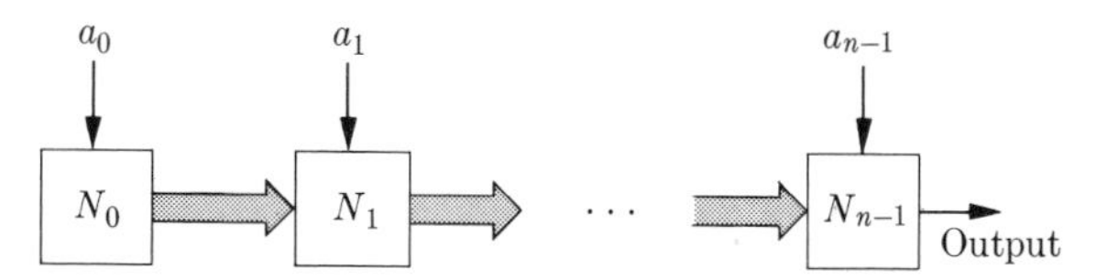

FIG. 10.3. Block diagram for Example 10.1.

obvious. In evaluating the number of 1's in a message, every digit has to be taken into account. The contribution by each one of the digits is transmitted by the interconnection between blocks!

What information should be transmitted by these interconnections? This is where the *state* concept enters. If we are called upon to count the number of 1's in a coded message, we may proceed by examining each digit and noting whether the number of appearances of 1's at any stage is even or odd. It is interesting here to note that we do not have to remember the exact number of 1's counted, because just by knowing whether the number is even or odd, we can finish the job. In conclusion, at any stage in the counting process, we have to know only whether the number of appearances of 1's so far is even or is odd. These two situations are termed two states. For the present problem, these two states are necessary and sufficient. It is impossible to reduce the number of states to one and still expect that the resultant circuit will provide the correct answer. At the same time, to define more than two states will result in redundancy and unnecessary complication of the typical cell to be designed.

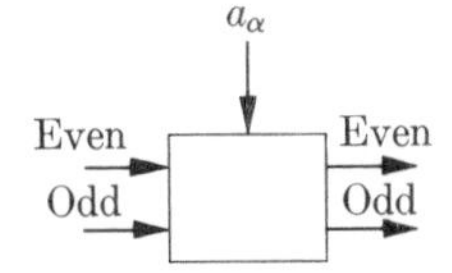

FIG. 10.4. Block diagram of a typical cell for Example 10.1.

With the notion of a state introduced, we can now draw the block diagram for the typical cell, as shown in Fig. 10.4. One of the three inputs is the digit assigned to this cell, and the other two inputs send in vital information concerning the state up to this cell. That is to say, the two inputs tell us whether the number of appearances of 1's so far is even or odd. There are two outputs for each typical cell. They are used to indicate the number of appearances of 1's up to and including this cell. This information is sent to the next cell.

The next task in the design of such a network is to synthesize the typical cell just defined. We would certainly ask, "How is this information transmitted?"

To answer this question, we have first of all to define the type of switching elements to be used. It is specified that this example is to be implemented with relays and with direct-coupled transistors.

Let us first discuss the implementation with relays.

It was established before that two states are defined. At the output terminals of any typical cell, only one of the two states is true; that is to say, the situation at that point can be fully described by one of the two states, but certainly not by both. How do we indicate which state is valid at that point?

One wire which interconnects two adjacent typical cells is assigned to each state. In the present problem, two wires are needed. One stands for the state in which the number of 1's counted so far is even and the other stands for the state in which the number of 1's is odd. This operation of assigning wires for different states is termed *state assignment*.

The operation of state assignment still does not answer the question, "How do we indicate which state prevails at the input or at the output of any typical cell?" The following assumption can then be made. Whenever a state is valid at a certain point, that is to say, the situation which the state represents prevails at that point, the wire which is assigned to this state will be at a specified voltage level. In this book this specified voltage will be designated as V_+. With this convention established, we can now proceed to design the typical cell.

A state transfer chart is then drawn, as shown in Table 10.2. The state in which an even number of 1's is counted is designated as A; the state in which an odd number of 1's is counted is designated as B. A subscript is used to denote at what point the state prevails. For example, A_t denotes that the number of 1's counted by the typical cell N_t and all its preceding cells is even; A_{t-1} denotes that the number of 1's counted by all the cells preceding cell N_t is even. The input binary digit, which is to be "examined" by the cell N_t, is defined as a_t.

TABLE 10.2

		a_t	
		0	1
Input states	A_{t-1}	A_t	B_t
	B_{t-1}	B_t	A_t

The state transfer chart for this example has two rows. Each row corresponds to one input state of N_t. Had there been three input states of N_t, the chart would have three rows. This state transfer chart has two columns, because only one bit is assigned to each cell, and one bit can be either 1 or 0. One column indicates the situation in which the input bit is 1, and in the other the input bit is 0.

When the input state is A_{t-1}, the number of 1's counted by all the cells preceding N_t is even. In this situation, if the input bit a_t is 0, then the number of 1's connected by N_t and all its preceding cells is still even. However, if $a_t = 1$, the number of 1's counted by N_t and all its preceding cells will be odd. This explains the first row of the chart. The second row of the chart can be reasoned in the same way.

This state transfer chart is then used to establish the following two switching functions:

$$A_t = A_{t-1}a'_t + B_{t-1}a_t, \tag{10.1}$$

$$B_t = A_{t-1}a_t + B_{t-1}a'_t. \tag{10.2}$$

The implementation of these switching functions, or the circuit for the typical cell, is shown in Fig. 10.5. The input bit a_t is employed to control the current in the relay coil. If $a_t = 1$, a current will be sent to the coil; if $a_t = 0$, no current flows through the relay coil. The relay contacts are used to transmit the voltage level V_+ and therefore indicate the state transfer.

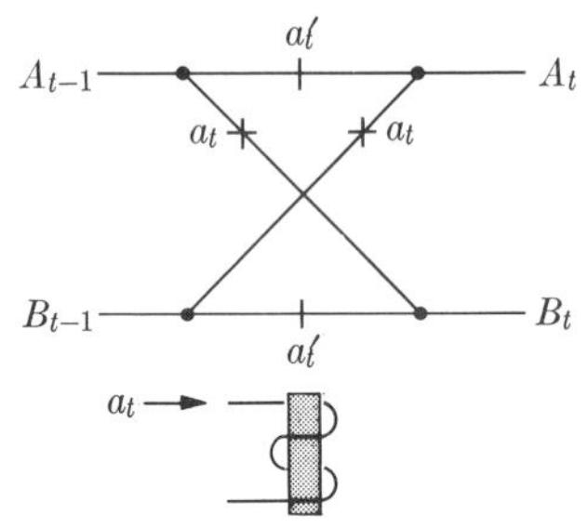

FIG. 10.5. The circuit for the typical cell of Example 10.1.

A typical cell has been designed and is shown in Fig. 10.5. The interconnection of typical cells is made by connecting the output wire of a cell to the corresponding input wire of its succeeding cell. The output wire and its corresponding input wire represent the same state. The complete circuit is shown in Fig. 10.6. Dashed lines are used to show the boundaries of typical cells.

If we examine the circuit in Fig. 10.6 from the first cell on the left, we will see that the first cell is simplified. This is done because to the left of this first cell, there is no digit examined; therefore, the number of 1's counted is 0, which can be considered to be even. Following this reasoning, we connect V_+ to the input wire representing the state in which the number of 1's counted is even. If the first digit is 0, the V_+ remains in state A. However, if a_0 is 1, V_+ will be transferred to state B. At the output, if V_+ appears in state A, then the number of digits that are 1 is even. If V_+ appears at state B, then it can be reasoned that the number of 1's in the given sequence is odd. This concludes the work for the design of the relay circuit specified in Example 10.1.

To summarize the design process, we can say that we must first distribute input variables to different cells. Next, we must identify the state to be used. Once the necessary and sufficient states are determined,

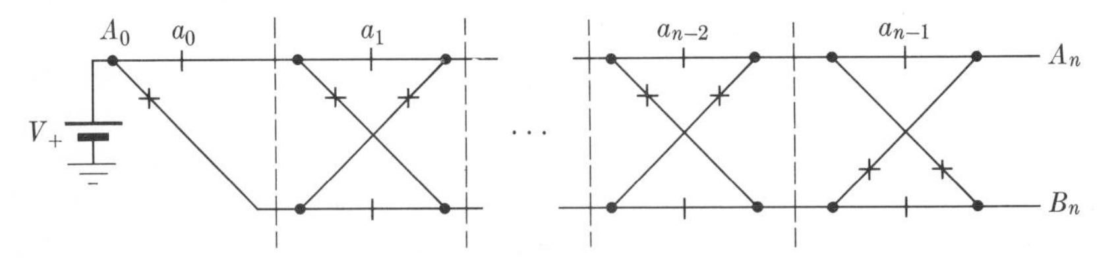

FIG. 10.6. The relay implementation for Example 10.1.

each state is assigned a specified voltage level on an interconnecting wire between cells. A state transfer chart is then constructed. From the transfer chart, a set of switching functions is established. The design of a typical cell is completed when the set of switching functions is properly implemented. Typical cells are then interconnected. If possible, certain simplifications can be made on the first few cells and on the last few cells. This concludes the design of a cascaded network.

At this point, there are some questions which should be answered. Why is just one input bit assigned to a typical cell in Example 10.1? There is a definite temptation to assign just one input variable to each typical cell, because it generally simplifies the design and yields optimum results. However, this does not mean that no attempt should be made to assign more than one input variable to one typical cell.

In designing the relay cascaded network for Example 10.1, we can assign two input bits to one typical cell. With this distribution, the necessary and sufficient states are still A and B, as defined before, but the state transfer chart has to be changed, as shown in Table 10.3. The

TABLE 10.3

		$a_\alpha a_\beta$ 00	01	10	11
Input states	A_{t-1}	A_t	B_t	B_t	A_t
	B_{t-1}	B_t	A_t	A_t	B_t

new transfer chart has four columns, because there are four input conditions to be considered. A set of two switching functions can be written from this chart:

$$A_t = (a'_\alpha a'_\beta + a_\alpha a_\beta)A_{t-1} + (a_\alpha a'_\beta + a'_\alpha a_\beta)B_{t-1}, \tag{10.3}$$

$$B_t = (a'_\alpha a'_\beta + a_\alpha a_\beta)B_{t-1} + (a_\alpha a'_\beta + a'_\alpha a_\beta)A_{t-1}. \tag{10.4}$$

These expressions are implemented in Fig. 10.7(a), and a simplified version is shown in Fig. 10.7(b). This typical cell, which examines two input bits, requires four transfer contacts or twelve springs. The typical cell shown in Fig. 10.5, which examines one input bit, needs two transfer contacts or six springs. Each design requires six springs per input bit.

The second question concerns the operation of state assignment. In Example 10.1, two states, A and B, are identified. State A is true if V_+ appears on one wire. State B is true if V_+ appears on the other wire. It is certainly logical to ask, "Why not use just one wire to do the job?" It seems possible to adopt the following convention. If V_+ appears on one wire, state A is true; if V_+ does not appear, state B is true. For

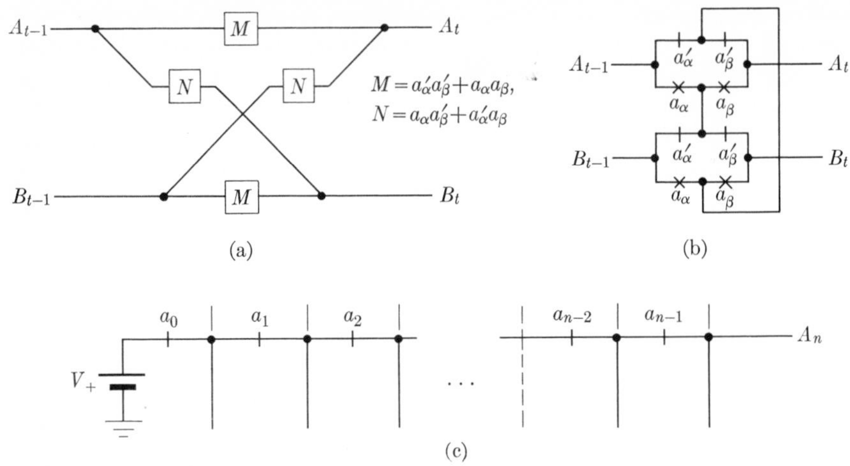

FIG. 10.7. (a) and (b) Circuits for the typical cell of Example 10.1. (c) Illustration of incorrect cascaded relay network for Example 10.1.

cascaded networks using relays as their switching components, this type of assignment actually does not work. This statement can be substantiated if we examine the entire cascaded relay network in Fig. 10.6. The voltage level V_+ is propagated from left to right. Whether it finally appears on terminal A or on terminal B depends on the number of 1's contained in the given sequence. Note that this voltage level originates only from the left. Nowhere in the entire cascaded structure can V_+ be generated. If the "one-wire" suggestion is adopted, the resultant cascaded network will be that shown in Fig. 10.7(c). This circuit obviously will produce erroneous results, because propagation of V_+ can be stopped at any cell. Once it is stopped, it can never appear at the output, even if the number of 1's contained in the given sequence is even. The basic reason for this phenomenon is that a relay switching element does not have regenerating capacity. However, transistors do.

To complete the second part of Example 10.1, implementation with direct-coupled transistor gates is investigated. As when designing a cascaded relay network, distribution of input variables among typical cells and state identification constitute the first and second steps in the design of a transistor cascaded network. Owing to the inverting capability of the transistor, the two voltage levels on one wire can be used to represent two states. To express it differently, a switching variable can be used to denote two states. In the present problem, one switching variable, J_t, can be used to represent the two states A and B. When $J_t = 1$, A_t is true and when $J_t = 0$, B_t is true. Using this designation,

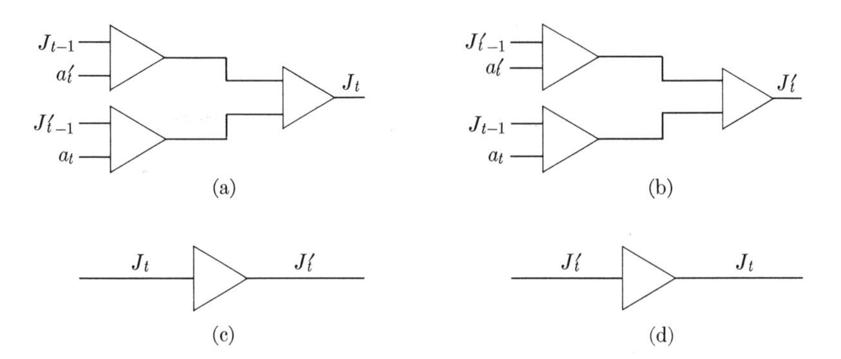

Fig. 10.8. The direct-coupled transistor circuits of a typical cell for Example 10.1.

we can rewrite Eqs. (10.1) and (10.2) as

$$J_t = J_{t-1}a'_t + J'_{t-1}a_t, \tag{10.5}$$

$$J'_t = J_{t-1}a_t + J'_{t-1}a'_t. \tag{10.6}$$

The design of a typical cell is completed when Eqs. (10.5) and (10.6) are implemented. The circuits are shown in Fig. 10.8. The circuits in Figs. 10.8(a) and 10.8(c) form a typical cell. An alternative design is to use the circuits shown in Figs. 10.8(b) and 10.8(d).▲

10.3 Implementation of symmetric functions by contactor networks. Another example is studied in this section, not only to illustrate once again the design of cascaded networks, but also to discuss the synthesis of a special class of switching functions.

Example 10.2. Given a message of nine binary digits, design a relay switching circuit which will indicate whenever the number of 1's contained in the message is exactly four.

If the straightforward approach is adopted, the establishment and manipulation of the switching function will be quite cumbersome. The iterative approach, or the design of a typical cell and cascading of a number of cells in series, seems to be an attractive alternative.

In this problem, there are clearly many choices we could make as to the number of inputs assigned to each typical cell. Different assignment schemes certainly require different typical cells. It is the designer's responsibility to make an intelligent choice.

Let us distribute one input variable or one bit to each typical cell. The information to be transmitted between cells in this case can be defined by the following states; among the digits counted so far:

A: No digit is 1.
B: One digit is 1.
C: Two digits are 1.
D: Three digits are 1.
E: Four digits are 1, or *valid*.
F: More than four digits are 1, or *invalid*.

When more than four digits counted are 1, then the circuit, according to its specification, will not give an indication; therefore, there is no need to distinguish the case in which five digits examined are 1 from the case in which six digits examined are 1. The term invalid is self-explanatory, because, as soon as more than four digits counted are 1, the circuit will not give an indication no matter what happens with the remaining digits to be counted.

The term *valid* is used to describe the situation where four and only four digits counted are 1.

A subscript is used to denote the point where certain states are true. For example, $A_t = 1$ means that among the binary digits counted by the typical cell N_t and all its preceding cells, no bit is 1.

The block diagram of a typical cell is shown in Fig. 10.9. The design of a typical cell actually amounts to providing appropriate connections between the terminal on the left and those on the right. A state transfer chart can easily be constructed, as shown in Table 10.4.

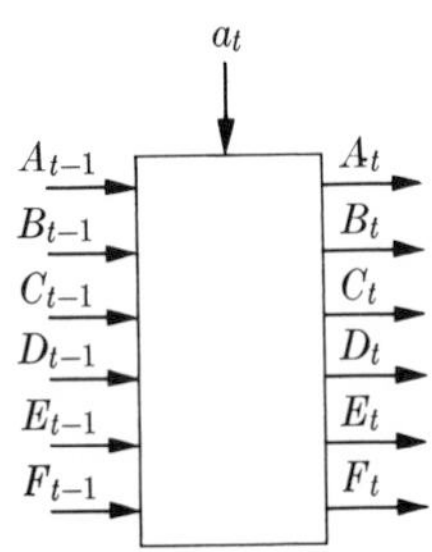

FIG. 10.9. Block diagram of a typical cell for Example 10.2.

TABLE 10.4

	Input variable a_t	
	0	1
A_{t-1}	A_t	B_t
B_{t-1}	B_t	C_t
C_{t-1}	C_t	D_t
D_{t-1}	D_t	E_t
E_{t-1}	E_t	F_t
F_{t-1}	F_t	F_t

Following the state transfer chart, we might think of employing six wires to represent the six states identified. However, note that whenever state F is reached, there are already more than four digits among the digits counted which are 1. According to the specification of the problem, the circuit should not make an indication, even if none of the remaining digits is 1. There is, therefore, no need to provide a wire for F to propagate V_+, whose appearance at the output is supposed to indicate that the number of 1's contained in the message is exactly four.

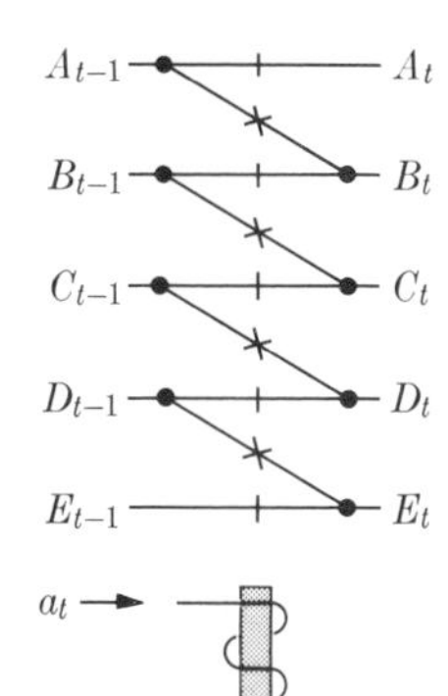

FIG. 10.10. Circuit of a typical cell for Example 10.2.

A set of switching functions can be established from Table 10.4, from which the circuit for a typical cell can be drawn. For a relay cascaded network, the circuit for a typical cell sometimes can be drawn from direct inspection of the state transfer chart. This is shown in Fig. 10.10.

The interconnection of the typical cells shown in Fig. 10.10 presents no problem. There are, however, extensive simplifications that can be achieved in the first few cells and in the last few cells of the chain.

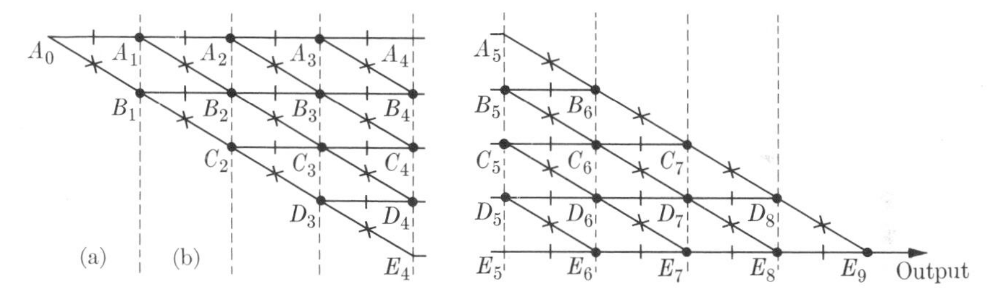

FIG. 10.11. The first four simplified cells for Example 10.2.

FIG. 10.12. The last four simplified cells for Example 10.2.

Let us first examine the situation at the beginning few cells. There is certainly no digit of 1 entered before the first cell. The voltage level V_+ which indicates the validity of the A state is connected to the input terminal A_0. The simplified first cell is shown in Fig. 10.11(a). It is immediately obvious that the second cell in the chain can also be simplified, because only its input terminals A_1 and B_1 are fed by the first cell. The simplified version is shown in Fig. 10.11(b). Using the same reasoning we recognize that the first four cells can be simplified as shown.

This circuit is required to transmit the V_+ to the output terminal only when the number examined contains four digits of 1; therefore, only the

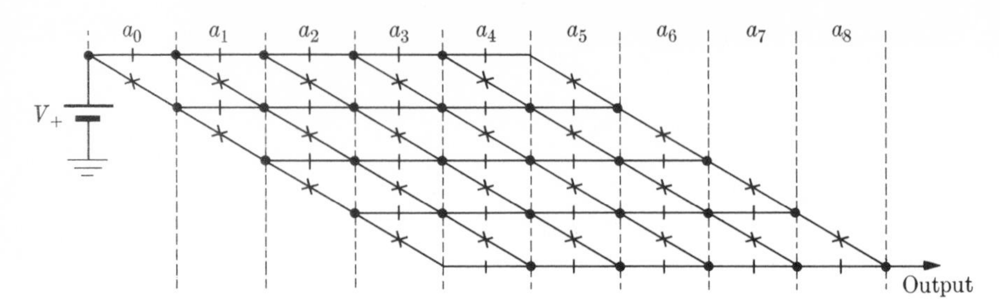

FIG. 10.13. The complete cascaded network for Example 10.2.

output terminal E of the last cell should be retained. This, of course, produces tremendous savings in the last cell. Furthermore, the three other cells preceding the last can also be simplified as shown in Fig. 10.12. The complete cascaded network is shown in Fig. 10.13. The problem given is solved by following the procedures necessary to design a cascaded network.▲

By using the iterative approach to solve a given problem, we do not need to establish the switching function for the complete circuit. However, it is interesting to see what such a function would look like for Example 10.2. If it is to be expressed in the disjunctive normal form, then one of the standard products is

$$a_0a_1a_2a_3a_4'a_5'a_6'a_7'a_8'.$$

This product represents a sequence of nine binary digits, four of which are 1's. In the process of finding other standard products which must be included in the function, we note that new ones can be found by interchanging any two variables. For instance, if a_1 and a_5 are interchanged, the following product is found:

$$a_0a_5a_2a_3a_4'a_1'a_6'a_7'a_8'.$$

All the standard products which should be included in the switching function can be generated by successively interchanging two variables. For this reason, the resultant function will have a very special characteristic; that is, the interchange of any two of $a_0, a_1, a_2, \ldots, a_8$ in the function will leave the function unaltered. Such a function is said to be symmetric with respect to $a_0, a_1, a_2, a_3, \ldots, a_8$. It is the purpose of this section to show that a symmetrical function can be implemented by using the iterative approach.*

* SH 1 and CA 1.

10.4 Another example.

EXAMPLE 10.3. Design a diode switching circuit which can examine any two numbers of n binary digits each and compare corresponding digits to detect whether they differ only in one corresponding pair of digits.

Let the two numbers be $a_{n-1}a_{n-2} \cdots a_1a_0$ and $b_{n-1}b_{n-2} \cdots b_1b_0$. The circuit is asked to compare a_0 with b_0, a_1 with b_1, ..., and indicate whenever one and only one differing pair of corresponding digits is found. There is a very practical implication in this problem. If these two numbers are binary equivalents of two standard products, then if they differ only in one pair of corresponding digits, they form a combinable pair and the variable, which is represented by that differing digit, can be eliminated.

To solve this problem, we distribute the $2n$ inputs into n typical cells. Each cell will have two input variables. The scheme is shown in Fig. 10.14.

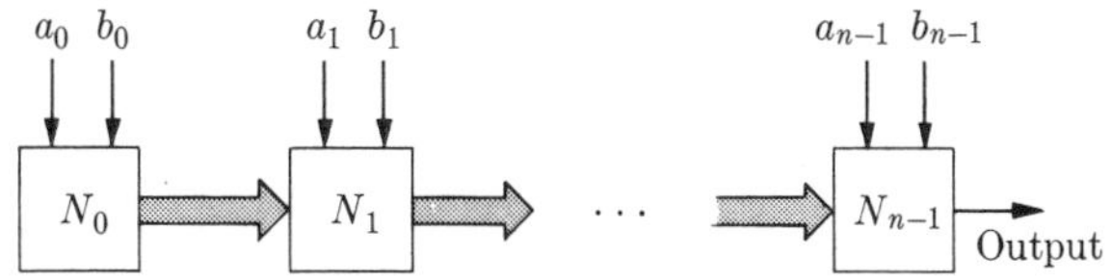

FIG. 10.14. Block diagram for Example 10.3.

Let us now examine the typical cell N_t. From the input at its left, this cell is told how many of the compared pairs of corresponding digits have been different. It should then be able to compare a_t and b_t, and by its output at the right let the next cell have the necessary information to proceed.

Now we investigate what information must be transmitted between typical cells; that is, we identify the necessary and sufficient states. Let us start from the left, since the typical cell N_0 compares a_0 and b_0. Cell N_0 should inform the next cell N_1 either that there is one corresponding pair of different digits, that is, a_0 and b_0 are different, or that there is no corresponding pair of different digits, that is, a_0 and b_0 are the same. After comparing a_1 with b_1, N_1 will indicate to the next stage N_2 one of the three possible situations:

A: No corresponding pair of different digits.
B: One corresponding pair of different digits.
C: More than one pair of different digits.

A subscript is used to show where certain states are true. The problem specifies that the circuit is expected to indicate whenever the two numbers differ only in one corresponding pair. There is no need to distinguish between cases in which two, three, or more pairs of corresponding digits are different. Using this reasoning, we can conclude that the information transmitted between cells should indicate one of the three situations listed above. Each one of the three situations is termed a *state*. With the states defined as above, we can draw the block diagram, shown in Fig. 10.15, for a typical cell.

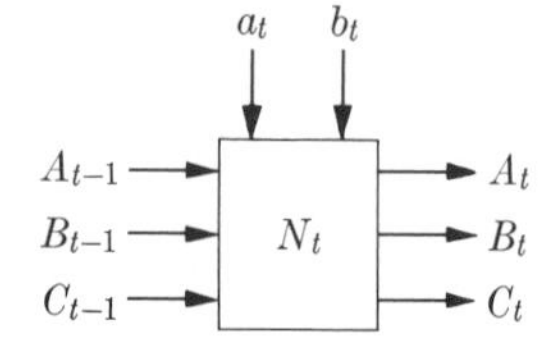

FIG. 10.15. Block diagram of a typical cell for Example 10.3.

The physical implementation of states in a diode cascaded network follows the same thinking used in a relay cascaded network, because diode gates, like relay gates, do not have the inversion capacity. The appearance of the voltage level V_+ at a specific point denotes that a corresponding state is true. The only difference between the two cascaded networks is that the voltage level V_+ is propagated from left to right with diode gates rather than with relay contacts. Since state C, defined above, represents a situation in which the circuit should not make an indication, the propagation of V_+ should be stopped whenever C is true. Therefore, only two input points and two output points are needed to indicate states A and B. A state transfer chart is shown in Table 10.5.

TABLE 10.5

		Input variables a_t, b_t			
		00	01	11	10
Input states	A_{t-1}	A_t	B_t	A_t	B_t
	B_{t-1}	B_t	C_t	B_t	C_t

Since there are two input variables for each cell, there are consequently four input conditions, represented by the four columns in the chart. Let us now examine the second row of this chart. The input state B_{t-1} conveys the information that one pair of corresponding digits is already found to be different. If the input variables are both 0 or both 1, the output state is still B_t. This corresponds to the first and the third columns. If the input variables differ in their values, then one differing pair of corresponding digits has to be added. This will transfer the state

B_{t-1} at the input into state C_t at the output. This is shown in columns two and four.

In order to design the circuits for the typical cell, a set of switching functions is established:

$$A_t = A_{t-1}a_tb_t + A_{t-1}a'_tb'_t, \tag{10.7}$$

$$B_t = B_{t-1}a_tb_t + B_{t-1}a'_tb'_t + A_{t-1}a_tb'_t + A_{t-1}a'_tb_t. \tag{10.8}$$

Each product in Eq. (10.7) represents one condition in which A_t will be 1. Each condition can be seen directly from the state transfer chart. The same can be said about Eq. (10.8).

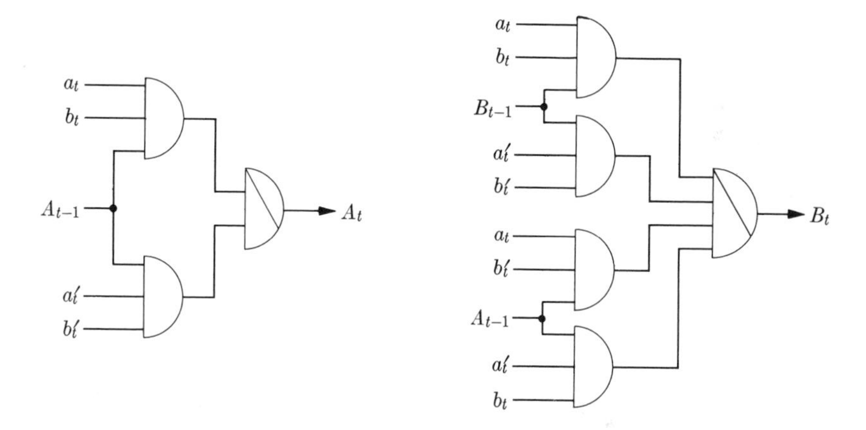

FIG. 10.16. Circuits for a typical cell for Example 10.3.

The implementation of Eqs. (10.7) and (10.8) is shown in Fig. 10.16. The restriction that each circuit may have at most two levels is observed. However, note that the output of one cell will be the input to its succeeding cell. Amplification must be performed at certain points, not only to restore the attenuated signal, but also to isolate interacting components.▲

10.5 Binary and decimal parallel adders. In this section both binary and decimal parallel adders are designed according to the iterative method. A binary adder is a switching circuit which produces the sum of two numbers expressed in the binary system.

Section 10.1 points out that a strictly parallel adder is prohibitively costly. A parallel adder, using the iterative scheme, is shown in Fig. 10.2. Our task now is to design the circuits for a typical cell N_i. In implementing such circuits, diode and transistor gates will be employed.

For a typical cell, the switching functions relating the inputs a_i, b_i, and c_{i-1}, and the outputs S_i and c_i, are established in Section 3.4 and are

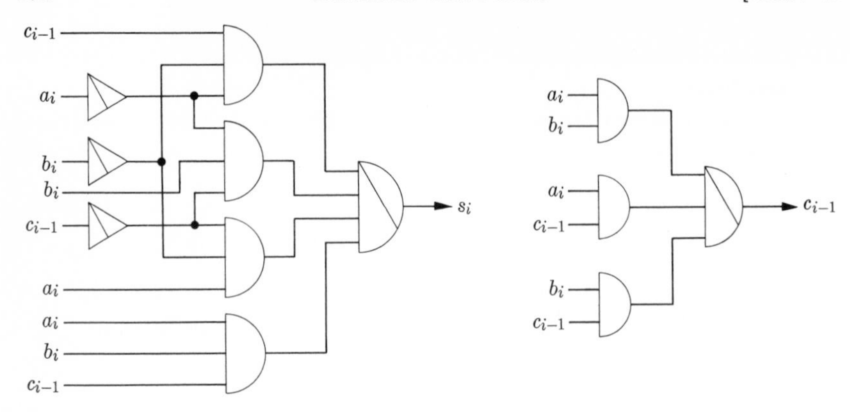

FIG. 10.17. A tentative design of a one-digit binary adder.

repeated below:

$$s_i = a_i'b_i'c_{i-1} + a_i'b_ic_{i-1}' + a_ib_i'c_{i-1}' + a_ib_ic_{i-1}, \tag{10.9}$$

$$c_i = a_i'b_ic_{i-1} + a_ib_i'c_{i-1} + a_ib_ic_{i-1}' + a_ib_ic_{i-1}. \tag{10.10}$$

One scheme of implementation is shown in Fig. 10.17. Equation (10.10) is simplified to

$$c_i = a_ib_i + a_ic_{i-1} + b_ic_{i-1}. \tag{10.11}$$

The circuits in Fig. 10.17 are of a two-level nature. The total requirements are 25 diodes and 3 transistors.

There is a very attractive feature in the carry circuit. Examining the block diagram in Fig. 10.2 again, we realize that the cell N_1 will not have all its inputs available until the carry forwarded by the cell N_0 arrives. The same can be said of all other cells. Therefore, in order to reduce the computing time needed for such an adder, it is imperative that each cell generate its carry as soon as possible. In the carry circuit in Fig. 10.17, if the two input digits a_i and b_i are each 1, a carry is generated without waiting for the arrival of a carry from the previous stage. However, there are shortcomings in this design. The outputs of this cell, generally, have to be amplified before they can be gated again. The hidden cost is not revealed until we try to use the outputs of one cell as inputs for the subsequent cell. An alternative implementation scheme is expressed by rewriting Eqs. (10.9) and (10.10):

$$s_i = c_{i-1}(a_i'b_i' + a_ib_i) + c_{i-1}'(a_i'b_i + a_ib_i'), \tag{10.12}$$

$$c_i = a_ib_i + c_{i-1}(a_i'b_i + a_ib_i'). \tag{10.13}$$

The following substitution is proposed:

$$M_i = a_i'b_i + a_ib_i'. \tag{10.14}$$

It can be readily seen that

$$M'_i = (a_i + b'_i)(a'_i + b_i) = a_ib_i + a'_ib'_i. \qquad (10.15)$$

Because of developments in Eqs. (10.14) and (10.15), Eqs. (10.12) and (10.13) can be written as

$$s_i = c_{i-1}M'_i + c'_{i-1}M_i, \qquad (10.16)$$

$$c_i = a_ib_i + c_{i-1}M_i. \qquad (10.17)$$

Now we have three switching functions to be implemented, namely M_i, s_i, and c_i, expressed in Eqs. (10.14), (10.16), and (10.17), respectively. Note that the expressions on the right-hand side of Eqs. (10.14) and (10.16) are identical in form. The former expression is in terms of a_i and b_i, and the latter is in terms of c_{i-1} and M_i. The successful implementation of one expression will reveal the means of realizing the other. It is really the iterative process in itself.

Since M_i is needed to realize s_i, we will first try to implement M_i. The expression in Eq. (10.14) has two switching variables. Each one appears in both primed and unprimed forms. Since an input variable is available only in its unprimed form, the appearance of primed variables indicates the need for inverters. To realize M_i, as expressed by Eq. (10.14), two inverters (in the present case, transistors) are needed to provide a'_i and b'_i. With the reduction of the number of needed negations in mind, we can rewrite M_i as

$$M_i = a'_ib_i + a_ib'_i = (a_i + b_i)(a'_i + b'_i) = (a_i + b_i)(a_ib_i)'. \qquad (10.18)$$

The last expression in Eq. (10.18) has the same number of literals as the original one, but it requires only one negation. The implementation of M_i via the last expression in Eq. (10.18) is shown in Fig. 10.18(a). Note that M_i in Fig. 10.18(a) is the output of a two-level diode switching circuit. It must be amplified before it can be used to generate s_i. A nand-gate is used in Fig. 10.18(b) to obtain M'_i. Doubts might be raised because the circuit in Fig. 10.18(b) generates M'_i instead of M_i. However, M_i and M'_i both are part of the function of s_i. We now see that M'_i is available, and, following the established pattern for realizing M'_i, we can rewrite s_i as

$$s_i = (c'_{i-1} + M'_i)(c'_{i-1}M'_i)'. \qquad (10.19)$$

The form of Eq. (10.19) suggests that it can be realized simply by using the circuit in Fig. 10.18(a), with different inputs. This is done in Fig. 10.18(c).

Examining the s_i circuit, we see that the carry forwarded by the previous cell is used in its primed form. Instead of generating c_i, c'_i should be pro-

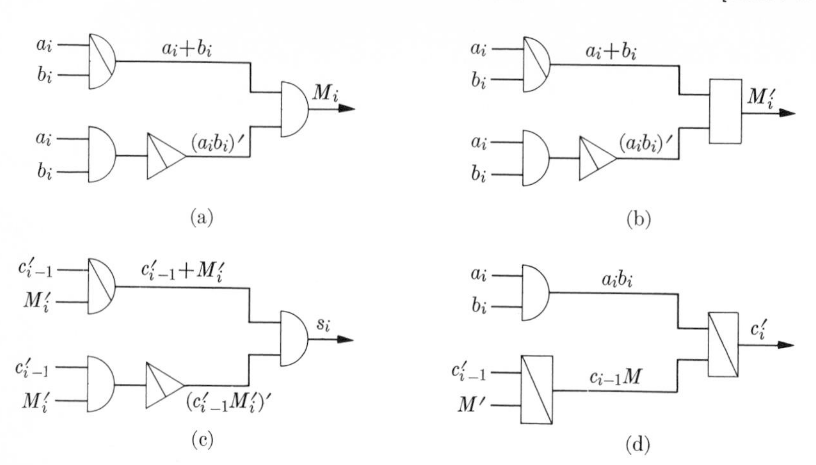

FIG. 10.18. The diode-transistor circuits for a typical cell of a binary parallel adder.

duced, which can then be used without inversion by the next cell. The resultant circuit is shown in Fig. 10.18(d).

The three circuits which generate M_i', s_i, and c_i' require eighteen diodes and five transistors. The carry output can be used by the next cell without further amplification.

A typical cell of a binary parallel adder which can add three bits simultaneously is termed a *full-adder*. A similar unit which can add only two bits at a time is termed a *half-adder*. The circuit of a half-adder can be derived from the circuit of a full-adder after certain deletions are made.

Completion of the design of its typical cell finishes the discussion on binary parallel adders. Now let us turn our attention to the design of a decimal parallel adder. The general situation is shown in the block diagram in Fig. 10.19, where the two operands are $x_{n-1}x_{n-2} \cdots x_2x_1x_0$ and $y_{n-1}y_{n-2} \cdots y_2y_1y_0$; x's and y's can be 0, 1, 2, 3, . . . , 9. The sum is expressed by

$$s_ns_{n-1}s_{n-2} \cdots s_2s_1s_0.$$

The iterative approach is preferable because of the large number of inputs. The block diagram of a typical cell is shown in Fig. 10.20.

The design of the one-digit decimal adder seems to be simple, but actually it is not, because x_t, y_t, s_t, c_{t-1}, and c_t are expressed in the decimal number system. If binary switching components are to be employed, all these variables have to be appropriately coded. The coding scheme adopted has a direct and extensive influence on the complexity of the resultant circuit.

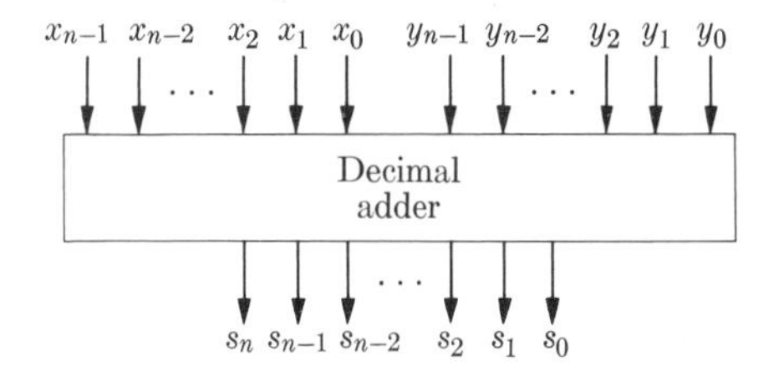

FIG. 10.19. Block diagram of a decimal parallel adder.

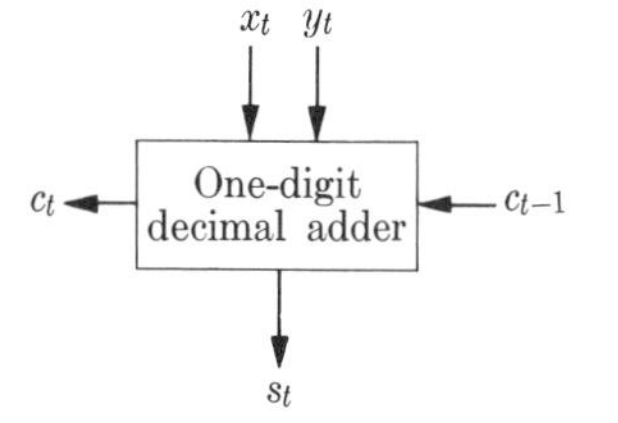

FIG. 10.20. Block diagram of a one-digit decimal adder.

Further study proves that the decimal code to be used must be specified. The BCD code, shown in Table 9.2, is considered first. Let the codes for x_t, y_t, and s_t be $a_{3t}a_{2t}a_{1t}a_{0t}$, $b_{3t}b_{2t}b_{1t}b_{0t}$, $u_{3t}u_{2t}u_{1t}u_{0t}$. Setting aside the carry c_{t-1} for the moment, the problem now is to produce a switching circuit which will yield $u_{3t}u_{2t}u_{1t}u_{0t}$, and c_t upon the receipt of $a_{3t}a_{2t}a_{1t}a_{0t}$ and $b_{3t}b_{2t}b_{1t}b_{0t}$. The advantage in using the BCD code is that $a_{3t}a_{2t}a_{1t}a_{0t}$ and $b_{3t}b_{2t}b_{1t}b_{0t}$ can be processed by using binary arithmetic, with slight modifications. This will be shown in the following.

There are two general cases to be considered. In the first case, the sum of x_t and y_t is less than 10; therefore c_t, the carry, is 0. In the second case, the sum of x_t and y_t is equal to or larger than 10, and c_t is 1. The first case does not introduce any complication. For example, if x_t and y_t are equal to 2 and 3, respectively, we expect that the combination of their respective BCD codes by binary addition will yield the BCD code for 5, which of course is the sum of 2 and 3. This is exactly the case as shown below.

$$\begin{array}{r} 2 \\ +\ 3 \\ \hline 5 \end{array} \qquad \begin{array}{r} 0010 \\ +\ 0011 \\ \hline 0101 \end{array}$$

In the second case, the sum of x_t and y_t is equal to or larger than 10. Not only do we expect the adder circuit to produce the code which correctly represents the sum digit, but we also expect it to forward a carry of 1 to the next stage. It would be desirable if these two operations could be completed by one integrated circuit which would process $a_{3t}a_{2t}a_{1t}a_{0t}$ and $b_{3t}b_{2t}b_{1t}b_{0t}$ according to binary arithmetic rules. However, in order to produce the carry and the sum digit in its coded form, certain modifications have to be made, as demonstrated in the following three subcases.

In the first subcase, the sum of x_t and y_t is equal to or larger than 16. If binary additions are used to process the codes of the operands, a carry is readily produced, but certain operations have to be performed to obtain

$u_{3t}u_{2t}u_{1t}u_{0t}$, which represents the correct sum digit. A simple calculation is shown below.

Decimal digit		Corresponding BCD code	
Augend	8		1000
Addend	+ 9		+ 1001
	17	Overflow	10001

In the above evaluation, the two codes are added as if they were binary numbers. The overflow indicates that c_t, the carry, is 1, but the resultant four bits do not represent the corresponding sum digit, which is 7 in this calculation. The reason for this discrepancy can be explained by the fact that the binary overflow carries 16 instead of 10, which a decimal carry is entitled to carry. To remedy this situation, 6 should be restored to obtain the correct sum digit:

$$\begin{array}{r} 0001 \\ +\ 0110 \\ \hline 0111 \end{array}$$

The code 0111 does indicate 7 in BCD code.

In the second subcase, the sum of x_t and y_t is equal to or larger than 12, but less than 16. If the two codes of the two operands are added according to binary addition, the resultant four bits do not represent any decimal digit in the BCD coding scheme, as can be seen from the following calculations.

Decimal digit		Corresponding BCD code
Augend	6	0110
Addend	+ 7	+ 0111
	13	1101

The resultant four bits do not form a code which can be used in the BCD coding scheme. If weights of 8, 4, 2, and 1 are given to the four bits from left to right, the result will be exactly 13. Certain operations are needed which will produce a carry of 1 and four bits which represent 3 in BCD code. Note that this is necessary whenever the 8-weighted and 4-weighted bits are 1. The remedial operation is simply to produce a carry immediately and to add 0110 to the resultant four bits. In the present calculation, the following results:

$$\begin{array}{lr} & 1101 \\ & +\ 0110 \\ \hline \text{Overflow} & 10011 \end{array}$$

If the overflow is ignored, the remaining four bits do represent 3 in the BCD coding scheme. This always produces the correct result, because 6 has been added to the sum and subsequently 16 subtracted from it, while ignoring the overflow. The correct sum, of course, will be obtained.

The third subcase occurs whenever the sum of the operands is equal to or larger than 10, but less than 12. This situation can be detected by noting that the resultant 8-weighted and 2-weighted bits are 1, and it can be corrected by the remedial operation used in the second subcase.

The above presentation shows that if the BCD coding scheme is used in a decimal adder, the two codes of the two operands can be added by binary addition. The resultant four bits is the code for the corresponding sum digits, provided that none of the following three conditions prevails:

(1) an overflow occurs,
(2) the 8-weighted and the 4-weighted bits are 1,
(3) the 8-weighted and the 2-weighted bits are 1.

If any of these conditions does occur, a carry of 1 is forwarded to the next digit, and the code 0110 is added to the resultant four bits to obtain the code for the corresponding sum digit.

The above discussion did not show how the carry c_{t-1} is treated. This is actually very simple. If $c_{t-1} = 1$, the corresponding code 0001 can be added to the codes for x_t and y_t. This only affects the addition of a_{0t} and b_{0t}. Everything else stays the same.

Since binary addition is used repeatedly when the BCD code is adopted, the binary full and half-adders are used in the implementation shown in Fig. 10.21. The circuits for the full binary adder and the half binary adder can be found or derived respectively from that shown in Fig. 10.18. This explains why the negatives of subsequent carries are used in Fig. 10.21.

The adoption of BCD codes in decimal adders transforms the addition in the decimal system into additions in the binary system. One of the undesirable features is that a carry is sometimes produced even when there is no overflow in the final binary addition. A delay could be introduced in forwarding a carry to the eagerly awaiting next stage. It would be desirable to have a coding scheme which, when used in decimal adders, retains the rules of binary addition and also removes any delay in carry propagation.

It is desirable to make the overflow in adding the codes of two operands the sole indication of a carry to be forwarded. In using the BCD code, further gating is needed to produce the carry only if the sum of the two operands is at least 10 and less than 16. If 0110, which represents 6 in BCD code, is always added to the codes of the two operands, then the presence of an overflow is the sole indication of a carry. To ensure that

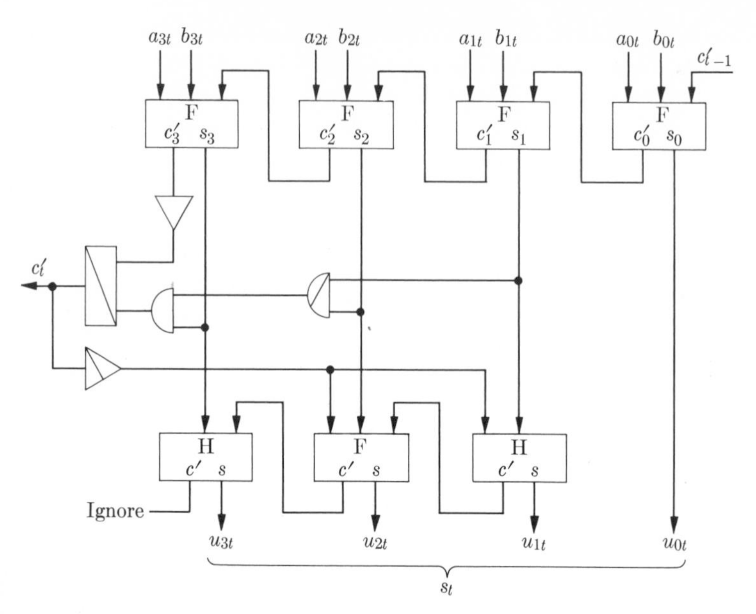

FIG. 10.21. The logical diagram of a one-digit decimal adder using BCD code. F represents a full binary adder, and H represents a half binary adder.

the code 0110 is always added, 0011 is added to the code of each operand to bring about the excess-3 code, shown in Table 9.3.

The implementation of a one-digit decimal adder, which employs excess-3 code, with binary full and half-adders, is listed as a problem.*

PROBLEMS

10.1 Given a message of ten binary digits, design a switching circuit with relays which will indicate whenever the number of 1's contained in the message is exactly four or exactly eight. Assign one binary digit to each cell. Show the complete circuit.

10.2. Solve Problem 10.1 by assigning two binary digits to one cell.

10.3. Design a switching circuit to examine a message of nine binary digits. The circuit will make an indication whenever the number of 1's in the message is exactly three or exactly six. Assign one binary digit to each cell. Show the complete circuit.

10.4. Solve Problem 10.3 by assigning three binary digits to one cell.

10.5. Implement the switching circuit specified in Problem 10.1 with direct-coupled transistor gates. Show only the schematic diagram of a typical cell.

---

* Further information on cascaded networks can be found in HE 1 and MC 3. For decimal arithmetic unit design see RI 1 and LE 1.

10.6. The switching circuit specified in Problem 10.3 is to be implemented with direct-coupled transistor gates. Show only the schematic diagram of a typical cell.

10.7. Design a switching circuit with relays to examine a message of n binary digits, where n is an integer. The circuit is to make an indication whenever the message has only one consecutive group of 1's. Assign one bit to each typical cell. Show the typical cell. *Note:* A consecutive group of 1's is formed by a string of adjacent 1's. For example, there is only one consecutive group of 1's in each of the following messages:

(a) 00001111100000,
(b) 00001000000.

10.8. Solve Problem 10.7 by assigning two binary digits to every typical cell.

10.9. Use diode-transistor gates to implement the switching circuit specified in Problem 10.7. Show the schematic diagram of the typical cell.

10.10. Design a switching circuit with relays to examine a message of n binary digits, where n is an integer. The circuit will indicate whenever the message has one or more consecutive groups of 1's. Assign one bit to each cell. Show the typical cell. [*Note:* For definition of "consecutive group," see Problem 10.7.]

10.11. Solve Problem 10.10 by assigning two binary digits to each typical cell.

10.12. Use diode-transistor gates to implement the switching circuit specified in Problem 10.10. Show the schematic diagram of the typical cell.

10.13. Implement a one-digit decimal adder which employs excess-3 code, with binary full and half-adders. Show the logical diagram of such an adder.

10.14. By comparing the design obtained in Problem 10.13 with that shown in Fig. 10.21, can you comment on the choice of BCD code and excess-3 code?

10.15. Let $A = A_3A_2A_1A_0$ and $B = B_3B_2B_1B_0$ be two integers between zero and fifteen inclusive, written in binary number system. Each of the above eight binary variables is represented by a switch which activates a relay coil. The contacts of the relays are to transmit the ground to one of three output terminals as follows. Terminal 1 is grounded if and only if $A > B$. Terminal 2 is grounded if and only if $A = B$. Terminal 3 is grounded if and only if $A < B$.

Design an optimum (minimum number of springs) contact network which satisfies these specifications.

10.16. Design a switching network which is used to examine n bits A_{n-1}, $A_{n-2}, \ldots, A_2, A_1, A_0$. The circuit is required to make an indication whenever the number of 1's contained in the n bits is equal to $1 + 4k$, where k is any positive integer.

(a) Use relays to implement the optimum circuit. Show the complete circuit by drawing the first few cells, the typical cell, the last few cells, and how an indication is made by the circuit.

(b) Repeat (a) using direct-coupled transistors.

CHAPTER 11

SEQUENTIAL CIRCUITS I

11.1 Introduction. The switching systems which have been discussed so far have one thing in common: the output at any instant is a function of the inputs at the same instant only. According to the definition given in Section 3.3, these circuits are termed *combinational* circuits. It is true that every switching system must have combinational circuits, but most of them have something more.

Chapter 1 emphasized that switching systems are implements for achieving automation in computation, control, and communication. In order to spare human operators drudgery, switching systems should possess as much facility as possible. Among other things, it is desirable to have switching systems capable of memorizing or storing information. Without this capacity, the usefulness of switching circuits is quite limited. It can be said without hesitation that the availability of stored information makes possible the realization of modern sophisticated computers, telephone switching systems, and control systems.

Sequential switching circuits can be divided into two classes: synchronous and asynchronous. Synchronous sequential switching circuits will be studied in this and the following three chapters. The understanding and insight gained will be relied upon to approach asynchronous sequential circuits in Chapter 15.

In this chapter, we will first introduce the general notion of synchronous sequential circuits. Next, storage elements will be discussed, and finally the general procedure for designing a synchronous sequential circuit will be presented.

11.2 The block diagram of a synchronous sequential switching circuit. The block diagram of a general synchronous sequential switching circuit is shown in Fig. 11.1.

It can be seen from this block diagram that a synchronous sequential circuit can be thought of as a combinational switching circuit with a memory. The combinational circuit has $p + k$ inputs, namely $x^1, x^2, \ldots, x^p$ and $Q^1, Q^2, \ldots, Q^k$. The inputs $x^1, x^2, \ldots, x^p$ are the actual inputs of the sequential circuit; the inputs $Q^1, Q^2, \ldots, Q^k$ denote the bits that can be obtained from the memory. The combinational circuit has $m + k$ outputs; $y^1, y^2, \ldots, y^m$ represent the actual outputs of the sequential circuit. The outputs $q^1, q^2, \ldots, q^k$ indicate the bits that are to be stored in the *memory*.

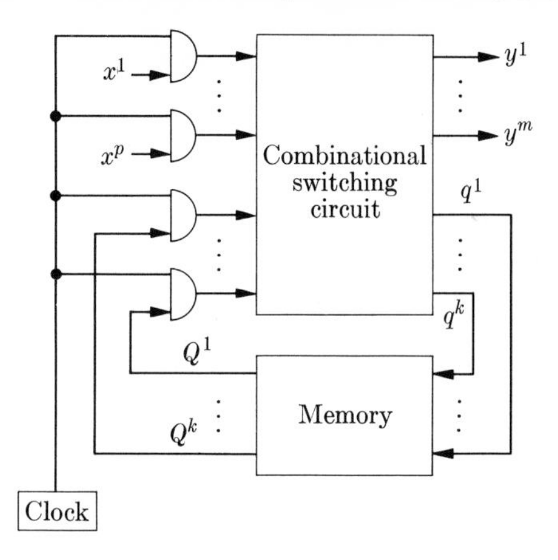

FIG. 11.1. Block diagram of a synchronous sequential circuit.

A memory is defined here as an aggregation of k binary storage devices. The characterization of a binary storage device will be discussed in the next section.

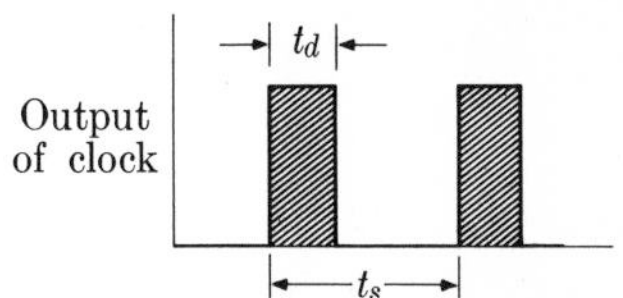

FIG. 11.2. The idealized waveform of the output of the clock.

The clock is actually a pulse generator. Its idealized output is shown in Fig. 11.2. Due to the presence of the and-gates at the inputs of the combinational circuit, the inputs to the sequential circuit have to be synchronized with the clock pulses. Since the inputs to the combinational circuit are in the form of pulses, its outputs are, in general, represented by pulses.

To illustrate the operation of a synchronous sequential circuit, let us examine the block diagram of a binary serial adder shown in Fig. 11.3. Even though the practical significance of such an adder cannot be over-

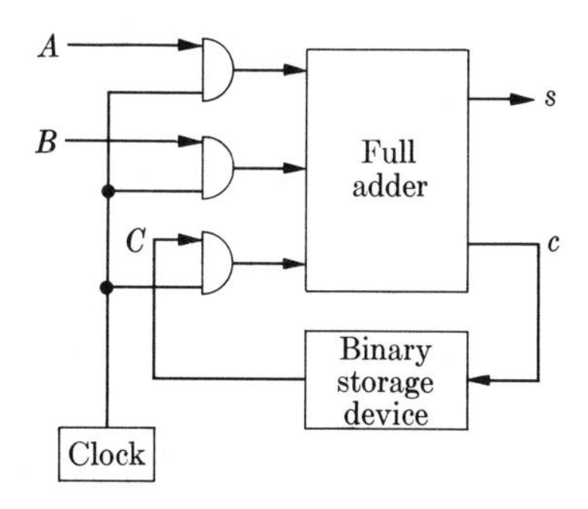

FIG. 11.3. Block diagram of a binary serial adder.

emphasized, the main point is that the diagram in Fig. 11.3 is a specific and concrete version of that in Fig. 11.1.

We can imagine that two numbers A and B are to be added serially and both are expressed in the binary number system as

$$A = a_n a_{n-1} \cdots a_1 a_0, \tag{11.1}$$

$$B = b_n b_{n-1} \cdots b_1 b_0. \tag{11.2}$$

It can be realistically assumed that each bit in A and B, the sum bit, s, and the carry generated, c, are all implemented by pulses. The output of the storage device, C, representing the carry stored, is in the form of a voltage level.

Assume that at the time instant t_0, we begin the serial addition. A clock pulse and pulses representing a_0 and b_0 appear simultaneously. A voltage level representing C_0, the carry bit stored in the memory at t_0, is also applied. The combinational circuit (the full adder in the present situation) accordingly produces s_0, which is the lowest order bit in the sum to be formed, and c_0, which represents the carry bit generated at t_0. Functionally, we express this as

$$s_0 = f(a_0, b_0, C_0), \tag{11.3}$$

$$c_0 = g(a_0, b_0, C_0), \tag{11.4}$$

where f is a switching function of three variables, namely a_0, b_0, and C_0, and g is also a switching function of the same three variables. Note that we have considered the delays developed in the combinational circuit in producing s_0 and c_0 as negligible. This assumption is made in our subsequent discussion on sequential switching circuits.

The subscripts on the switching variables denote the time instants at which the variables are considered. This is a distinct and important point in studying synchronous sequential switching circuits.

At the time instant t_0, a pulse, representing c_0, is sent into the binary storage. If this carry appears without delay at the output of the memory, it will be added again with a_0 and b_0. This, of course, may produce erroneous results. To avoid this difficulty, a certain delay has to be incorporated into the storage device. The *delay* in a storage device is defined as the time interval between the instant that a bit is sent into the device and the instant that this bit can be sensed at its output. By examining the idealized waveform of the clock pulses, we see that this delay has to be larger than the width of the clock pulse, t_d, but smaller than the period of the clock pulses, t_s. In general, the following relationship is all that is needed:

$$C_{\alpha+1} = c_\alpha, \tag{11.5}$$

where c_α denotes the bit sent into the storage during the presence of the αth clock pulse, and $C_{\alpha+1}$ denotes the bit sensed from the storage during the presence of the $(\alpha + 1)$th clock pulse. It is very interesting to examine the switching function in Eq. (11.5) and observe that it is somewhat different from the switching functions for combinational switching circuits. Note that "time" enters into Eq. (11.5). An equation of this type is sometimes called a *difference equation.*

At the time instant t_1 $(t_1 = t_0 + t_s)$, the second clock pulse and pulses representing a_1 and b_1 appear simultaneously. The output of the binary storage device provides a voltage level representing C_1, which is equal to c_0. Without delay, the full adder produces s_1 and c_1 according to the relationships

$$s_1 = f(a_1, b_1, C_1), \tag{11.6}$$

$$c_1 = g(a_1, b_1, C_1). \tag{11.7}$$

This operation is continued until all the bits in the sum have been generated.

With the understanding achieved above, it is not hard for us to see that the following functions can be established for the general synchronous sequential circuit in Fig. 11.1:

$$y_n^{l_1} = f^{l_1}(x_n^1, x_n^2, \ldots, x_n^p; Q_n^1, Q_n^2, \ldots, Q_n^k), \tag{11.8}$$

$$q_n^{l_2} = g^{l_2}(x_n^1, x_n^2, \ldots, x_n^p; Q_n^1, Q_n^2, \ldots, Q_n^k), \tag{11.9}$$

$$Q_{n+1}^{l_2} = q_n^{l_2}, \tag{11.10}$$

where l_1 and l_2 are integers, and $1 \leq l_1 \leq m$, $1 \leq l_2 \leq k$.

11.3 Binary storage. Since, in general, the design of the memory constitutes the first step in the design of a sequential circuit, and since a memory consists of a number of binary storage devices, it is desirable that a binary storage device should be studied first.

Not every kind of storage device applicable to synchronous sequential circuits will be discussed here.* We will discuss only the bistable transistor circuit shown in Fig. 11.4. This circuit is also called a toggle, a latch, a binary, and, very commonly, a flip-flop.

Examination of the operation of the circuit in Fig. 11.4 will convince us that such a device meets the following basic specifications for a binary storage device.

First, a binary storage device must have two distinct states to represent the truth values of a switching variable, and it must be able to remain in one state indefinitely until it is directed to do otherwise. In the circuit

* For more information, see RI 2.

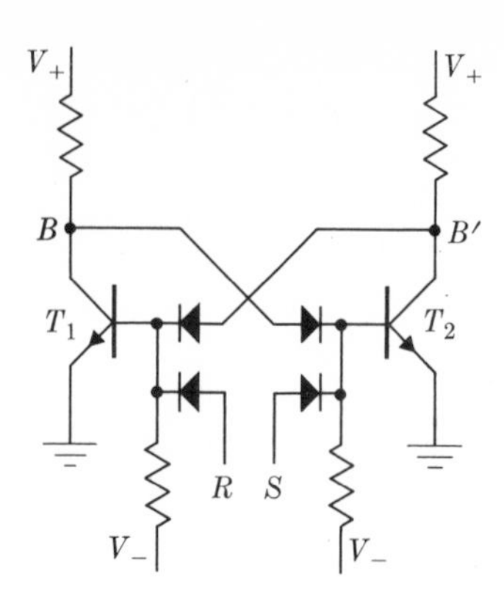

FIG. 11.4. Schematic diagram of an RS-type binary storage device.

in Fig. 11.4, the 1-state can be represented by the situation in which V_+ appears at B (transistor T_1 is cut off) and ground appears at B' (transistor T_2 conducts heavily). The 0-state is then implemented by having V_+ at B' (T_2 is cut off) and ground appears at B (T_1 conducts heavily). If no input signal is applied to R or S, any state can stay indefinitely.

Secondly, we should be able to sense what state the storage device is in. In other words, means must be provided so that the truth value of the stored bit can be detected. In the circuit in Fig. 11.4, the voltage level at B represents the truth value of a switching variable, say B; then the voltage level at B' provides the truth value of B'.

Thirdly, means must be provided to set or reset the storage device, so that it can receive the bit to be stored. Whenever a bit of truth value 1 is stored in a storage, the device is said to be *set*. The operation which stores a 0-bit in a device is called the *reset* operation, and the device is said to be *reset*.

When a positive pulse with sufficient amplitude and width is applied to terminal R, T_1 starts conducting. Owing to the amplification and inversion of T_1, a much stronger negative pulse is impressed upon the base of T_2, which reduces the conduction of T_2 and sends an amplified positive pulse to the base of T_1. The conduction in T_1 keeps on increasing and the conduction in T_2 keeps on decreasing until the former conducts heavily and the latter is entirely cut off. The circuit then reaches state 0. The reset operation is thus completed. The set operation can be accomplished by applying the pulse at terminal S.

Finally, we note that it does take time for the flip-flop (Fig. 11.4) to make a transition from one state to another. This constitutes the delay. At times, additional delays are deliberately introduced.

The characteristic of the binary storage device in Fig. 11.4 can be clearly summarized by a truth table (Table 11.1).

TABLE 11.1

B_n	0	0	0	0	1	1	1	1
R_n	0	0	1	1	0	0	1	1
S_n	0	1	0	1	0	1	0	1
B_{n+1}	0	1	0	X	1	1	0	X

TABLE 11.2

B_n	0	0	0	0	1	1	1	1
J_n	0	0	1	1	0	0	1	1
K_n	0	1	0	1	0	1	0	1
B_{n+1}	0	0	1	1	1	0	1	0

In Table 11.1, B_n is the bit stored in the storage at $t = t_n$. When $R_n = 1$, a positive pulse with sufficient width and amplitude is applied to terminal R at $t = t_n$. When $R_n = 0$, no input is applied to terminal R at $t = t_n$. When $S_n = 0$, no input is applied to terminal S at $t = t_n$. When a positive pulse with sufficient width and amplitude is applied to terminal S at $t = t_n$, then $S_n = 1$. Note that X is placed in both column four and column eight. This does not imply that whenever one of these two input combinations is true, the value of B_{n+1} can be either 1 or 0. What is actually indicated here is that these two input combinations will never happen. The inputs to terminals R and S cannot both be 1 at the same time. In other words, the following relationship has to be observed:

$$R_n S_n = 0. \tag{11.11}$$

The flip-flop characterized by Table 11.1 is considered the RS-type flip-flop.

There are other types of flip-flops. The JK-type flip-flop is characterized by Table 11.2.

Transistor flip-flops are used extensively in constructing counters, accumulators, and other small storage units in switching systems.

11.4 The design of counters. The design of counters, binary and decimal, is discussed here not only because of their extensive applications in switching systems, but also because of the fact that their design illustrates the basic considerations involved in the design of a general synchronous sequential switching circuit.

EXAMPLE 11.1. Design a counter which counts incoming pulses and displays in the binary number system the number of pulses counted. The counter is to return to its initial state after receiving every 16 pulses. Use RS-type flip-flops.

In designing a sequential switching circuit, the consideration of the memory generally precedes consideration of the combinational circuit. Since a memory consists of a number of binary storage devices, the foremost question is: How many binary storage devices are needed in the memory? The answer depends on how much the memory has to remember.

Quantitatively, this means that the number of binary storage devices needed is determined by the number of states the memory has to store and display. This answer might sound still very vague. Let us try to clear up this point by pursuing our example.

According to the specifications given, the counter to be designed is to display the number of pulses counted. At any instant, the number of pulses counted by the sequential circuit is the *state* of the circuit at that time. Let A denote the state in which no pulse is counted by the circuit, let B denote the state in which one pulse is counted, and so on. It would seem that it is necessary to define an infinite number of states, and that an infinite number of flip-flops is needed. However, an additional specification in the example states that after receiving 16 pulses, the counter should return to its initial state. Therefore, A can be used to represent the state in which the number of pulses counted is $16l$ (l is an integer, zero included), B the state in which the number of pulses counted is $16l + 1$, etc.

Note that the number of states in the present example is obviously 16. However, in the design of a general sequential switching circuit, the identification of necessary and sufficient states is an important operation. The construction of a state transition table (Table 11.3) generally facilitates the operation of state identification. Furthermore, this table constitutes a necessary step in the design of the combinational circuit.

TABLE 11.3

Present state	Next state		Present state	Next state	
	$V_n = 0$	$V_n = 1$		$V_n = 0$	$V_n = 1$
A_n	A_{n+1}	B_{n+1}	I_n	I_{n+1}	J_{n+1}
B_n	B_{n+1}	C_{n+1}	J_n	J_{n+1}	K_{n+1}
C_n	C_{n+1}	D_{n+1}	K_n	K_{n+1}	L_{n+1}
D_n	D_{n+1}	E_{n+1}	L_n	L_{n+1}	M_{n+1}
E_n	E_{n+1}	F_{n+1}	M_n	M_{n+1}	N_{n+1}
F_n	F_{n+1}	G_{n+1}	N_n	N_{n+1}	O_{n+1}
G_n	G_{n+1}	H_{n+1}	O_n	O_{n+1}	P_{n+1}
H_n	H_{n+1}	I_{n+1}	P_n	P_{n+1}	A_{n+1}

Subscripts are used to denote the instances when the states are true. For example, $A_n = 1$ indicates that at $t = t_n$ the state of the circuit is represented by A. V is used to denote the input pulse. $V_n = 0$ indicates that at $t = t_n$ no pulse is sent into the counter, while $V_n = 1$ indicates that at $t = t_n$ a pulse is sent into the counter. The state transition table can be easily understood. For example, the first row of the table indicates that if at $t = t_n$ the state of the circuit is A and no pulse is sent in, then at $t = t_{n+1}$ the state of the circuit is still A. However, if one pulse is sent into the counter at that instant, necessary transitions will take place, and at $t = t_{n+1}$ the state of the circuit will be B.

It is desirable that only necessary and sufficient states be identified, because the number of states to be stored determines the minimum number of flip-flops needed. The example under study specifies that the number of states to be stored is 16. How many binary storage devices or flip-flops are needed? Since the content of each binary storage can be either 0 or 1, 16 different combinations can be formed with four flip-flops. Each combination is used to represent one state. The following question naturally arises: How do we assign the available 16 combinations to 16 states? In the design of a general sequential circuit, the operation of state assignment has an extensive influence on the complexity of the necessary combinational switching circuit. In the present problem, the designer does not have the freedom to assign freely one combination to any one of the 16 states, because it is specified that the display should be made in the binary number system. That is to say, state A has to be represented by 0000, B by 0001, and so on.

At this point, if the four flip-flops to be used are of the RS type, the remaining problems in the counter design are clearly displayed in the block diagram of Fig. 11.5.

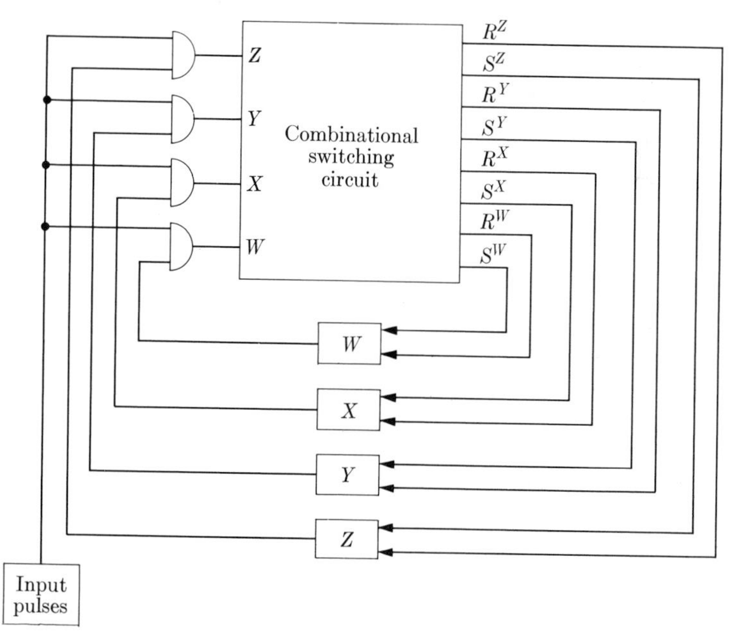

FIG. 11.5. A block diagram showing the completion of the design of memory for Example 11.1.

The task now is to design a combinational switching circuit which has four input variables and eight outputs, as shown.

Before we establish the eight switching functions for the eight outputs, note that the input pulses have to be synchronized with the clock pulses. If this synchronization is not achieved, then the memory of the counter will not change its content, even though pulses are being sent in. Table 11.3 also shows that the memory will change and must change its state only when an input pulse is sent in. This explains that in Fig. 11.5, the source of input pulses replaces the clock.

TABLE 11.4

THE STATE TRANSITION TABLE FOR EXAMPLE 11.1

Number of rows	W_n	X_n	Y_n	Z_n	W_{n+1}	X_{n+1}	Y_{n+1}	Z_{n+1}
1	0	0	0	0	0	0	0	1
2	0	0	0	1	0	0	1	0
3	0	0	1	0	0	0	1	1
4	0	0	1	1	0	1	0	0
5	0	1	0	0	0	1	0	1
6	0	1	0	1	0	1	1	0
7	0	1	1	0	0	1	1	1
8	0	1	1	1	1	0	0	0
9	1	0	0	0	1	0	0	1
10	1	0	0	1	1	0	1	0
11	1	0	1	0	1	0	1	1
12	1	0	1	1	1	1	0	0
13	1	1	0	0	1	1	0	1
14	1	1	0	1	1	1	1	0
15	1	1	1	0	1	1	1	1
16	1	1	1	1	0	0	0	0

The switching functions of the eight outputs can be established from the state transition table (Table 11.4). This table is obtained from the original state transition table, Table 11.3, by replacing states with their respective flip-flop combinations. The column $V_n = 0$ is omitted, because no transition is needed in that situation.

Table 11.4 can be considered as the combination of four separate truth tables for W_{n+1}, X_{n+1}, Y_{n+1}, and Z_{n+1}, respectively. The switching functions that have to be established here are S^W, R^W, S^X, R^X, S^Y, R^Y, S^Z, and R^Z. It would seem strange that the truth table established does not explicitly involve these eight variables. Actually it does not present any difficulty because S^W and R^W are related to W_{n+1} by the equations

$$S_n^W R_n^W = 0, \tag{11.12}$$

$$W_{n+1} = S_n^W + W_n(R_n^W)'. \tag{11.13*}$$

Equations (11.12) and (11.13) are true because RS-type flip-flops are to be used. The subscript n is added to indicate the time.

Let us start by trying to establish a switching function for S_n^W. It is obvious that S_n^W should be 1 when W_n is 0 and W_{n+1} is 1. Only by setting W at $t = t_n$ can we expect to have the bit stored in W to be 1 at $t = t_{n+1}$. With this criterion in mind, we examine the column under W_n and the column under W_{n+1}, and obtain the function

$$S_n^W(W_n, X_n, Y_n, Z_n) = m_7. \tag{11.14}$$

Note that only one standard product is entered, because only in row eight does $W_n = 0$ and $W_{n+1} = 1$. To meet this requirement, S_n^W has to be 1. Examine row nine, and see that it shows that

$$W_n = 1 \qquad \text{and} \qquad W_{n+1} = 1.$$

This means that S_n^W can be either 0 or 1. No matter which value S_n^W takes, W_{n+1} will be 1. Therefore, m_8 actually constitutes a don't-care condition. Other don't-care conditions can be found from rows 10, 11, 12, 13, 14, and 15. The switching function for S_n^W can be rewritten as

$$\begin{gathered} S_n^W(W_n, X_n, Y_n, Z_n) = m_7, \\ \text{don't care conditions: } m_8, m_9, m_{10}, m_{11}, m_{12}, m_{13}, \text{ or } m_{14}. \end{gathered} \tag{11.15}$$

Before function simplification is begun, it is important to point out that the combinational circuit being designed is a multiterminal network. The simplification should be done in such a manner that all eight functions are considered at the same time. If the tabulation method is used, the remaining seven functions should be expressed in the same form as Eq. (11.15). If the map method is used, Eq. (11.15) can be mapped as shown in Fig. 11.6(a).

Since Eq. (11.15) employs only four input variables, it is more convenient to use the map method. Following this decision, there is no need to write the remaining seven functions before mapping them. The appropriate maps can be constructed directly from the state transition table. These are shown in Fig. 11.6(b), (c), (d), (e), (f), (g), and (h).

---

* This equation can be justified by Table 11.1.

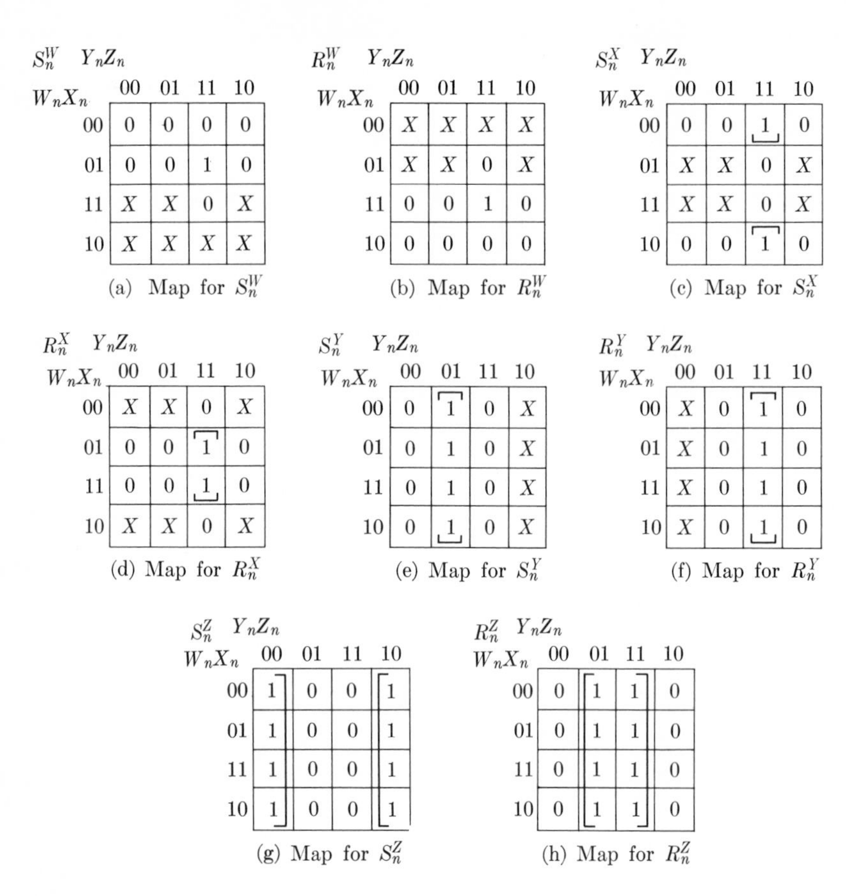

FIG. 11.6. Maps used to simplify switching functions for Example 11.1.

In Fig. 11.6(b), a map for the switching function R_n^W is shown. This map is established from Table 11.4, especially the column under W_{n+1}. In row one, W_{n+1} is to be 0. Since W_n is already 0, there is no absolute need to reset the binary storage. So long as S_n^W is 0, R_n^W can be either 0 or 1. This don't-care condition prevails when the state of the flip-flop at t_n is represented by 0000. This explains why an X is placed in the block 0000 on the map. To establish the map for R_n^W, we need pay attention only to the rows where W_{n+1} is 0. In row sixteen, note that while $W_{n+1} = 0$, $W_n = 1$. This situation requires that R_n^W be 1, and it is so indicated on the map.

The above discussion shows that if the map method is used, the maps for different switching functions can be constructed directly from the state transition table as soon as the type of flip-flop is known.

Proper groupings are displayed in Fig. 11.6. A set of eight functions is tabulated below:

$$S_n^W = W_n'X_nY_nZ_n, \tag{11.16}$$
$$R_n^W = W_nX_nY_nZ_n, \tag{11.17}$$
$$S_n^X = X_n'Y_nZ_n, \tag{11.18}$$
$$R_n^X = X_nY_nZ_n \tag{11.19}$$
$$S_n^Y = Y_n'Z_n, \tag{11.20}$$
$$R_n^Y = Y_nZ_n, \tag{11.21}$$
$$S_n^Z = Z_n', \tag{11.22}$$
$$R_n^Z = Z_n. \tag{11.23}$$

The implementation of these switching expressions is routine. This completes the design called for in Example 11.1; however, there are two points which need further clarification.▲

First of all, some readers might remark at this point that such a binary counter as specified in Example 11.1 could have been designed by inspection. Why were so many words spent on this simple and easy circuit? The design of this counter is actually used as a vehicle to introduce the reasoning involved and the steps taken in the design of a general synchronous sequential switching circuit. In the process of designing such a counter, the first step is the establishment of a state transition table showing sufficient and necessary states. The second step is the determination of the number of flip-flops to be used to form the memory. Thirdly, available combinations must be assigned to the states established. After the completion of the state assignment, the switching functions for the combinational switching circuit must be found and simplified. The combinational circuit is then implemented. This completes the entire design process.

The orderly procedure above will be found to be very useful, because the design of even simple counters cannot always be achieved by the cut-and-try process. Problems of this nature are provided at the end of this chapter.

The second point to be clarified concerns the definition of an optimum sequential switching circuit. Generally speaking, a switching circuit can be judged by its cost and its performance. In sequential switching circuits, the cost evaluation involves not only the installation expenses and the switching components used in the combinational circuit, but also includes the flip-flops used to form the memory. The number of flip-flops used, the way state assignments are made, and the complexity of the necessary combinational circuit are intimately related. The intimate relationship among these factors is chiefly responsible for the challenging and perplexing nature of sequential circuit design. The number of flip-flops employed is sometimes used as a quick and rough measuring rod of the worth of a switching circuit.

EXAMPLE 11.2. Design a counter which counts incoming pulses and displays in the binary number system the number of pulses counted. The counter is to return to its initial state after receiving every ten pulses. T-type binary storage devices are to be used.

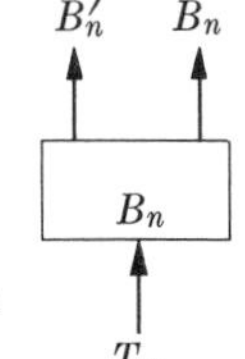

FIG. 11.7. Block diagram of a T-type flip-flop.

TABLE 11.5

B_n	0	0	1	1
T_n	0	1	0	1
B_{n+1}	0	1	1	0

The block diagram of a T-type flip-flop is shown in Fig. 11.7. The operating characteristic of a T-type flip-flop can be expressed by a truth table, as in Table 11.5.

From Table 11.5, the following switching function can be established:

$$B_{n+1} = B_n'T_n + B_nT_n'. \tag{11.24}$$

The number of states in the present example is ten, as can be easily derived from the given specifications. Let A denote the state in which the number of pulses counted is $10l$ (l is an integer, zero included), B the state where the number of pulses counted is $10l + 1$, etc.

TABLE 11.6

THE STATE TRANSITION TABLE FOR EXAMPLE 11.2

Present state	Next state	
	$V_n = 0$	$V_n = 1$
A_n	A_{n+1}	B_{n+1}
B_n	B_{n+1}	C_{n+1}
C_n	C_{n+1}	D_{n+1}
D_n	D_{n+1}	E_{n+1}
E_n	E_{n+1}	F_{n+1}
F_n	F_{n+1}	G_{n+1}
G_n	G_{n+1}	H_{n+1}
H_n	H_{n+1}	I_{n+1}
I_n	I_{n+1}	J_{n+1}
J_n	J_{n+1}	A_{n+1}

Subsequently a state transition table can be constructed, as in Table 11.6. In the table, $V_n = 0$ indicates that at t_n no pulse is sent in, and $V_n = 1$ indicates that at t_n one pulse is sent in. The same reasoning used in establishing Table 11.3 is applied here.

Since the memory of this counter must distinguish ten different states, four flip-flops are needed. If the specification that the display should be made in the binary number system were not given, the designer would have the complete freedom and the *responsibility* to assign ten of the sixteen available combinations to the ten states. Since state assignment has a direct influence on the complexity of the combinational circuit, and since there are so many alternatives in making the state assignment*, the designer would have a difficult and interesting task indeed. In the present example, since the binary number system is used, state A has to be represented by 0000, state B by 0001, etc.

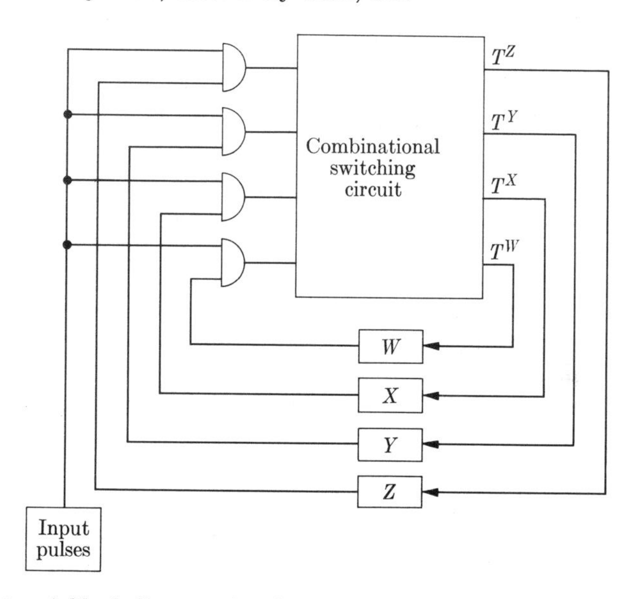

FIG. 11.8. A block diagram showing the completion of the design of memory for Example 11.2.

The schematic diagram of this decimal counter is shown in Fig. 11.8. As in the development of Example 11.1, the input pulses are used as clock pulses. There remains to be designed a combination switching circuit which has four input variables and four outputs. A new state transition table is drawn so that necessary switching functions can be established.

---

* MC 4.

TABLE 11.7

THE STATE TRANSITION TABLE FOR EXAMPLE 11.2

Number of rows	W_n	X_n	Y_n	Z_n	W_{n+1}	X_{n+1}	Y_{n+1}	Z_{n+1}
1	0	0	0	0	0	0	0	1
2	0	0	0	1	0	0	1	0
3	0	0	1	0	0	0	1	1
4	0	0	1	1	0	1	0	0
5	0	1	0	0	0	1	0	1
6	0	1	0	1	0	1	1	0
7	0	1	1	0	0	1	1	1
8	0	1	1	1	1	0	0	0
9	1	0	0	0	1	0	0	1
10	1	0	0	1	0	0	0	0

Table 11.7 is obtained by substituting the states for their representing combinations for the states. The column under $V_n = 0$ is omitted, because no transition is needed in that situation.

From Table 11.7, switching functions for T^W, T^X, T^Y, and T^Z can be found. Then simplification can be carried out either by the map method or by the tabulation method. Since only four input switching variables are involved, the map method is preferable. Consequently, maps for the four switching functions can be constructed directly from Table 11.7 and from Eq. (11.24), which presents the characteristic of a T-type flip-flop.

Four maps for T^W, T^X, T^Y, and T^Z are shown in Fig. 11.9(a), (b), (c), and (d), respectively. Let us examine the map in Fig. 11.9(a). The switching function for T^W is mapped by examining the columns under W_n and W_{n+1} of Table 11.7. In row one, $W_n = 0$ and $W_{n+1} = 0$. This means that if a pulse is received at t_n, the content of W should not be changed; T_n^W must be 0 in this situation. Therefore, a 0 is placed in the block 0000. Now let us examine row eight, where $W_n = 0$ and $W_{n+1} = 1$. This indicates that if a pulse is received at t_n, the state of W must be changed from 0 to 1; consequently, $T_n^W = 1$. Therefore, a 1 is placed in the block 0111. By going through each row of Table 11.7, we can conclude that T_n^W is either 0 or 1 under the conditions specified by W_n, X_n, Y_n, and Z_n. But there are six don't-care conditions shown on the map. Where do they come from? Note that the four flip-flops used can provide sixteen combinations. Only ten of them have been assigned to represent the ten states sufficient and necessary for this problem. The remaining six combinations, 1010, 1011, 1100, 1101, 1110, and 1111, are discarded. These six combinations will never appear in the memory. It follows that it is

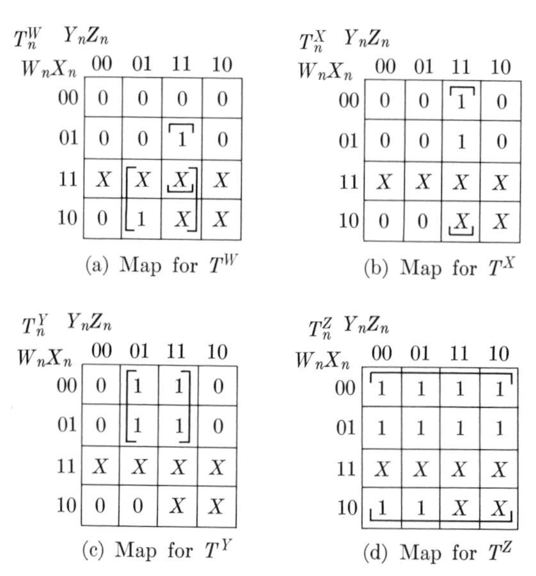

FIG. 11.9. Maps used to simplify switching functions for Example 11.2.

quite unnecessary to specify what the next state will be if the present state is one of the six listed above. Therefore, the six combinations actually provide six don't-care conditions to every one of the four switching functions we try to simplify.

Actually, it is very easy to construct maps for necessary switching functions, once the type of the flip-flop is known. Proper groupings are carried out in Fig. 11.9.

The simplified switching functions for T^W, T^X, T^Y, and T^Z are

$$T_n^W = W_nZ_n + X_nY_nZ_n, \tag{11.25}$$

$$T_n^X = Y_nZ_n, \tag{11.26}$$

$$T_n^Y = W_n'Z_n, \tag{11.27}$$

$$T_n^Z = 1. \tag{11.28}$$

The implementation of the four expressions is quite simple.▲

Examination of the two block diagrams in Figs. 11.5 and 11.8 exposes a very interesting problem. At $t = t_n$, W_n or the bit stored in W is used as an input to the combinational circuit, but at the same time, a new bit is sent into W to be stored. There is a great danger that the combinational circuit receives W_{n+1} instead of W_n as its input. Erroneous results, of course, would be obtained. This same problem also exists in X, Y, and Z. One way to keep this from happening is to install an appropriate delay in the output terminal of the flip-flops. If we do this, we can be sure that at t_n, W_n, X_n, Y_n, and Z_n are used by the combinational circuit as its inputs.*

11.5 The operation of multiplication and the design of a shift register. In Section 3.10, the method generally used to carry out the operation of multiplication is presented. The switching function for producing the partial product is described by Eq. (3.35), and mention is made that further development will be continued in Chapter 11. Discussion of multiplication has been delayed, because binary storage devices are needed to store the accumulated sum and to carry out proper shifting. Since binary storage devices have already been introduced in this chapter, the design of a binary multiplier can now be resumed. All the component circuits needed in a multiplier, except one, have already been presented. The design of a multiplier demonstrates how switching circuits can be judiciously combined to perform more complicated operations. Furthermore, it also helps to show one of the applications of a shift register. The block diagram of a binary multiplier which is capable of handling a multiplicand of three bits and a multiplier of three bits is shown in Fig. 11.10.

In the previous discussion on sequential switching circuits, one clock is introduced in Fig. 11.1 to synchronize the operations of the circuit. Note that two clocks are used in the multiplier circuit. The outputs of these two clocks are shown in Fig. 11.11.

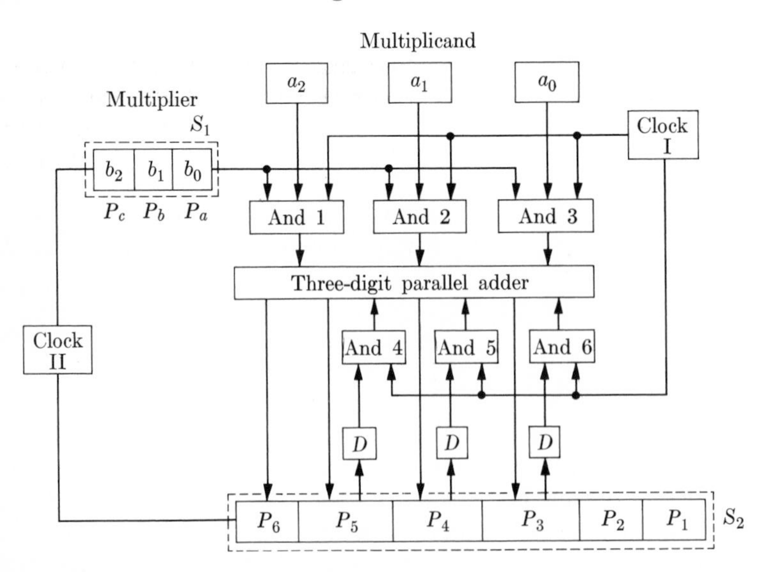

FIG. 11.10. Block diagram of a binary multiplier which can handle a multiplicand of three bits and a multiplier of three bits.

* Further discussion on counter design can be found in RI 1 and KA 3.

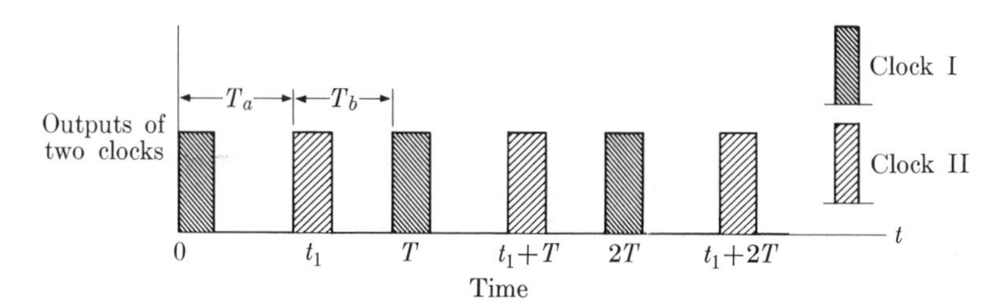

FIG. 11.11. The outputs of the two clocks used in the multiplier circuit.

At the start of the multiplication operation, the three bits of the multiplicand, a_2, a_1, and a_0, are stored in three flip-flops. The three bits of the multiplier, b_2, b_1, and b_0, are stored in the three flip-flops of a shift register S_1, whose characteristics will be defined later. Shift register S_2 has six flip-flops. At the start of the operation, all six bits stored in S_2 are 0.

The operation of this multiplier circuit can best be explained by an example. Let the multiplicand, a_2, a_1, a_0, be 111 and the multiplier, b_2, b_1, b_0, be 101. The steps taken and the intermediate results are tabulated in Table 11.8.

There are several points that need clarification. The time indicated at the right-hand side of the table corresponds to the time indicated in Fig. 11.11. For example, at $t = 0$, a pulse from clock I is applied to all six and-gates. Through and-gates 1, 2, and 3, the first partial product 111 is formed and sent to the parallel adder. The stored bits in P_3, P_4, and P_5 of S_2 are sent to the parallel adder through and-gates 4, 5, and 6. The first accumulated sum 111 is placed back into P_5, P_4, and P_3. We might ask whether the new bit contents in P_5, P_4, and P_3 might enter into the adder and produce erroneous results. This is possible, but is avoided here by the introduction of the delay device at the output of P_5, P_4, and P_3 and also by the finite width of the pulses from clock I. A delay is a device which introduces a pure time delay into a signal. For example, if a signal is applied to a delay device at t_0, the output of the delay device will be 0 until $t_0 + \Delta$, at which time the original signal appears as its output. An *RC* integrating circuit attached to the output of a flip-flop generally provides the necessary delay to enable it to be sensed and set or reset at the same time in a pulsed sequential switching circuit. In the two counting circuits designed in the previous section, this feature is assumed for all the flip-flops used.

At t_1, a pulse from clock II is applied to all flip-flops in shift registers S_1 and S_2. A *shift register* is a chain of flip-flops connected in such a way that upon receiving a shift pulse, the content of a flip-flop will be transmitted to its right (or left), while receiving the content of the flip-flop to its left (or right). When S_1 shifts to the right at t_1, the contents in its three flip-flops P_c, P_b, and P_a will be 010, respectively. The purpose of

TABLE 11.8

ILLUSTRATING THE STEPS AND INTERMEDIATE RESULTS IN THE MULTIPLIER CIRCUIT IN FIG. 11.10

Cycle	Step						Contents of S_2: P_6	P_5	P_4	P_3	P_2	P_1	Time
First cycle	Multiplicand $a_2a_1a_0$		1	1	1								
	Multiplier $b_2b_1b_0$		1	0	1								
													$t = 0$
	First partial product		1	1	1								
	Contents of P_5, P_4, and P_3		0	0	0		0	0	0	0	0	0	
	First accumulated sum		1	1	1		0	1	1	1	0	0	
													$t = t_1$
	Both S_1 and S_2 shift to the right by one bit						0	0	1	1	1	0	
													$t = T$
Second cycle	Second partial product		0	0	0								
	Contents of P_5, P_4, and P_3		0	1	1								
	Second accumulated sum		0	1	1		0	0	1	1	1	0	
													$t = t_1 + T$
	Both S_1 and S_2 shift to the right by one bit						0	0	0	1	1	1	
													$t = 2T$
Third cycle	Third partial product		1	1	1								
	Contents of P_5, P_4, and P_3		0	0	1								
	Third accumulated sum	1	0	0	0		1	0	0	0	1	1	
	If desired both S_1 and S_2 shift to the right by one bit												$t = 2T + t_1$
	This clears S_1. S_2 has to have an additional flip-flop					0	1	0	0	0	1	1	
							Product						

this shifting to the right is to move b_1 into a position to generate the second partial product. When S_2 shifts to the right at t_1, the contents of its six flip-flops are 001110, as shown. The contents are shifted to the right in order to place the first accumulated sum in such a position that it can be added to the second partial product. In pencil and paper calculation, we usually "shift" the partial product to the left. This, of course, is equivalent to shifting the accumulated sum to the right. This completes one cycle. Two more cycles are needed to complete the computation in the present example. The product is displayed in shift register S_2.

The block diagram shown in Fig. 11.10 is intended to illustrate how a multiplication process can be performed by properly connecting several simple switching circuits. Numerous variations are available.* For example, the parallel adder and the shift register can be combined, and result in substantial component saving. Such a combination is called an *accumulator*.

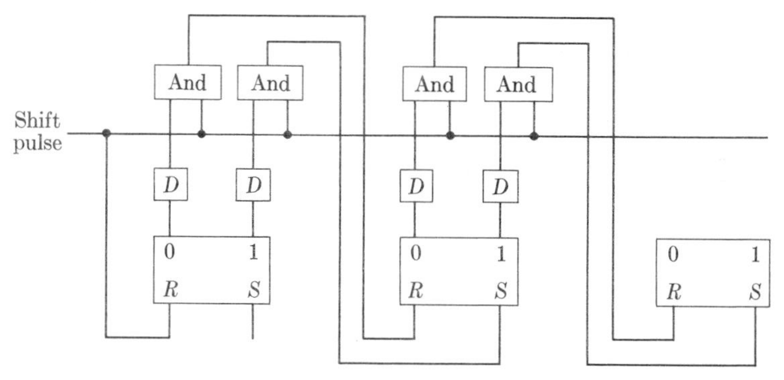

FIG. 11.12. A three-cell block of a right-shifting shift register.

The characteristic of a shift register has already been defined above. A three-cell block of a right-shifting shift register is shown in Fig. 11.12. *RS*-type flip-flops are used. The delay units installed at the output terminals of the flip-flops enable each one to transmit its content to the cell at its right-hand side, while receiving the content from the cell at its left-hand side.

PROBLEMS

11.1. If the serial binary adder shown in Fig. 11.3 is used to generate the sum of two numbers, each of which has $n + 1$ bits, how many clock pulses are needed to complete the operation?

11.2. Design a counter which counts incoming pulses and displays in the binary number system the number of pulses counted. The counter is to return to its initial state after receiving every fifteen pulses. Use *T*-type binary storage devices.

11.3. Design a counter which counts incoming pulses and displays in the binary number system the number of pulses counted. The counter is to return to its initial state after receiving every nine pulses. Use *RS*-type binary storage devices.

---

* RI 1, ES 1, FR 2, LE 3, and RO 3.

11.4. Use JK-type flip-flops to implement a counter which displays in the binary number system the number of incoming pulses counted. The counter is to return to its initial state after receiving every thirteen pulses.

11.5. Design a decimal counter which displays in excess-3 code the number of incoming pulses counted. Use (a) T-type flip-flops, (b) RS-type flip-flops, (c) JK-type flip-flops.

11.6. Use RS-type flip-flops to implement a counter which displays the following number sequence: 1, 3, 5, 7, 9, 11, 12, 13, 14, 15, for every ten pulses received. The binary number system is to be used.

11.7. Design a counter which displays the following number sequence: 0, 2, 1, 5, 4, 3, 9, 8, 7, for every nine pulses received. BCD code and T-type flip-flops are to be used.

11.8. Implement a counter with JK-type flip-flops which displays the number sequence: 7, 8, 5, 3, 2, 6, 9, 1, 4, for every nine pulses received. Excess-3 code is to be used.

11.9. A delay element can be considered as a storage device which delays its input information one or more time intervals before presenting it at its output terminal. (A time interval is the time elapsed between two consecutive clock pulses.) Hence, it has a single input terminal and a single output terminal. The state of a single time interval delay storage element Q at time $\tau + 1$ depends only on its input I at time τ. In other words,

$$Q_{\tau+1} = I_{\tau}.$$

Since a delay element (defined above) is a storage device, it is possible to use it to replace a flip-flop when designing counters.

Design a counter that has the following counting sequence:

A	B	C	D
1	1	0	0
0	1	1	0
0	0	1	1
1	0	0	1
0	1	0	1
1	0	1	0
0	1	0	0
0	0	1	0
0	0	0	1
1	0	0	0

Use delay elements as storage devices and determine the simplest input equations (fewest number of literals) for each of the delay elements.

CHAPTER 12

SEQUENTIAL CIRCUITS II: FROM CIRCUIT SPECIFICATIONS TO STATE TABLE

12.1 Introduction. The model of a synchronous sequential circuit is established in the previous chapter. By designing counting circuits and shift registers, we have illustrated the general steps that must be taken in the design of a sequential switching circuit. It should be pointed out, however, that even though counters and shift registers are sequential circuits and are widely used in switching systems, the completion of their design does not mean that all the difficulties and considerations in synthesizing a general synchronous sequential circuit have been exposed. In this chapter and the following two chapters we intend to disclose all the difficulties and try to solve them.

The specifications for a sequential switching circuit to be designed are generally given in the form of a statement of several sentences. The first task in circuit design is to express the given specifications in the form of a table, called the state transition table, abbreviated as *state table.** In Chapter 11, we did not encounter any difficulty in establishing state tables for counting circuits. These isolated instances, however, are not proof that the transformation of circuit specifications from a statement of words into a table is routine. Unfortunately, there is no established step-by-step procedure for executing this transformation. Several cases will be considered in this chapter.

12.2 Parity-bit generators. The coding problem in switching systems is discussed in Sections 9.4 and 9.6. Three coding schemes, BCD, excess-3, and cyclic, were introduced. Section 10.2 points out that certain error-detecting schemes must be incorporated in a large switching system to discover possible errors in its operation. The introduction of a parity bit into a code is a widely used and simple method of error detection. In using the parity bit for error detection, we have to design a parity-bit generator, a device which generates appropriate parity bits for a given code. For example, if odd-parity checking is adopted, the parity bit for the code sequence 0000 should be 1.

---

* The characterization and representation of sequential circuits can also be made with graphs and matrices. See HO 3, AU 1, AU 2, SE 2, MC 7, OT 1, BU 2, EL 1, and FR 1.

A parity-bit generator can operate in the parallel mode, that is, all the bits of a code sequence are sent to the circuit at the same time. The design of a parallel-mode parity-bit generator is generally carried out by the iterative approach introduced in Chapter 10. As a matter of fact, the resultant circuit for Example 10.1 can be considered a parallel-mode parity-bit generator.

A parity-bit generator can also operate in the serial mode, that is, the bits of a code sequence are sent to the circuit one at a time. Such a generator is, of course, a sequential switching circuit.

EXAMPLE 12.1. Design a serial parity-bit generator for BCD code, excess-3 code, or cyclic code of four binary digits, with RS-type flip-flops and diode gates.

From what has been presented in the previous chapter, we know that our first step is to convert the given specifications into a state table. In designing the counting circuit, we did not encounter any problem in obtaining a state table. Here we are confronted with the problem of where to begin.

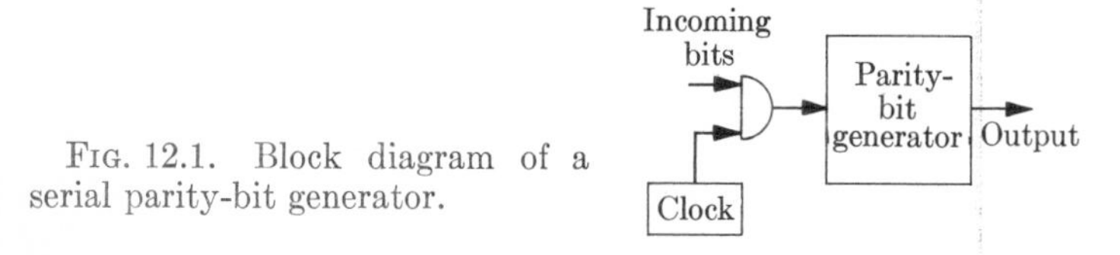

FIG. 12.1. Block diagram of a serial parity-bit generator.

We will use the block diagram of the circuit shown in Fig. 12.1 to clarify the situation. The four bits of a code sequence are sent to the circuit through one input lead. The pulses representing the bits are synchronized with the clock pulses. The bits of a code sequence enter the circuit one at a time. When the fourth bit is received, the circuit produces the parity bit to be added to the original code sequence. In other words, the circuit to be designed examines four successive bits, produces an output (the parity bit), and gets ready to receive the next four bits. This cyclic operation suggests that an initial state can be defined. The *initial state* is the state the circuit is in when it embarks on the task of examining four successive bits. The establishment of the notion of an initial state provides a welcome opening for drawing the state diagram in Fig. 12.2.

The initial state is designated as A. The parity-bit generating circuit is at this state when it has just finished examining four bits and is ready to examine the next four bits successively, or should we say, to start another cycle. The first bit of the cycle can be either 1 or 0. Upon receiving a 0-bit, the state of the circuit is changed from A to B. A directional link showing this transition is drawn between A and B. A notation 0/0 is

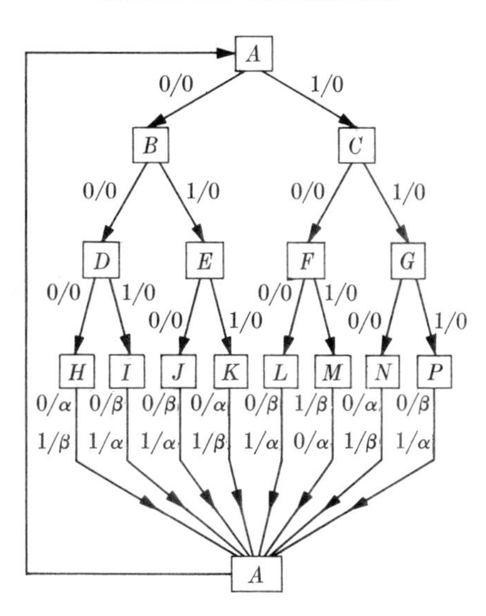

FIGURE 12.2

placed alongside the link. The 0 above the slanted bar indicates that the circuit, while at state A, receives a 0-bit. The 0 under the slanted bar indicates that the sequential circuit, while at state A, produces no output when an 0-bit is received. If the first bit of the cycle is 1, the circuit changes its state from A to C. The notation 1/0 is placed alongside the directional link between A and C. This indicates that the circuit, while at state A, receives a 1-bit and produces no output. Before the second bit of the cycle arrives, the state of the circuit has already settled either in state B or in state C.

The second bit of the cycle can of course be either 1 or 0. Therefore, before the third bit of the cycle arrives, the circuit is in one of the four states D, E, F, or G. The arrival of the third bit will transfer the state of the circuit to one of the eight states, H, I, J, K, L, M, N, or P. If the state of the circuit is at H, then the first three bits of the cycle are 0, 0, and 0. If the state of the circuit is at M, the first three bits of the cycle are 1, 0, and 1, respectively.

The diagram in Fig. 12.2 shows that upon receiving the fourth bit of the cycle, the circuit will return to state A, because four bits constitute a cycle. After examining the four bits of a cycle, the circuit must return to its initial state to start another one. It is also indicated in the diagram that there are two kinds of outputs, α and β, made by the circuit after receiving the fourth bit. The output α denotes that the parity bit for the code sequence is 1, and the output β denotes that the parity bit for the code sequence of this cycle is 0. For example, if the state of the circuit is J

TABLE 12.1

Present state	Next state		Output	
	0	1	0	1
A	B	C	0	0
B	D	E	0	0
C	F	G	0	0
D	H	I	0	0
E	J	K	0	0
F	L	M	0	0
G	N	P	0	0
H	A	A	α	β
I	A	A	β	α
J	A	A	β	α
K	A	A	α	β
L	A	A	β	α
M	A	A	α	β
N	A	A	α	β
P	A	A	β	α

when it receives a 0-bit, the output is β. This happens because the code sequence of this cycle is 0100. To keep the number of 1's contained odd, the parity bit must be 0. On the other hand, if the state of the circuit is J when it receives a 1-bit, the output must be α. In that case, the code sequence of this cycle is 0101. In order to keep the number of 1's contained odd, the parity bit must be 1.

Note that the state diagram was not introduced in the previous chapter. Its introduction there was not necessary, because state tables can be easily constructed for the design of counters or shift registers. The state diagram is used here as an intermediate step in transforming given circuit specifications into a state table. If the state table can be easily constructed, there is no need to obtain the state diagram first.

To establish the state table from the state diagram is a simple matter, because the states and the transitions between them are well defined. From the state diagram in Fig. 12.2, the state table in Table 12.1 is made. The establishment of the state table constitutes the first step in the design of the parity-bit generating circuit.

By examining Fig. 12.2 or Table 12.1, we see that the resultant circuit will be able to provide an odd parity bit for any four-bit code. If the parity-bit generating circuit is used for a specific coding scheme, certain code sequences will never appear. For example, if BCD code is used, the six code sequences 1010, 1011, 1100, 1101, 1110, and 1111 will never be

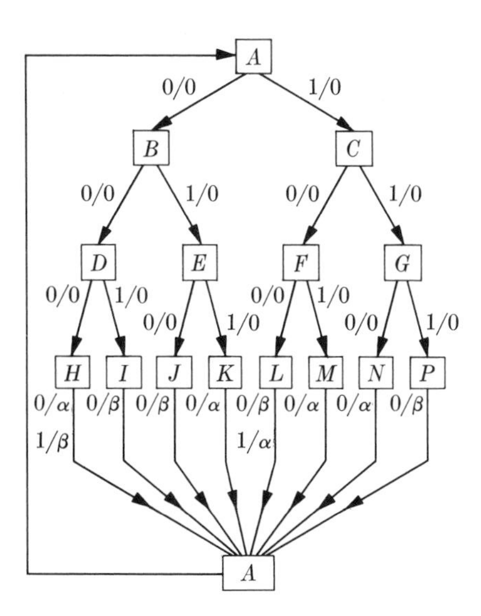

FIGURE 12.3

applied to the circuit in a cycle. This observation brings about some interesting modifications of the original state diagram and state table.

Let us now construct the state diagram, and later the state table, of an odd parity-bit generating circuit for BCD code. It is assumed that the 1-weighted bit appears first in a cycle. Subsequently, 2-, 4-, and 8-weighted bits appear, in that order.

Since six code sequences among the possible sixteen will never be applied to the circuit, the state diagram can be modified to that shown in Fig. 12.3. This state diagram differs from Fig. 12.2 in the reduced number of entries following the arrival of the fourth bit. It looks as if this were another exercise in constructing a state diagram, but actually the resultant state table shown in Table 12.2 provides us with a new opportunity and a new challenge.

Note that in Table 12.2, crosses are placed in certain blocks. For example, crosses are found in the I-row and the two 1-columns. The interpretation of the cross is this: if the state of the circuit is at I and the fourth bit is 1, the next state and the output are not specified. It would seem that when the circuit state is at I, the 1-, 2-, and 4-weighted bits are 0, 0, and 1, respectively. If the 8-weighted bit is 1, the corresponding parity should be 1, and the circuit must be returned to its initial state. This would be so if such a code sequence were sent to the circuit, but, since the BCD code is used, this sequence will never occur. It would be advantageous to leave the next state and the output unspecified. Those unspecified entries, or don't-care conditions, can help to simplify the

TABLE 12.2

Present state	Next state		Output	
	0	1	0	1
A	B	C	0	0
B	D	E	0	0
C	F	G	0	0
D	H	I	0	0
E	J	K	0	0
F	L	M	0	0
G	N	P	0	0
H	A	A	α	β
I	A	$\times$	β	$\times$
J	A	$\times$	β	$\times$
K	A	$\times$	α	$\times$
L	A	A	β	α
M	A	$\times$	α	$\times$
N	A	$\times$	α	$\times$
P	A	$\times$	β	$\times$

resultant design, provided that they are intelligently used. They, therefore, provide the designer with a new opportunity and a new challenge. The design of the parity-bit generator will be continued in Example 13.1.▲

12.3. A sequential switching circuit without an initial state. The design of a sequential switching circuit is introduced in the previous section. Note that an initial state is established first. In Example 12.1, the circuit is asked to examine four input bits, produce an output, and get ready to receive the next four input bits. Each cycle of operation consists of examining four bits and producing an appropriate output. The state in which the circuit starts each cycle is identified as its initial state. After the completion of each cycle, the circuit returns to its initial state.

There are sequential circuits whose operations are not cyclic in nature; no initial state can be found. This does not, however, necessarily complicate the task of establishing the state table.

EXAMPLE 12.2. Design a sequential switching circuit with flip-flops and transistor gates to examine a train of binary digits. The output of the circuit must be 1 when the last four bits received are all 1.

To explain the given problem further, a hypothetical train of bits, their corresponding instances of occurrence, and the outputs of the sequential circuit are shown at the top of the next page.

Increase in time
⟶

Time instants	t_1	t_2	t_3	t_4	t_5	t_6	t_7	t_8	t_9	...
Input bit	0	0	1	1	1	1	1	0	0	...
Output	0	0	0	0	0	1	1	0	0	...

The time intervals between pairs of consecutive bits do not have to be equal, but each one of them must be an integral multiple of the period of the clock pulses, because the input bits are synchronized with clock pulses. Note also that there is always a delay before the circuit produces the output. For example, at t_6 the circuit receives the fourth consecutive 1-bit. However, the output of 1 cannot be expected to appear exactly at t_6.

If we try to locate an initial state for the state diagram under discussion, our efforts will definitely be in vain, because there is no initial state to be found. Re-examining the given specification of the circuit, we begin to understand that in order for the circuit to satisfy the requirement it must have the capacity to remember or store the last three bits received. By having the last three bits received at hand, the circuit is in a position to decide what the output should be whenever it receives a fourth bit. Therefore, the states of the sequential circuit can be made to indicate the eight possible combinations of the last three bits received. In other words, eight states are defined, while each state represents one possible combination of the last three bits received.

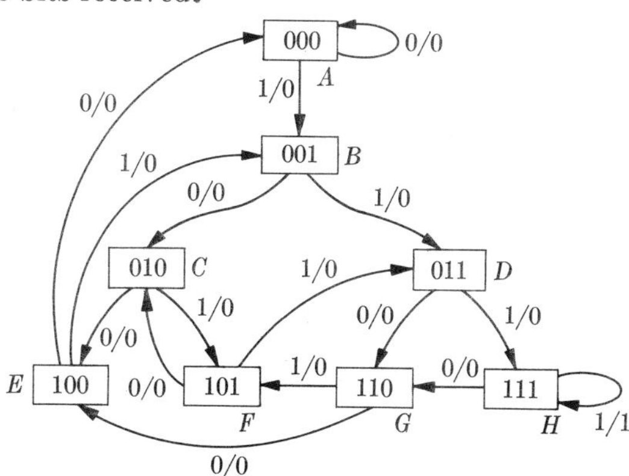

FIGURE 12.4

The transition between states is of course determined by the input bit received. The state diagram is shown in Fig. 12.4. Each state is designated by its corresponding combination of the last three bits received. For example, 110 is used to designate the circuit state in which the last bit

TABLE 12.3

Present state	Next state		Output	
	0	1	0	1
A	A	B	0	0
B	C	D	0	0
C	E	F	0	0
D	G	H	0	0
E	A	B	0	0
F	C	D	0	0
G	E	F	0	0
H	G	H	0	1

received is 0, the next to last 1, and the bit before the last two is also 1. This scheme of designation is included because it facilitates the task of identifying next states.

Once the state diagram is constructed, only the letter designation is retained in the corresponding state table, shown in Table 12.3. This example is to be continued in Example 13.2.▲

PROBLEMS

12.1. Construct the state diagram and the state table for a synchronous sequential circuit which examines the pulses from an input line. The circuit should return to its initial state after receiving every five pulses. The output is 1 whenever four and only four of every five pulses received are 1.

12.2. Construct the state diagram and the state table for a synchronous sequential circuit which examines the pulses from an input line. The circuit is returned to its initial state after receiving every five pulses. The output is 1 whenever there is one and only one consecutive group* of 1's in every five pulses received.

12.3. Construct the state diagram and the state table for a sequential circuit which examines the synchronized pulses from two input lines. The circuit should return to its initial state after receiving every four pairs of pulses. The output is 1 whenever there is one and only one pair among the four pairs examined which consists of a 1 and a 0.

12.4. A synchronous sequential circuit which has two input lines is to be designed. The circuit has an initial state which is reached after receiving every five pairs of synchronized input pulses. The output of the circuit is 1 whenever the number of pairs of input pulses which are both 1 or 0 is odd. Construct the state diagram and the state table.

---

* "Consecutive group" is defined in Problem 10.7.

12.5. A synchronous sequential circuit is to be designed. The output of the circuit is 1 whenever the last four pulses received through the input line are of the following pattern.

Time instant	t_n	t_{n+1}	t_{n+2}	t_{n+3}
Input bit	1	1	0	1

Construct the state diagram and the state table.

12.6. A synchronous sequential circuit is to be designed. The output of the circuit is 1 whenever the last five pulses received through the input line are of the following pattern.

Time instant	t_n	t_{n+1}	t_{n+2}	t_{n+3}	t_{n+4}
Input bit	1	1	0	1	1

Construct the state diagram and the state table.

12.7. Design a synchronous sequential circuit to be used for error-checking. BCD coded messages are sent into the circuit serially through an input line. The circuit is to indicate whenever an undefined bit combination occurs. Construct the state diagram and the state table.

12.8. Design a synchronous sequential circuit which examines messages serially, each of which has five binary digits. The circuit is to indicate whenever each message has two and only two 1's. Construct the state diagram and the state table.

CHAPTER 13

SEQUENTIAL CIRCUITS III: SIMPLIFICATION OF STATE TABLES*

13.1 Introduction. In the previous chapter, the considerations involved in constructing a state table for a given sequential switching circuit are discussed. State diagrams are used as an intermediate means in transforming given specifications into state tables.

Note that in establishing a state table, our only concern is that the state table obtained faithfully reflects the specifications given. We do not pay attention to the number of states the resultant state table possesses. Is it then true that the number of states has no bearing on the complexity of the resultant circuit? The answer is definitely no! It is not at all hard to see why the number of states is intimately related to the complexity of the resultant circuit.

Chapter 11 shows how the states of a sequential circuit are implemented with binary storage devices. The number of states to be implemented determines the number of binary storage devices needed. For example, if sixteen states are to be implemented, then at least four binary storage devices are needed. For each binary storage device, the necessary combinational switching circuits for setting or resetting purposes must be provided. Therefore, the number of states is inextricably related to the resultant circuit.

It appears to us at this time, even though the number of states defined does influence the resultant circuit, they are defined according to a set of given specifications. It seems that the number of states is beyond our control and, therefore, we must accept and implement them; this, however, is not always true.

This chapter will show that for a set of given specifications, the corresponding state table is not unique. In other words, to a certain extent, we can control the number of states for a given problem, and consequently we do have the responsibility of deciding the number of states to be implemented.

13.2 Equivalent states and completely specified state table reduction. Before the equivalence between states is defined, it will be profitable to try to reduce a given state table.

---

* Relevant references ME 2, MO 1, AU 1, AU 2, GI 1, GI 2, GI 3, PA 1, HO 3, NE 1, SI 1, and SI 2.

EXAMPLE 13.1. Continue the design of the serial parity-bit generator specified in Example 12.1.

The state table for the parity-bit generator which can handle any four-bit code is established in Table 12.1. This table is repeated in Table 13.1. If we examine row I and row L, we find that these two rows are identical. No matter whether the circuit is initially at I or L, if the input is 0, the output will be β and the circuit will go into state A. No matter whether the circuit is initially at I or L, if the input is 1, the output will be α and the next state of the circuit will be A.

TABLE 13.1

Present state	Next state		Output	
	0	1	0	1
A	B	C	0	0
B	D	E	0	0
C	~~F~~ E	D ~~G~~	0	0
D	H	I	0	0
E	~~J~~ I	H ~~K~~	0	0
~~F~~	~~L I~~	~~H M~~	~~0~~	~~0~~
~~G~~	~~N H~~	~~I P~~	~~0~~	~~0~~
H	A	A	α	β
I	A	A	β	α
~~J~~	~~A~~	~~A~~	~~β~~	~~α~~
~~K~~	~~A~~	~~A~~	~~α~~	~~β~~
~~L~~	~~A~~	~~A~~	~~β~~	~~α~~
~~M~~	~~A~~	~~A~~	~~α~~	~~β~~
~~N~~	~~A~~	~~A~~	~~α~~	~~β~~
~~P~~	~~A~~	~~A~~	~~β~~	~~α~~

The above situation makes it quite clear that state I and state L are the same, so far as the output of the circuit is concerned. Therefore, in Table 13.1, row L is crossed out, and all the L's in the table are replaced by I's. This operation amounts to the elimination of state L.

The same elimination process is continued until no two rows can be found that are identical. The state table is reduced to that shown in Table 13.2. The number of states is reduced from fifteen to seven. ▲

At this point, we should be very interested in justifying the validity of the above elimination process, which is intuitively convincing. We should also look into the possibility of further reduction, even though there is no identical pair among the remaining seven rows. To satisfy these two points, the *equivalence between states* is to be defined first.

TABLE 13.2

Present state	Next state		Output	
	0	1	0	1
A	B	C	0	0
B	D	E	0	0
C	E	D	0	0
D	H	I	0	0
E	I	H	0	0
H	A	A	α	β
I	A	A	β	α

Let us examine a sequential circuit, T, which has a finite number of states; among them S_1 and S_2. If T initially is at S_1, and any arbitrary sequence of input combinations, X, is applied to T, then a sequence of output combinations is produced which may be designated as $Y_{s_1}(X)$.

To offer a tangible interpretation to the above statements, let us examine the parity-bit generator discussed in Example 13.1. State I can be taken as S_1. The number of input combinations is equal to 2^p, where p is the number of inputs of the sequential circuit. Since the parity-bit generator has only one input, there are only two input combinations, namely 0 and 1. If there were two inputs to the circuit, there would be four input combinations, namely 00, 01, 10, and 11.

The number of output combinations is equal to 2^m, where m is the number of outputs of the sequential circuit. Since there is only one output in the parity-bit generator, there are two output combinations, namely 0 and 1.

We can now perform an "experiment" on the circuit. Suppose that at $t = t_0$, while the parity-bit generator is at state I, a 0 is applied to the circuit. We see from Table 13.1 that the corresponding output of the circuit is β and the state of the circuit will change to A. At $t = t_1$ ($t_1 = t_0 + t_s$),* a 0 is applied. The corresponding output is 0 and the circuit will transfer to state B. At $t = t_2$ ($t_2 = t_1 + t_s$), the input is 1. Table 13.1 dictates that the corresponding output is 0 and the circuit moves to state E. At $t = t_3$ ($t_3 = t_2 + t_s$), 1 is again applied. The state of the circuit is then transferred to H and the output is 0.

To summarize what has been done, we see that a sequence of input combinations has been applied to the circuit when the circuit is initially at state I. This sequence can be expressed as

$$X_1\colon 0, 0, 1, 1. \tag{13.1}$$

* t_s is the time interval between two clock pulses.

The corresponding sequence of output combinations, $Y_I(X_1)$, can then be written:

$$Y_I(X_1)\colon\ \beta, 0, 0, 0. \tag{13.2}$$

We can now return to our original task, to define the equivalence between states.

If T is initially at S_2, and the same sequence of input combinations X is applied, then a sequence of output combinations is produced which may be designated as $Y_{s_2}(X)$.

S_1 and S_2 are said to be equivalent if $Y_{s_1}(X)$ and $Y_{s_2}(X)$ are identical.

The above definition can be justified if we again examine the block diagram of the general synchronous sequential switching circuit shown in Fig. 11.1. Note that two separate blocks are employed to illustrate the combinational circuit and the memory of a sequential switching circuit. The diagram has been drawn in this manner to facilitate our understanding. The performance or characteristic of a synchronous sequential switching circuit can be adequately represented by the block diagram in Fig. 13.1.

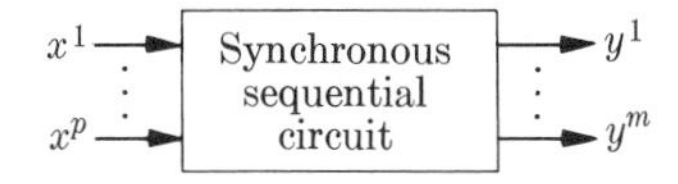

FIG. 13.1. Block diagram of a synchronous sequential circuit.

All we can observe is the sequence of input combinations and its corresponding sequence of output combinations. If *any* arbitrary sequence of input combinations, X, is applied to a synchronous sequential circuit, and if the condition for state equivalence presented above is met, then the corresponding sequence of output combinations will be the same; no matter whether the state of the circuit is initially at S_1 or at S_2 when X is applied. Then, so far as we are concerned, S_1 and S_2 are the same; S_1 can be replaced by S_2, or vice versa.

In order to reduce the number of states in a state table, we must locate equivalent pairs, if any, from among the existing states. The definition made above concerning the equivalence between states seems to suggest that we can identify equivalent pairs by feeding arbitrary sequences of input combinations into the circuit when it is initially at S_1, then repeating the operation when the initial circuit state is at S_2, and finally observing corresponding output sequences. There is no difficulty in finding the corresponding sequence of output combinations once the sequence of input combinations is determined. This can be accomplished by using the established state table. The main problem in using this approach to locate an equivalent pair is the necessity of satisfying the stipulation that two states are equivalent if they produce the same sequence of output combinations with respect to *any arbitrary sequence* of input combinations. We can immediately see that this amounts to an endless task, because the number of arbitrary sequences of input combinations is infinite. This is so for two reasons: first, at each input instant, the number of possible input combinations is equal to 2^p, where p is the number of input variables; and secondly, the number of input combinations contained in each sequence, or the *length* of each sequence, can be any integer.

To overcome the difficulty of infinite input combinations, the following approach is suggested. We restrict the number of input combinations contained in each sequence, or the length of each sequence, to 1. With this restriction, the number of arbitrary sequences is finite and equal to 2^p. Instead of sending an infinite number of arbitrary sequences into the circuit, it is now necessary to send only 2^p sequences, each of whose lengths is 1. The immediate complaint about this suggestion is that any two states cannot be declared equivalent based on this test, because it does not satisfy the requirement stated in the definition. To remedy this shortcoming, we require not only that the output combination corresponding to each of the 2^p input combinations be the same, but also that the circuit be transformed into the same next state when the initial state of the circuit is either at S_1 or at S_2. It can easily be seen that the satisfaction of this modified requirement automatically qualifies S_1 and S_2 to be considered as equivalent states. This also justifies the elimination process performed in Example 13.1.

TABLE 13.3

Present state	Next state		Output		New state	Next state	
	0	1	0	1		0	1
A	B	C	0	0	I	II	I
B	E	C	1	0	II	~~II~~ III	I
C	D	A	0	0	I	II	I
D	E	A	1	0	II	~~II~~ III	I
E	E	E	1	0	~~II~~ III	~~II~~ III	~~II~~ III

Questions the reader might ask are: Are there equivalent states whose corresponding rows are not identical? If so, how can they be located? These questions can be answered by trying to reduce the state table shown in Table 13.3.

Note in Table 13.3 that the search for identical rows will result in no reduction of the number of states. However, this does not necessarily mean that there are no equivalent states among the five in Table 13.3.

For this reason another approach, which will lead to the identification of the minimum number of states, must be introduced.

In trying to locate identical rows in a state table, we are looking for states whose output combinations and next states are identical for each possible input combination. For two states to be considered equivalent, it is absolutely essential that their output combinations be identical. It is, however, not necessary that their next states be the same. Instead of comparing the entire rows, we propose to examine only the output columns of two states. In other words we start the reduction process by grouping states according to their output patterns.

The output pattern of a state is an orderly array in which the output combinations corresponding to every input combination, when the circuit is in that state, are displayed. For example, in Table 13.3, the output pattern of state A is (0, 0) and the output pattern of state B is (1, 0).

Grouping the states in Table 13.3 according to their output pattern, we obtain

$$\frac{\mathrm{I}(0,\,0)}{A,\,C}\quad\frac{\mathrm{II}(1,\,0)}{B,\,D,\,E} \tag{13.3a}$$

The above shows that states A and C are equivalent if the length of the input sequence is 1. This condition is *necessary*, but certainly *not sufficient* for establishing equivalence between states. This grouping by output patterns shows, however, that the most we can accomplish is the replacement of states A and C by a new state I, and states B, D, and E by another new state II. This is denoted in the columns on the right-hand side of Table 13.3.

Since state A is included in the new state I, a I is entered in row A in the new state column. When the input is 0, the next state for A is B, which is included in the new state II, and a II is thus entered under the new zero next state column. The right-hand columns in Table 13.3 are completed in the same way. Note that the output column is omitted, because in doing the grouping, the outputs of new states are already fixed as shown in (13.3a).

Once the new columns are completed, we can start to check and see whether the number of new states is adequate. In the present problem, we are going to check whether the two new states defined in (13.3a) can be substituted for the original five states. This is done by examining the rows which belong to the same new state: row A and row C in Table 13.3 correspond to new state I. The next state entries are II and I when the inputs are 0 and 1, respectively. No difficulty is encountered. Rows B, D, and E all correspond to new state II. So far as the columns on the right-hand side are concerned, row B and row D are identical. If we, however, compare row E with either row B or row D, a contradiction is found. When the input is 1, the next state for state II is II, according to row E, but the next state for state II is I according to row B or row D. This contradiction reveals that E cannot be grouped with B and D. A new state, III, is created:

$$\frac{\text{I}(0, 0)}{A, C} \; \frac{\text{II}(1, 0)}{B, D} \; \frac{\text{III}(1, 0)}{E}. \tag{13.3b}$$

Note that E is taken away from state II and represented by state III. Certain alterations must be made accordingly in the columns on the right-hand side of Table 13.3. State E is originally represented by II. Because of this new grouping, any II which is a replacement of E must be replaced by III. This is done in the table.

The above checking process reveals that the number of states cannot be reduced to two, and subsequently a new state is added. The same checking procedure must be employed to see whether the number of states can be reduced to three. No contradiction is found, and therefore a new state table can be drawn up (Table 13.4) which is equivalent to Table 13.3, but has only three states.

TABLE 13.4

Present state	Next state		Output	
	0	1	0	1
I	II	I	0	0
II	III	I	1	0
III	III	III	1	0

By using the output-grouping method, we can obtain the minimum number of states for a given design problem. This claim is based on the fact that to start the reduction process, the initial number of new states is equal to the number of output patterns present. No additional state is introduced unless a contradiction is encountered.

Let us try to use this method to reduce further the state table in Table 13.2. The result will reveal that the minimum number of states is seven, as shown.

To conclude this section, the following summary can be made. To reduce a given state table or to locate possible equivalent states, we can first search for identical rows. Any two states whose corresponding rows are identical are equivalent. If desirable, one of the two states can be eliminated. This reduction process is carried out just because of the ease of its execution. The second elimination process, based on output patterns, must then be attempted. For a sequential circuit which has an initial state, reduction by elimination of identical rows is, in general, sufficient.

TABLE 13.5

Present state	Next state		Output	
	0	1	0	1
A	B	C	0	0
B	D	E	0	0
C	F	G	0	0
D	H	I	0	0
E	J	~~K~~ H	0	0
F	L	M	0	0
G	N	~~P~~ L	0	0
H	A	A	α	β
I	A	×	β	×
J	A	×	β	×
~~K~~	~~A~~	~~×~~	~~α~~	~~×~~
L	A	A	β	α
M	A	×	α	×
N	A	×	α	×
~~P~~	~~A~~	~~×~~	~~β~~	~~×~~

13.3 Reduction of incompletely specified state table. The state table considered in the previous section is termed completely specified because each entry is fixed. There are situations in which certain entries in a state table are not prescribed, for example, Table 12.2, which corresponds to the parity-bit generator for BCD code.

The reduction procedure presented in the previous section for completely specified state tables can easily be applied to incompletely specified cases. To illustrate this transition, we continue Example 13.1 and try to reduce the state table in Table 12.2.

Table 12.2 is repeated in Table 13.5. Only two pairs of equivalent states are identified for discussion purposes. States H and K are equivalent. This is made possible by assigning, in row K, to the unspecified next state entry A and to the unspecified output entry β. If this is done, row H and row K become identical and consequently their corresponding states are equivalent. States P and L are made equivalent in the same fashion. Note that the same reductions were carried out when Table 13.1 was simplified. There was no question asked at that point. In fact, we were very happy to be able to find two rows which were identical. There is, however, a very interesting question that must be answered here. It is true that by assigning the unspecified entries in row K, states H and K become identical. We should ask, however: in doing this, have we overlooked some other assignments for the unspecified entries which will eventually lead to a better overall reduction?

TABLE 13.6(a)

B	BD CE													
C	BF CG	DF EG												
D	BH CI	DH EI	FH GI											
E	BJ CK	DJ EK	FJ GK	HJ IK										
F	BL CM	DL EM	FL GM	HL IM	JL KM									
G	BN CP	DN EP	FN GP	HN IP	JN KP	LN MP								
H	×	×	×	×	×	×	×							
I	×	×	×	×	×	×	×	×						
J	×	×	×	×	×	×	×	×	✓					
K	×	×	×	×	×	×	×	✓	×	×				
L	×	×	×	×	×	×	×	×	✓	✓	×			
M	×	×	×	×	×	×	×	✓	×	×	✓	×		
N	×	×	×	×	×	×	×	✓	×	×	✓	×	✓	
P	×	×	×	×	×	×	×	×	✓	✓	×	✓	×	×
	A	B	C	D	E	F	G	H	I	J	K	L	M	N

TABLE 13.6(b)

B	~~BD CE~~ ×													
C	~~BF CG~~ ×	~~DF EG~~ ×												
D	~~BH CI~~ ×	~~DH EI~~ ×	~~FH GI~~ ×											
E	~~BJ CK~~ ×	~~DJ EK~~ ×	~~FJ GK~~ ×	~~HJ IK~~ ×										
F	~~BL CM~~ ×	~~DL EM~~ ×	~~FL GM~~ ×	~~HL IM~~ ×	JL KM									
G	~~BN CP~~ ×	~~DN EP~~ ×	~~FN GP~~ ×	HN IP	~~JN KP~~ ×	~~LN MP~~ ×								
H	××	××	××	××	××	××	××							
I	××	××	××	××	××	××	××	××						
J	××	××	××	××	××	××	××	××	✓					
K	××	××	××	××	××	××	××	✓	××	××				
L	××	××	××	××	××	××	××	××	✓	✓	××			
M	××	××	××	××	××	××	××	✓	××	××	✓	××		
N	××	××	××	××	××	××	××	✓	××	××	✓	××	✓	
P	××	××	××	××	××	××	××	××	✓	✓	××	✓	××	××
	A	B	C	D	E	F	G	H	I	J	K	L	M	N

In order to effect the best reduction possible, we must first undertake an exhaustive search for all possible equivalences between existing states. For example, in Table 13.5, H can be considered equivalent to K. This is, however, only one of possibly many equivalences between K and other states. A systematic process is desirable to uncover all possible equivalences between states. With all possibilities listed, we are then in a better position to make an intelligent selection among them.

The systematic search for all possible equivalences can be illustrated by continuing Example 13.1. Note that the chart in Table 13.6(a) has as many cells as it has possible pairs between existing states in Table 13.5. The cell that is located in row B and column A is called the B-A cell. In the B-A cell, we record whether or not it is possible for states A and B to be equivalent. If so, what does it imply? This information can be obtained by comparing row A and row B in Table 13.5. The output pattern for row A is $(0, 0)$ and the output pattern for row B is also $(0, 0)$. Thus it is possible for A and B to be equivalent. The *necessary implications* for this equivalence are that B and D are equivalent, and C and E are also equivalent. This can be observed from the next state columns for A and B. This explains the entries in the B-A cell. By comparing row H with row A in Table 13.5, we see that their output patterns are different. It is absolutely impossible to group H and A together. This fact is denoted by placing a cross in the H-A cell. Since row J and row I are identical, these two states are equivalent without any implication, so a check mark is entered in the J-I cell. The entries in other cells are obtained in the same way.

To display all the information about possible equivalences between any pair of existing states, we examine the only cell in column N. Since a cross is present in the P-N cell, we know that P and N can never be equivalent. With this in mind, we examine all other cells to see if the equivalence between another pair depends on the equivalence of P and N. If there is any, a cross is entered in that cell to denote that it is impossible to establish equivalence between its two corresponding states. In the present problem, PN is not implied elsewhere. At the conclusion of this searching process, an additional cross is entered in the P-N cell.

Then we move left to column M. A check mark is found in the N-M cell. This means that states N and M can be made equivalent. Since the P-M cell is marked by a cross, a search has to be undertaken to see if MP is entered in other cells. A cross is entered in the G-F cell because of the presence of MP in the cell. Since no other cells contain MP as an entry, an additional cross is put in the P-M cell. This means that from now on this cell can be ignored. This process is continued until no single cross appears in any cell. The resultant table is shown in Table 13.6(b). Two identical charts are used to facilitate the understanding of the process. In practice, only one chart is actually needed.

TABLE 13.7

N	
M	MN
L	MN, PL
K	KMN, PL
J	KMN, JPL
I	KMN, $IJPL$
H	$HKMN$, $IJPL$
G	$HKMN$, $IJPL$
F	$HKMN$, $IJPL$
E	EF, $HKMN$, $IJPL$
D	DG, EF, $HKMN$, $IJPL$
C	DG, EF, $HKMN$, $IJPL$
B	DG, EF, $HKMN$, $IJPL$
A	DG, EF, $HKMN$, $IJPL$
Final	A, B, C, DG, EF, $HKMN$, $IJPL$

The next step in the reduction process is to extract all possible groupings among existing states. Each grouping consists of states which can be made equivalent. Let us start from the right-most column N; no grouping can be established. Accordingly, nothing is entered in row N of Table 13.7.

In column M, a possible grouping of MN is found. This is recorded in row M of Table 13.7. Note that in carrying out this process, we have to pay attention only to the cells which are void of crosses. In column L, another grouping involving states L and P is found. The entries in row L of Table 13.7 are MN and PL. They represent all possible groups found up to column L.

Column K of Table 13.6(b) reveals two possible groupings, namely MK and NK. The entries for row K would seem to be MK, NK, MN, and PL. However, the first three groupings suggest a grouping, KMN. Therefore, the entries in row K are KMN and PL. Using the same reasoning, the entries in row J are found to be KMN and JPL.

An examination of column I determines the entries in row I of Table 13.7 to be KMN, $IJPL$. Note that the new grouping $IJPL$ is formed, because column I suggests groupings IJ, IL, and IP. Since JPL already form a grouping, and the state I can be grouped with every state in the grouping, the new group $IJPL$ is formed.

The same reasoning is used to complete the entries in Table 13.7. The entries in the Final row of the table are obtained by listing all the entries in row A and all the states of the given state table which are missing from the entries in row A.

The next task is to select the groupings among those listed in the Final row. In carrying out this selection, we have to observe two rules. First, every state in the original state table has to be included in at least one grouping of the selection. Note that each grouping of the selection implies a state in the new state table. This requirement ensures that every state in the given table will be represented. It is also interesting to note that a given state of the original table may appear in more than one grouping of the selection.* Second, the groupings in the selection must be so chosen that all the *necessary implications* are satisfied. What this means is that if the equivalence among the states in a grouping depends on the equivalence of some other states, those states should belong to a grouping in the selection. For example, let us examine the Final row of Table 13.7 and Table 13.5. If the grouping EF is to be included in the selection, the states J and L must appear in a grouping of the selection. This is so because the equivalence between states E and F depends on the equivalence between states J and L. By the same reasoning, states K and M must also appear in a grouping of the selection.

Now we are in a position to continue Example 13.1. The first rule requires that every state in the given table has to be represented. Therefore, the selection will include every grouping listed in the Final row of Table 13.7. By examining Table 13.5, we realize that the equivalence of states D and G depends on the equivalence between H and N and the equivalence between I and P. The second rule requires that states I and P appear in one grouping and H and N appear in one grouping in the selection. Since I and P do appear in the grouping $IJPL$ and H and N do appear in $HKMN$, the necessary implications are satisfied for states D and G. Further examination will also show that the implications of states E and F are also satisfied. The selection is

$$A, B, C, DG, EF, HKMN, IJPL.$$

Each grouping is represented in the reduced table by a new state. The resultant state table is that shown in Table 13.2.

At this point, the reader might say that by using the simpler approach presented in the previous section, the same resultant state table can be obtained. Why must we follow this more complicated process? The reason is very simple. By following this exhaustive search process, we can rest assured that the unspecified entries in the state table are used to our best advantage. By following the method presented in the previous section, we might be haunted by the fear that we had not done the best we could, and in general, this fear might be quite justified.

The tabulation approach presented in this chapter is actually a general one. It is as applicable to reducing completely specified as well as unspecified state tables.

---

* The groupings of states are not disjoint.

This concludes Example 13.1. The state tables for parity-bit generators are reduced. Their implementation will be undertaken in Example 14.1.

13.4 Illustrative examples. Two examples will be presented to further demonstrate the application of the reduction methods presented in the previous two sections.

EXAMPLE 13.2. Continue the design of the sequential switching circuit specified in Example 12.2.

The state table for the specified sequential switching circuit is shown in Table 12.3 and repeated in Table 13.8.

TABLE 13.8

Present state	Next state		Output		New state	Next state	
	0	1	0	1		0	1
A	A	B	0	0	I	I	~~I~~ IV
B	~~C~~ A	D	0	0	~~I~~ IV	I	~~I~~ III
~~C~~	~~E A~~	~~F B~~	~~0~~	~~0~~			
D	~~G~~ ~~C~~ A	H	0	0	~~I~~ III	I	II
~~E~~	~~A~~	~~B~~	~~0~~	~~0~~			
~~F~~	~~C~~	~~D~~	~~0~~	~~0~~			
~~G~~	~~E A~~	~~F~~	~~0~~	~~0~~			
H	~~G~~ ~~C~~ A	H	0	1	II	I	II

The reduction process is initiated by locating identical rows. This eliminates states C, E, F, and G. After examining the remaining four rows, we realize that there are only two different output patterns, namely (0, 0) and (0, 1). An attempt is made to see if two states are enough to cover the remaining four. The tentative grouping is

$$\frac{\text{I}(0,\,0)}{A,\,B,\,D}\;\frac{\text{II}(0,\,1)}{H}\,. \tag{13.4a}$$

Substitutions are made in rows A, B, D, and H of Table 13.8. A contradiction is noticed in row D. Knowing that D cannot be grouped with A, B, we introduce a new state III. The grouping is

$$\frac{\text{I}(0,\,0)}{A.\,B}\;\frac{\text{II}(0,\,1)}{H}\;\frac{\text{III}(0,\,0)}{D}\,. \tag{13.4b}$$

A contradiction is subsequently noticed in row B. Another new state IV is introduced. The resultant grouping is

$$\frac{\text{I}(0,\,0)}{A}\ \frac{\text{II}(0,\,1)}{H}\ \frac{\text{III}(0,\,0)}{D}\ \frac{\text{IV}(0,\,0)}{B}. \tag{13.4c}$$

In other words, rows A, B, D, and H constitute the resultant state table.

The tabulation method is used to reduce the state table in Table 13.8. The chart for identifying equivalence between states is shown in Table 13.9(a). The presence of a cross in the H-G cell indicates that H and G

TABLE 13.9(a)

B	AC BD						
C	AE BF	CE DF					
D	AG BH	CG DH	EG FH				
E	✓	CA DB	EA FB	GA HB			
F	AC BD	✓	EC FD	GC HD	AC BD		
G	AE BF	CE DF	✓	GE HF	AE BF	CE DF	
H	×	×	×	×	×	×	×
	A	B	C	D	E	F	G

TABLE 13.9(b)

B	~~AC BD~~						
C	AE BF	~~CE DF~~					
D	~~AG BH~~	~~CG DH~~	~~EG FH~~				
E	✓	~~CA DB~~	EA FB	~~GA HB~~			
F	~~AC BD~~	✓	~~EC FD~~	~~GC HD~~	~~AC BD~~		
G	AE BF	~~CE DF~~	✓	~~GE HF~~	AE BF	~~CE DF~~	
H	××	××	××	××	××	××	××
	A	B	C	D	E	F	G

cannot be grouped together. Consequently any pair of states whose equivalence depends on the equivalence between H and G can never be represented by one state. Not only do we place an additional cross in the H-G cell, but we also place a cross in any cell which implies the equivalence between H and G. This process is continued until no cell is left with only one cross. This situation is shown in Table 13.9(b). In practice, only one chart is needed.

To extract possible groupings among states, we start from the right-most column G. No possible equivalence among states is found. Accordingly, nothing is entered in row G of Table 13.10. There is no entry made in row F of Table 13.10. Column E of Table 13.9(b) indicates that it is possible to establish the equivalence between states E and G; an entry, EG, is thus recorded in row E of Table 13.10. Column D produces no new entry. Column C of Table 13.9(b) suggests groupings CG and CE. Considering the already existing grouping EG, we enter in row C of Table 13.10 the grouping CGE. The listing in Table 13.10 is completed when columns B and A of Table 13.9(b) are examined.

TABLE 13.10

G	
F	
E	EG
D	EG
C	CGE
B	BF, CGE
A	BF, $ACGE$
Final	BF, $ACGE$, D, H

The state table in Table 12.3 has only two kinds of output patterns, namely (0, 0) and (0, 1). We, therefore, are tempted to try to select only two groupings, to be represented by two new states, among those listed in the Final row of Table 13.10. However, we immediately realize that no selection of two groupings can be made to satisfy the requirement that all states in the original table be represented in the new table. To satisfy this rule, the following selection is made:

$$B(BF),\ A(ACGE),\ D,\ H. \tag{13.5}$$

Now we must ascertain whether this selection satisfies all the necessary implications. An examination of Table 13.8 reveals that the equivalence between states B and F brings in no implication. Note, however, that the equivalence between states A and C demands that states A and E belong to one grouping in the selection, and states B and F belong to one grouping in the selection. This is accomplished in the selection in (13.5). Further examination shows that all other implications are satisfied.

The resultant state table is that shown in Table 13.8. ▲

EXAMPLE 13.3. Reduce the state table (Table 13.11) of a sequential circuit.

TABLE 13.11

Present state	Next state				Output			
	00	01	10	11	00	01	10	11
A	C	D	×	×	×	×	×	×
B	A	H	F	C	×	×	×	×
C	H	×	×	A	0	×	1	×
D	F	×	H	×	×	×	0	×
E	F	A	×	×	1	×	×	×
F	×	×	C	×	×	×	×	×
G	×	×	D	E	×	×	×	×
H	A	B	G	×	×	×	×	×

TABLE 13.12

B	AC DH						
C	CH	AH AC					
D	CF	AF FH	××				
E	CF AD	AF AH	××	✓			
F	✓	CF	✓	CH	✓		
G	✓	~~DF CE~~ ×	AE	DH	✓	~~CD~~ ×	
H	AC BD	~~FG~~ ×	AH	AF GH	AF AB	CG	DG
	A	B	C	D	E	F	G

A few attempts to reduce the given table by locating identical rows or comparing output patterns will convince us that the tabulation method should be employed. Furthermore, it is intended to use this example to bring out some important points in using the tabulation method to reduce a state table. The procedure to establish the table shown in Table 13.12 is routine. The approach to extract possible groupings employed in the previous two examples can certainly be used here. However, another approach will be introduced.

The extracting procedure is launched by assuming that all states in the given state table can be included in one and only one grouping. Note that this assumption is quite in line with our desire to include as many states in one grouping as possible.

Examination of column A of Table 13.12 does not reveal any contradiction of the assumption. It is so recorded in row A of Table 13.13. Column B of Table 13.12 reveals that state B cannot be grouped with either state G or H. This means there are at least two groupings of states. This is shown in row B of Table 13.13. Note that B does not appear with either G or H in the same grouping. Column C indicates that state C cannot be grouped together with states D or E. Therefore, four groupings are listed in row C of Table 13.13. Columns D and E do not produce any new grouping, because there is no crossed cell in these two columns. A cross is found in the G-F cell, which indicates that states F and G cannot appear jointly in any grouping. Row F of Table 13.13 lists the changes made. Column G of Table 13.12 does not initiate any new grouping. Since every state of the given state table is included in at least one grouping of row G, the listings in the Final row of Table 13.13 are the same as those in row G.

TABLE 13.13

A	$ABCDEFGH$
B	$ABCDEF$, $ACDEFGH$
C	$ABCF$, $ABDEF$, $ACFGH$, $ADEFGH$
D	$ABCF$, $ABDEF$, $ACFGH$, $ADEFGH$
E	$ABCF$, $ABDEF$, $ACFGH$, $ADEFGH$
F	$ABCF$, $ABDEF$, $ACFH$, $ACGH$, $ADEFH$, $ADEGH$
G	$ABCF$, $ABDEF$, $ACFH$, $ACGH$, $ADEFH$, $ADEGH$
Final	$ABCF$, $ABDEF$, $ACFH$, $ACGH$, $ADEFH$, $ADEGH$

Each grouping in the Final row is termed a *maximal compatible* of the given table. It is easy to understand that each grouping is termed a compatible, because it is possible to represent all the states by one state in the resultant state table. Each grouping is termed a maximal compatible, because it cannot include even a single additional state and still constitute a compatible. For example, the grouping $ABCF$ cannot include another state and still remain a compatible.

The next step is to make a selection from among the maximal compatibles. This selection has to cover every state of the given table and produce a state table which consists of a minimum number of states. From the two previous examples, we can see that this selection is essentially a cut-and-try process.

The state table in Table 13.11 exhibits only two output patterns, namely (0, ×, 1, ×) and (1, ×, 0, ×). Therefore, in starting the selection process, two groupings are selected.

There are many ways to pick two from those listed in the Final row of Table 13.13. *ABCF* and *DEGH* are chosen. *ABCF* is a maximal compatible listed. *DEGH* is formed by deleting *A* from the maximal compatible *ADEGH*, since *A* is already covered by *ABCF*. This deleting operation makes use of the fact that a portion of a compatible is also a compatible. Note that by choosing *ABCF* and *DEGH*, we have covered every state in Table 13.11. The remaining task is to examine whether all implications of these two groupings are satisfied.

Let us look first into the implications of *ABCF*. If the input combination is 00, the next states for *A*, *B*, *C*, and *F* are *C*, *A*, *H* and ×, respectively. Consequently *CAH* must appear in at least one grouping of the selection. Since this is not satisfied, we have to either replace *ABCF* by another grouping or introduce an additional grouping which contains *ACH*. The latter is undertaken. This is possible because *ACH* appears in the maximal compatibles found. The selection of groupings is *ABCF*, *DEGH*, *ACH*.

We should now continue to check the implications of *ABCF*. When the input combination is 01, the next states are *D*, *H*, ×, and ×. Since *DH* appears in the grouping *DEGH*, this implication is satisfied. The two other cases where the input combinations are 10 and 11 are then examined.

Since the implications of *ABCF* are all satisfied, we should then investigate the next states of *DEGH*. It is found that every one of the four next state groups appears in at least one of the groupings listed.

The implications of *ACH* are then checked. It is noted that when the input combination is 01, the next states are *D*, ×, and *B*. Since *BD* does not appear in any one of the groupings listed, we decide to introduce a new grouping *BD*. This is allowable because *BD* appears in the maximal compatible *ABDEF*. The selection of groupings is now expressed as *ABCF*, *DEGH*, *ACH*, and *BD*.

The implications of *ACH* are satisfied. Examination of *BD* initiates subsequent alterations. The final selection of groupings is

$$ACFH,\ ADEGH,\ ABDE, \text{ and } CG. \tag{13.6}$$

Note that certain states (for example, *A*) appear in more than one grouping and also that portions of certain maximal compatibles are entered in the final selection.

If we represent the grouping *ACFH* by 1, *ADEGH* by 2, *ABDE* by 3, and *CG* by 4, the reduced state table shown in Table 13.14 is obtained. Note that when the input combination is 11, the next state for state 1 can be state 1, state 2, or state 3. This can be explained by examining the

TABLE 13.14

Present state	Next state				Output			
	00	01	10	11	00	01	10	11
1	1	3	4	1, 2, 3	0	×	1	×
2	1	3	2	2, 3	1	×	0	×
3	1	2	1	1, 4	1	×	0	×
4	1, 2	1, 2, 3, 4	2, 3	2, 3	0	×	1	×

original state table (Table 13.11). The next states for *ACFH*, when the input combination is 11, are ×, *A*, ×, and ×. Since *A* appears in three groupings represented by 1, 2, 3, the next state entry can be any one of the three. However, the next state for state 1 is definitely 1, when the input combination is 00, because in this case the next states for *ACFH* are *C*, *H*, ×, and *A*, respectively, and *ACH* appears only in the grouping *ACFH*, which is represented by state 1. The other entries can be explained in the same way. ▲

PROBLEMS

13.1. Simplify the state table established in Problem 12.1 so that the number of rows contained in the table is a minimum.

13.2. Reduce the state table obtained in Problem 12.2 to one with the minimum number of rows.

13.3. Reduce the state table obtained in Problem 12.3 to one with the minimum number of rows.

13.4. Simplify the state table obtained in Problem 12.4 to one with the minimum number of rows.

13.5. Simplify the following state table.

Present state	Next state		Output	
	0	1	0	1
A	*C*	*D*	0	0
B	*B*	*B*	1	0
C	*B*	*G*	1	0
D	*E*	*F*	0	0
E	*B*	*A*	1	0
F	*C*	*D*	0	0
G	*E*	*F*	0	0

13.6. Reduce the state table obtained in Problem 12.5 to one with the minimum number of rows.

13.7. Reduce the state table obtained in Problem 12.6 to one with the minimum number of rows.

13.8. Reduce the state table derived in Problem 12.7 to one with the minimum number of rows.

13.9. Reduce the state table derived in Problem 12.8 to one with the minimum number of rows.

13.10. Simplify the following state table.

Present state	Next state		Output	
	0	1	0	1
A	G	B	0	0
B	F	I	1	1
C	H	E	1	0
D	F	C	1	1
E	G	C	1	0
F	D	E	1	1
G	A	F	0	0
H	G	B	0	0
I	A	E	1	0

13.11. Reduce the following state table to one with a minimum number of rows.

Present state	Next state				Output			
	00	01	11	10	00	01	11	10
A	A	D	×	G	0	×	0	×
B	×	D	E	×	×	1	0	1
C	×	B	K	F	1	1	1	×
D	D	×	G	×	0	×	×	1
E	D	×	G	A	0	0	×	1
F	×	×	I	J	1	×	×	1
G	D	×	G	A	×	×	×	1
H	D	×	I	J	1	×	0	×
I	×	H	I	J	1	×	×	1
J	D	H	×	J	×	×	0	1
K	×	A	A	×	0	×	0	×

13.12. Reduce the following state table to one with the minimum number of rows.

Present state	Next state				Output			
	00	01	11	10	00	01	11	10
A	B	×	×	D	0	×	×	1
B	×	C	×	×	×	0	×	0
C	A	×	×	×	×	×	0	0
D	×	H	×	×	1	×	×	×
E	×	×	G	×	0	1	×	×
F	×	×	×	A	×	×	×	×
G	×	D	×	×	×	×	1	1
H	×	×	×	K	×	0	×	×
I	E	×	×	×	0	×	1	×
J	×	×	F	×	×	×	0	×
K	×	I	×	×	×	×	×	0
L	J	×	×	×	×	1	×	1

CHAPTER 14

SEQUENTIAL CIRCUITS IV: STATE ASSIGNMENT AND THE COMPLETION OF DESIGN

14.1 Introduction. We have shown how a given set of specifications can be incorporated into a state table to facilitate the design of a synchronous sequential switching circuit with a finite number of states. Methods of reducing the number of states in a state table are also presented.

This chapter will show how a state table can be implemented. The implementation of the state table is, of course, the completion of the design of the sequential switching circuit. First, a memory is designed to realize the states specified in a state table. Then a combinational switching circuit is designed to ensure that proper state transitions are executed and outputs produced.

14.2 The design of the memory. The first step in the design of the memory is the determination of the number of binary storage devices to be used. We can determine this from the number of states in a given state table. The reader might conclude at this point that knowing the minimum number of binary storage devices needed would complete the first step in the design of the memory. This would be correct if the cost and performance of a sequential switching circuit were determined solely by the number of binary storages used. Unfortunately, the cost of the necessary combinational circuit must be taken into account. It can easily be seen that the number of binary storage devices employed influences the complexity of the necessary combinational circuit. There is, however, no conclusive evidence that the memory with the least number of binary storage devices always brings about the simplest combinational circuit, even though this is generally the case.

A cut-and-try approach is the only means available for determining the number of binary storage devices to be used. In the development which follows, we will use the least number of binary storage devices to implement a given state table, knowing that it generally represents a good choice, but not always the best.

EXAMPLE 14.1 Continue the design of the serial parity-bit generator specified in Example 13.1.

The state table for such a serial parity-bit generator for any four-bit code was established in Table 12.1 and then reduced to that shown in Table 13.2. In Table 12.1, there are fifteen states. Their implementation requires at least four flip-flops to provide the necessary fifteen bit combinations. (In using four flip-flops, there are actually sixteen bit combinations available.) The reduced state table (Table 13.2) has only seven states. Since three flip-flops are capable of providing eight bit combinations, the least number of flip-flops needed is three. The three flip-flops used are designated as X, Y, and Z.

It was stated before that one bit combination is used to represent one state. A bit combination is a set of bits stored in all the flip-flops of the memory. For example, if there are three flip-flops X, Y, and Z in the memory, the eight available bit combinations are

X	Y	Z
0	0	0
0	0	1
0	1	0
0	1	1
1	0	0
1	0	1
1	1	0
1	1	1

(14.1)

The bit combination 001 occurs when 0-bits are stored in X and Y, and a 1-bit is stored in Z. Whenever any specific bit combination prevails in the memory, the sequential circuit is in its corresponding state.

Let us pursue our example further. The eight bit combinations provided by flip-flops X, Y, and Z are available for implementing the seven states of Table 13.2. A new problem not encountered in the design of counters arises. How do we assign seven of the eight available bit combinations to the seven states? This operation of assigning bit combinations to states is termed state assignment. It is true that no matter how state assignment is done, the memory will have three flip-flops, but for each specific state assignment scheme a corresponding combinational swithcing circuit will have to be designed. It is, therefore, very easy to see that we must try to make a state assignment such that the corresponding combinational switching circuit will be the best in every respect. Unfortunately, a systematic method for arriving at such a state assignment scheme has yet to be found. There are, however, several helpful guide lines toward a good state assignment scheme. These guide lines will be presented in this chapter.

Let us continue Example 14.1 and try the following state assignment scheme:

$$\begin{array}{rccc} A & 0 & 0 & 0 \\ B & 0 & 0 & 1 \\ C & 0 & 1 & 0 \\ D & 0 & 1 & 1 \\ E & 1 & 0 & 0 \\ H & 1 & 0 & 1 \\ I & 1 & 1 & 0 \\ \text{Unused} & 1 & 1 & 1 \end{array} \tag{14.2}$$

Out of many possible assignment schemes, this one is arbitrarily chosen to illustrate once again how the corresponding combinational switching circuit is designed when a state assignment scheme is given. Furthermore, it will be used to demonstrate the effectiveness of the guide lines presented later.

Replacing the states with their respective bit combinations, we obtain from Table 13.2 the state table in Table 14.1. The design procedure from here on has already been presented in Section 11.4.

The remaining task is the design of a combinational switching circuit which has four input variables W_n, X_n, Y_n, and Z_n, and eight outputs R^X, S^X, R^Y, S^Y, R^Z, S^Z, α, and β. As an example, let us try to find R^X, the switching function of the reset terminal of flip-flop X. This can be accomplished by examining the X_n column and the two X_{n+1} columns in Table 14.1. Note that when W_n, X_n, Y_n, and Z_n are 0, X_{n+1} is 0. Since X_n is 0 already, R^X can be either 0 or 1. m_0 is entered as a don't-care condition. When W_n, X_n, Y_n, Z_n are 0, 1, 0, and 1, respectively, X_{n+1} should be 0, according to Table 14.1. Since X_n is 1, R^X must be 1 to

TABLE 14.1

Present state			Next state						Output	
			$W_n = 0$			$W_n = 1$			$W_n = 0$	$W_n = 1$
X_n	Y_n	Z_n	X_{n+1}	Y_{n+1}	Z_{n+1}	X_{n+1}	Y_{n+1}	Z_{n+1}		
0	0	0	0	0	1	0	1	0	0	0
0	0	1	0	1	1	1	0	0	0	0
0	1	0	1	0	0	0	1	1	0	0
0	1	1	1	0	1	1	1	0	0	0
1	0	0	1	1	0	1	0	1	0	0
1	0	1	0	0	0	0	0	0	α	β
1	1	0	0	0	0	0	0	0	β	α

R^X

W_nX_n \ Y_nZ_n	00	01	11	10
00	X	X	0	0
01	0	1	X	1
11	0	1	X	1
10	X	0	0	X

S^X

W_nX_n \ Y_nZ_n	00	01	11	10
00	0	0	1	1
01	X	0	X	0
11	X	0	X	0
10	0	1	1	0

R^Y

W_nX_n \ Y_nZ_n	00	01	11	10
00	X	0	1	1
01	0	X	X	1
11	X	X	X	1
10	0	X	0	0

S^Y

W_nX_n \ Y_nZ_n	00	01	11	10
00	0	1	0	0
01	1	0	X	0
11	0	0	X	0
10	1	0	X	X

R^Z

W_nX_n \ Y_nZ_n	00	01	11	10
00	0	0	0	X
01	X	1	X	X
11	0	1	X	X
10	X	1	1	0

S^Z

W_nX_n \ Y_nZ_n	00	01	11	10
00	1	X	X	0
01	0	0	X	0
11	1	0	X	0
10	0	0	0	1

FIGURE 14.1

ensure that X_{n+1} will be 0. Therefore, m_5 is a term in R^X. After every 0 in the two X_{n+1} columns is taken care of, the following switching function is obtained:

$$R^X(W_n, X_n, Y_n, Z_n) = m_5 + m_6 + m_{13} + m_{14}, \qquad (14.3)$$

$$\text{don't-care conditions: } m_0,\ m_1,\ m_8,\ m_{10},\ m_7, \text{ or } m_{15}.$$

The first four don't-care conditions, m_0, m_1, m_8, and m_{10}, are obtained from Table 14.1. The remaining two don't-care conditions, m_7 and m_{15}, are included because the bit combination 111 which corresponds to $X_n = 1$, $Y_n = 1$, and $Z_n = 1$ is not used in the present assignment scheme.

Switching functions for other output variables can likewise be established. Approaches to simplify such a set of switching functions are presented in Chapter 9.

The maps in Fig. 14.1 are used to obtain the following set of switching functions (α_n and β_n are obtained directly from Table 14.1):

$$\begin{aligned}
R^X &= X_nZ_n + X_nY_n,\\
S^X &= W_nX_n'Z_n + W_n'X_n'Y_n,\\
R^Y &= W_n'Y_n + X_nY_n,\\
S^Y &= W_n'X_n'Y_n'Z_n + W_n'X_nY_n'Z_n' + W_nX_n'Z_n',\\
R^Z &= X_nZ_n + W_nZ_n,\\
S^Z &= W_n'X_n'Y_n' + W_nX_nY_n'Z_n' + W_nX_n'Y_nZ_n',\\
\alpha_n &= W_n'X_nY_n'Z_n + W_nX_nY_nZ_n',\\
\beta_n &= W_nX_nY_n'Z_n + W_n'X_nY_nZ_n'.
\end{aligned} \qquad (14.4)$$

If we adopt the state assignment scheme in (14.2), we will have to implement the switching functions in (14.4).

14.3 Useful considerations. Even though the implementation of the switching functions (14.4) will complete the design, we are not yet ready to do it. By adopting the considerations which will be presented in this section, we may be able to obtain a better assignment scheme, so that its corresponding set of switching functions to be implemented is much simpler than (14.4).

W_nX_n \ Y_nZ_n	00	01	11	10
00	A	B	D	C
01	E	H	X	I
11	E	H	X	I
10	A	B	D	C

(a)

W_nX_n \ Y_nZ_n	00	01	11	10
00	B	D	H	E
01	I	A	X	A
11	H	A	X	A
10	C	E	I	D

(b)

FIG. 14.2. (a) Present state map (P-map). (b) Next state map (N-map).

To bring about a better state assignment scheme, we construct the two maps in Fig. 14.2. The present state map, P-map, is actually a graphical display of the state assignment scheme made in (14.2). For example, the bit combination 000 is used to realize state A; therefore, two areas, 0000 and 1000, are labeled A. The first bit is W, the input, and the last three bits are X, Y, and Z, respectively. The bit combination 111 is not used, and the two areas 0111 and 1111 are labeled X, which represents a don't-care condition. We might ask whether a P-map of three variables X, Y, and Z would do if the graphical display of the state assignment scheme only is wanted. Why is the input variable W involved? The input variable W is introduced in the P-map so that a next state map, called the N-map, can be established.

The N-map is derived from the P-map. The entries on the N-map are determined by the state table (Table 13.2). For example, the area 0000 in the P-map is labeled A. By examining the first row of Table 13.2, we see that when the present state is A and the input W is 0, the next state is B; therefore, the corresponding area on the N-map is labeled B. Other entries on the N-map can be explained in the same way. At this time, we will of course ask: What use can we make of the P-map and its corresponding N-map? They have been established to show how the state assignment scheme of (14.2) can be improved.

Note that on the N-map, state A appears in four areas. Each area, of course, represents an input combination at t_n which will transfer the state of the circuit to A at t_{n+1}. Since state A is represented by the bit combination 000, X_{n+1}, Y_{n+1}, and Z_{n+1} will be 0 whenever any one of the four input combinations prevails. This means that every one of the corresponding four standard products of these four areas will either be in the expression or appear as don't-care conditions for R^X, R^Y, and R^Z. If we reexamine the maps for R^X, R^Y, and R^Z in Fig. 14.1, we see that every one of the four areas 0101, 0110, 1101, and 1110 is labeled either 1 or X. The fact that A appears in four areas of the N-map is dictated by the state table, and we can do nothing about it. We can, however, decide where these four areas should be.

If the four areas of the N-map where A appears are adjacent and form a rectangle, they will contribute to the simplification of switching functions for R^X, R^Y, and R^Z. The assignment scheme of (14.2) does not place these four areas within a rectangle. This is why, for example, the switching function for R^X has two terms of two literals each, instead of one term of two literals, as it would if these four areas actually formed a rectangle. What must we do to make these four areas form a rectangle? The answer is found by examining the two maps in Fig. 14.2. On the N-map, A appears in areas 0101 and 1101, because A is the next state of H. A also appears in areas 0110 and 1110, because A is the next state of I. In order to arrange the four A-labeled areas in the N-map so that they will form a rectangle, we have to make H-labeled and I-labeled areas in the P-map adjacent and form a rectangle. This can be achieved by assigning to states H and I bit combinations which differ in only one variable. In other words, states H and I are to be given adjacent assignments.

By generalizing what we have observed in this example about state assignment, we put forward the following simple rule.

Rule 1. *Two or more states which have the same next state should be given adjacent assignments.*

To find the states which have the same next state is a very simple matter. This can be accomplished from the following tabulation:

A	H, I
B	A
C	A
D	B, C
E	B, C
H	D, E
I	D, E

(14.5)

The left-hand column lists the next states and the right-hand column lists the present states. For example, if the present state is either H or I, the next state is A. The tabulation (14.5) clearly shows that the states in each of the following groups should be given adjacent assignments:

$$(B, C),\ (D, E),\ (H, I). \tag{14.6}$$

By making use of Rule 1, we can simplify the switching circuit of every flip-flop employed in the memory. In the above example, by giving states H and I adjacent assignments, we can expect to simplify the switching functions for R^X, R^Y, and R^Z.

We can employ the same reasoning which produced Rule 1 to arrive at the following rule.

Rule 2. Two or more states which are the next states of a state should be given adjacent assignment.

Note that those states which are the next states of a state are adjacent on the N-map. For example, from Table 13.2, we see that both B and C are the next states of A, and they are adjacent on the N-map in Fig. 14.2. If these states are given adjacent assignments, we can expect that the combinational switching circuits for all except one flip-flop will be simplified.

To find states which claim to be the next states of a state is a trivial operation. They can be detected by simply examining each row of a given state table. For the present problem, Table 13.2 suggests the following group, according to Rule 2:

$$(B, C),\ (D, E),\ (H, I). \tag{14.7}$$

In this particular example, the groupings of states recommended by Rule 1 and Rule 2 are the same. This is not always the case, because the effectiveness of Rule 1 is more extensive than that of Rule 2. The grouping scheme suggested by Rule 1 takes precedence over that suggested by Rule 2.

Following the grouping scheme suggested by both (14.6) and (14.7), we propose the following state assignment scheme:

A	0	0	0
B	0	0	1
C	0	1	1
D	1	1	1
E	1	1	0
H	1	0	0
I	1	0	1
Unused	0	1	0

(14.8)

Note that (B, C), (D, E), and (H, I) are all given adjacent assignments.

TABLE 14.2

Present state			Next state						Output	
			$W_n = 0$			$W_n = 1$				
X_n	Y_n	Z_n	X_{n+1}	Y_{n+1}	Z_{n+1}	X_{n+1}	Y_{n+1}	Z_{n+1}	$W_n = 0$	$W_n = 1$
0	0	0	0	0	1	0	1	1	0	0
0	0	1	1	1	1	1	1	0	0	0
0	1	1	1	1	0	1	1	1	0	0
1	1	1	1	0	0	1	0	1	0	0
1	1	0	1	0	1	1	0	0	0	0
1	0	0	0	0	0	0	0	0	α	β
1	0	1	0	0	0	0	0	0	β	α

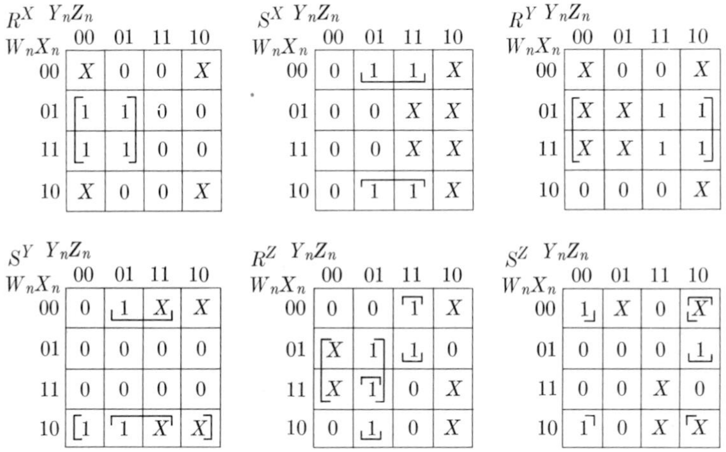

R^X

W_nX_n \ Y_nZ_n	00	01	11	10
00	X	0	0	X
01	1	1	0	0
11	1	1	0	0
10	X	0	0	X

S^X

W_nX_n \ Y_nZ_n	00	01	11	10
00	0	1	1	X
01	0	0	X	X
11	0	0	X	X
10	0	1	1	X

R^Y

W_nX_n \ Y_nZ_n	00	01	11	10
00	X	0	0	X
01	X	X	1	1
11	X	X	1	1
10	0	0	0	X

S^Y

W_nX_n \ Y_nZ_n	00	01	11	10
00	0	1	X	X
01	0	0	0	0
11	0	0	0	0
10	1	1	X	X

R^Z

W_nX_n \ Y_nZ_n	00	01	11	10
00	0	0	1	X
01	X	1	1	0
11	X	1	0	X
10	0	1	0	X

S^Z

W_nX_n \ Y_nZ_n	00	01	11	10
00	1	X	0	X
01	0	0	0	1
11	0	0	X	0
10	1	0	X	X

FIGURE 14.3

Replacing the states with their respective bit combinations, we obtain from Table 13.2 the state table in Table 14.2. We can then use Table 14.2 to establish the maps for R^X, S^X, R^Y, S^Y, R^Z, S^Z, shown in Fig. 14.3. A set of switching functions for the multiterminal combinational switching circuit is then obtained:

$$\begin{aligned}
R^X &= X_nY_n', & S^X &= X_n'Z_n, \\
R^Y &= X_n, & S^Y &= W_nX_n' + X_n'Z_n, \qquad (14.9)\\
R^Z &= X_nY_n' + W_nY_n'Z_n + W_n'Y_nZ_n, & S^Z &= X_n'Z_n' + W_n'Y_nZ_n', \\
\alpha_n &= W_n'X_nY_n'Z_n' + W_nX_nY_n'Z_n, & \beta_n &= W_nX_nY_n'Z_n' + W_n'X_nY_n'Z_n.
\end{aligned}$$

If we compare the set of switching functions in (14.9) with that in (14.4), we see immediately that the state assignment scheme in (14.8) is better than that in (14.2), because the former requires a much simpler combinational switching circuit.

We do not, however, want to create the impression that by following Rules 1 and 2, a unique state assignment scheme will automatically be reached. As a matter of fact, under the guidance of Rules 1 and 2, we can generally find many state assignment schemes.

The state assignment scheme of (14.8) satisfies both (14.6) and (14.7). The scheme shown below also possesses that same quality:

$$\begin{array}{rccc} A & 0 & 0 & 0 \\ B & 0 & 1 & 0 \\ C & 0 & 1 & 1 \\ D & 1 & 1 & 1 \\ E & 1 & 1 & 0 \\ H & 1 & 0 & 0 \\ I & 1 & 0 & 1 \\ \text{Unused} & 0 & 0 & 1 \end{array} \tag{14.10}$$

The substitution of the assignment scheme of (14.10) into Table 13.2 yields the state table in Table 14.3. The maps for R^X, S^X, R^Y, S^Y, R^Z, and S^Z shown in Fig. 14.4, are established from Table 14.3. A set of switching functions is obtained:

$$\begin{aligned} R^X &= Y'_n, & S^X &= Y_n, \\ R^Y &= X_n, & S^Y &= X'_n, \\ R^Z &= X_nY'_n + W'_nZ_n, & S^Z &= W_nX'_nY'_n + W'_nY_nZ'_n, \\ \alpha_n &= W'_nX_nY'_nZ'_n + W_nX_nY'_nZ_n, & \beta_n &= W_nX_nY'_nZ'_n + W'_nX_nY'_nZ_n. \end{aligned} \tag{14.11}$$

TABLE 14.3

Present state			Next state						Output	
			$W_n = 0$			$W_n = 1$			$W_n = 0$	$W_n = 1$
X_n	Y_n	Z_n	X_{n+1}	Y_{n+1}	Z_{n+1}	X_{n+1}	Y_{n+1}	Z_{n+1}		
0	0	0	0	1	0	0	1	1	0	0
0	1	0	1	1	1	1	1	0	0	0
0	1	1	1	1	0	1	1	1	0	0
1	1	1	1	0	0	1	0	1	0	0
1	1	0	1	0	1	1	0	0	0	0
1	0	0	0	0	0	0	0	0	α	β
1	0	1	0	0	0	0	0	0	β	α

R^X

W_nX_n \ Y_nZ_n	00	01	11	10
00	X	X	0	0
01	1	1	0	0
11	1	1	0	0
10	X	X	0	0

S^X

W_nX_n \ Y_nZ_n	00	01	11	10
00	0	X	1	1
01	0	0	X	X
11	0	0	X	X
10	0	X	1	1

R^Y

W_nX_n \ Y_nZ_n	00	01	11	10
00	0	X	0	0
01	X	X	1	1
11	X	X	1	1
10	0	X	0	0

S^Y

W_nX_n \ Y_nZ_n	00	01	11	10
00	1	X	X	X
01	0	0	0	0
11	0	0	0	0
10	1	X	X	X

R^Z

W_nX_n \ Y_nZ_n	00	01	11	10
00	X	X	1	0
01	X	1	1	0
11	X	1	0	X
10	0	X	0	X

S^Z

W_nX_n \ Y_nZ_n	00	01	11	10
00	0	X	0	1
01	0	0	0	1
11	0	0	X	0
10	1	X	X	0

FIGURE 14.4

Since the set of switching functions of (14.11) is the simplest among the three we have found so far, the state assignment scheme of (14.10) is better than the two previously attempted. Note that it is obtained through a cut-and-try process, and we have no way of telling whether the assignment scheme of (14.10) is the best that can be made. Before the set of switching functions of (14.11) is implemented, another assignment approach will be introduced in the next section.

14.4 Partition approach.* In the previous section, two rules are presented which can be used as guide lines to reach a state assignment scheme. The basic idea used in arriving at the two rules is to assign proper bit combinations to the states so that extensive simplifications of the resultant switching functions can be executed.

In this section, another method will be introduced. The basic idea of the new approach is this: the state assignment should be made in such a way that each bit of the next state depends on as few bits of the present state as possible. Applying this basic idea to Example 14.1, we will try to find a state assignment scheme such that X_{n+1}, Y_{n+1}, or Z_{n+1}, the bits of the next state, will depend on as few bits as possible in X_n, Y_n, and Z_n, the bits of the present state. Once this is achieved, the corresponding set of switching functions for the multiterminal combinational switching

* HA 2, ST 1, HA 3, and CU 2.

circuit will be quite simple. This new method must still seem very vague, but it will become clear as the presentation progresses.

To achieve the assignment scheme specified above, we introduce the *operation of partition*. The operation of partition is the distribution of all the states of a sequential switching circuit into blocks. Each state of the sequential circuit belongs to one and only one block.* The collection of all the blocks in an operation of partition is termed the partition, designated as P. For example, the serial parity-bit generator to be designed in Example 14.1 has seven states: A, B, C, D, E, H, and I. It is by itself a partition, because we can consider that each state forms a block. If we put states B and C into a block, D and E into another block, and H and I into another block, another partition is formed. This can be represented by the notation

$$P_1 = (A; \overline{B, C}; \overline{D, E}; \overline{H, I}). \tag{14.12}$$

It is clear that with a given set of states, numerous forms of partition can be achieved. In order to help ourselves find the state assignment scheme specified previously in this section, we look for partitions which have the *substitution property*. A partition of a sequential switching circuit is said to possess the substitution property if any two states of a block, under any possible input combination, yield the next two states which also belong to a simple block of the same partition. The partition of (14.12) for Example 14.1 has the substitution property. From Table 13.2, we see that when the input is 0, the next states for B and C are D and E, respectively. Note that B and C belong to a block of the partition, and D and E belong to a block of the partition. This is not enough, however, to claim that the partition of (14.12) has the substitution property with respect to Table 13.2. We must see if the next states of B and C, when the input is 1, belong to a block. This checking process has to be continued for every pair of states in every block of the partition.

Before showing how we can find a given sequential switching circuit partition with the substitution property, it will be worthwhile to demonstrate how such a partition can help us reach a desirable state assignment scheme. This will be done by continuing Example 14.1. For this problem, three schemes have already been proposed. We want to see if the partition method will render a better scheme.

Note that the partition of (14.12) has four blocks. We can use two of three available bits to form four combinations to represent the four blocks. Since no block in the partition has more than two states, the remaining 1-bit can be used to distinguish the two states in a block. One possible

* For relaxation of this restriction see ST 1.

state assignment scheme is then proposed:

$$\begin{array}{cccc} A & 0 & 0 & X \\ B & 0 & 1 & 0 \\ C & 0 & 1 & 1 \\ D & 1 & 1 & 1 \\ E & 1 & 1 & 0 \\ H & 1 & 0 & 0 \\ I & 1 & 0 & 1 \end{array} \tag{14.13}$$

Note that the first two bits are used to form four combinations: 00, 01, 11, and 10. Each of them is employed to represent one block. The third bit is used to distinguish the two states within a block. Since there is only one state in the 00 block, state A can be either 000 or 001.

The partition of (14.12) suggests the assignment scheme of (14.13). We consider the assignment scheme of (14.13) promising, because the partition of (14.12) has the substitution property. With the substitution property available, the first two bits of the next state can be determined solely from the first two bits of the present state and the input. In other words, X_{n+1} or Y_{n+1} will be a function of only X_n, Y_n, and W_n, where X, Y, and Z are the three bits and W is the input. With this knowledge, we can see that R^X, R^Y, S^X, and S^Y will be, at most, functions of three variables, X_n, Y_n, and W_n, instead of the four possible.

TABLE 14.4

Present state			Next state						Output	
			$W_n = 0$			$W_n = 1$			$W_n = 0$	$W_n = 1$
X_n	Y_n	Z_n	X_{n+1}	Y_{n+1}	Z_{n+1}	X_{n+1}	Y_{n+1}	Z_{n+1}		
0	0	X	0	1	0	0	1	1	0	0
0	1	0	1	1	1	1	1	0	0	0
0	1	1	1	1	0	1	1	1	0	0
1	1	1	1	0	0	1	0	1	0	0
1	1	0	1	0	1	1	0	0	0	0
1	0	0	0	0	X	0	0	X	α	β
1	0	1	0	0	X	0	0	X	β	α

Substituting the assignment scheme of (14.13) into Table 13.2, the state table in Table 14.4 is obtained. The maps for R^X, S^X, R^Y, S^Y, R^Z, and S^Z shown in Fig. 14.5 are established from Table 14.4. Note that the first row of Table 14.4 actually implies two rows, because the bit combination of the present state can be either 000 or 001. By proper grouping, the

R^X

W_nX_n \ Y_nZ_n	00	01	11	10
00	X	X	0	0
01	1	1	0	0
11	1	1	0	0
10	X	X	0	0

S^X

W_nX_n \ Y_nZ_n	00	01	11	10
00	0	0	1	1
01	0	0	X	X
11	0	0	X	X
10	0	0	1	1

R^Y

W_nX_n \ Y_nZ_n	00	01	11	10
00	0	0	0	0
01	X	X	1	1
11	X	X	1	1
10	0	0	0	0

S^Y

W_nX_n \ Y_nZ_n	00	01	11	10
00	1	1	X	X
01	0	0	0	0
11	0	0	0	0
10	1	1	X	X

R^Z

W_nX_n \ Y_nZ_n	00	01	11	10
00	X	1	1	0
01	X	X	1	0
11	X	X	0	X
10	0	0	0	X

S^Z

W_nX_n \ Y_nZ_n	00	01	11	10
00	0	0	0	1
01	X	X	0	1
11	X	X	X	0
10	1	X	X	0

FIGURE 14.5

following set of switching functions is obtained:

$$
\begin{aligned}
R^X &= Y'_n, \\
S^X &= Y_n, \\
R^Y &= X_n, \\
S^Y &= X'_n, \\
R^Z &= W'_n Z_n, \\
S^Z &= W_n Y'_n + W'_n Y_n Z'_n, \\
\alpha_n &= W'_n X_n Y'_n Z'_n + W_n X_n Y'_n Z_n, \\
\beta_n &= W_n X_n Y'_n Z'_n + W'_n X_n Y'_n Z_n.
\end{aligned}
\tag{14.14}
$$

The set of switching functions of (14.14) is simpler than that of (14.11). It is very interesting to compare the assignment scheme of (14.13) with that of (14.10).

The above presentation demonstrates that a proper partition with the substitution property does help us to reach a favorable state assignment scheme. The question now is: Given a state table of a sequential switching circuit, how do we find a partition with the substitution property?

The method used to find a partition with the substitution property, if any, is simple, but tedious. It is carried out by following the definition of the substitution property. Let us try to find possible partitions with the substitution property for Table 13.2.

A pair of states, say A and B, is chosen. In other words, we are attempting to see if there is any partition in which A and B belong to one block and which has the substitution property. This is recorded in row 1 of (14.15):

$$\begin{array}{ll} 1 & \overline{A, B} \\ 2 & \overline{A, B, D}; \quad \overline{C, E} \\ 3 & \overline{A, B, D, H}; \overline{C, E, I} \\ 4 & \overline{A, B, C, D, E, H, I} \end{array} \tag{14.15}$$

If the input is 0, the next states for A and B are B and D, respectively. According to the definition of the substitution property, B and D must also belong to a block. Since B and A are already assumed to be in one block, A, B, and D must all belong to one block. If the input is 1, the next states for A and B are C and E, respectively; C and E must also belong to one block. The result is summarized in row 2 of (14.15).

The next states for B and D are found from Table 13.2. The resultant grouping is shown in row 3 of (14.15).

The next states for D and H are then identified. The result, shown in row 4 of (14.15), indicates a trivial partition with the substitution property.

After the failure of this attempt, we should continue our search by picking another pair of states. It becomes obvious now that this searching process is indeed quite tedious.

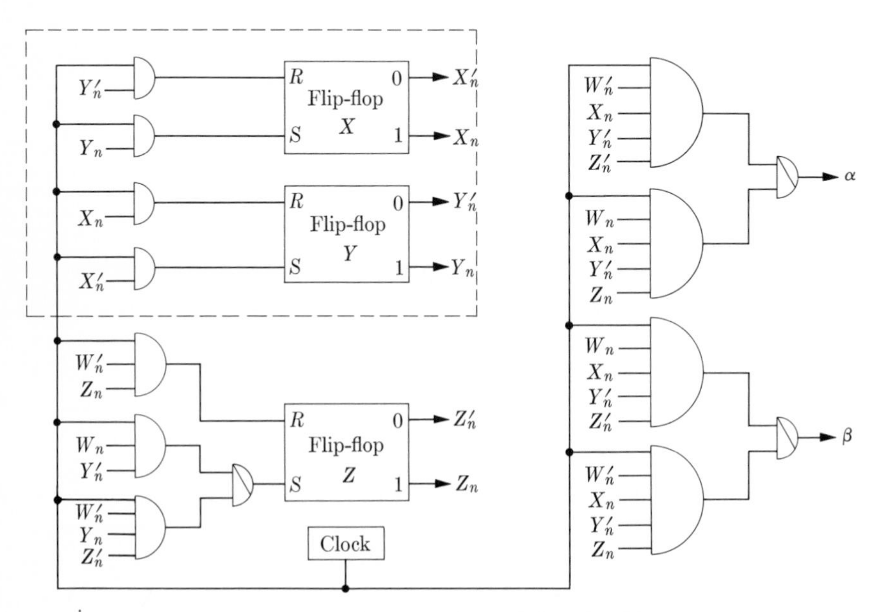

FIG. 14.6. Symbolic diagram of a serial parity-bit generator.

The same trivial result is obtained when the starting pair has A as a member. Let us now try a pair involving B and C. The steps are tabulated below:

$$\begin{array}{ll} 1 & \overline{B, C} \\ 2 & \overline{B, C};\ \overline{D, E} \\ 3 & \overline{B, C};\ \overline{D, E};\ \overline{H, I} \\ 4 & \overline{B, C};\ \overline{D, E};\ \overline{H, I};\ \overline{A} \end{array} \tag{14.16}$$

The final result is the partition of (14.12).

The complete design of the serial parity-bit generator is shown in Fig. 14.6. Since the partition of (14.12) is employed, and since the first two bits X and Y are used to represent the four blocks in that partition, the operation of the portion enclosed by the dashed lines in Fig. 14.6 is independent of the rest of the sequential circuit.* This completes Example 14.1 and the design of the serial parity-bit generator. ▲

14.5 Illustrative examples. Several guide lines have been presented in the previous two sections to help us in the search for a state assignment scheme which will produce an optimum resultant circuit. Two more examples will be presented in this section.

TABLE 14.5

Present state	Next state		Output	
	0	1	0	1
A	A	B	0	0
B	A	D	0	0
D	A	H	0	0
H	A	H	0	1

EXAMPLE 14.2. Continue the design of the sequential switching circuit specified in Example 12.2.

The state table for the specified sequential switching circuit is established in Table 12.3 and reduced in Table 13.8. The resultant state table is Table 14.5.

* An interesting approach is to decompose a sequential circuit into several cascaded subcircuits. See GI 5 and YO 1. Another approach can be found in AR 1.

Following the rules established in Section 14.3, this tabulation is established from Table 14.5:

Next states	Present states
A	A, B, D, H
B	A
D	B
H	D, H

(14.17)

The following assignment scheme is respondent to the suggestions which we can draw from (14.17):

A	0	0
B	0	1
D	1	0
H	1	1

(14.18)

Since only two flip-flops are used, the effect of using the considerations presented in the previous two sections is not noticeable.

TABLE 14.6

Present state		Next state				Output, Z	
		$W_n = 0$		$W_n = 1$			
X_n	Y_n	X_{n+1}	Y_{n+1}	X_{n+1}	Y_{n+1}	$W_n = 0$	$W_n = 1$
0	0	0	0	0	1	0	0
0	1	0	0	1	0	0	0
1	0	0	0	1	1	0	0
1	1	0	0	1	1	0	1

T^X X_nY_n

W_n	00	01	11	10
0	0	0	[1	1]
1	0	1	0	0

T^Y X_nY_n

W_n	00	01	11	10
0	0	[1	1]	0
1	[1]	1]	0	[1

FIGURE 14.7

Substituting (14.18) into Table 14.5, we obtain Table 14.6. We further specify that two T-type flip-flops be used. The switching functions for the two flip-flops, X and Y, are obtained by establishing the maps for T^X and T^Y shown in Fig. 14.7, from Table 14.6 and subsequent grouping. The

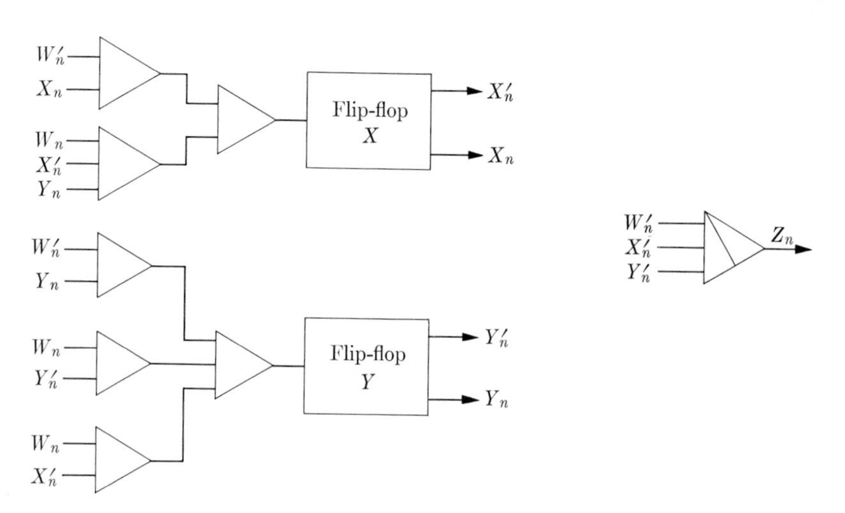

FIG. 14.8. Symbolic diagram of the sequential switching circuit specified in Example 12.2.

TABLE 14.7

Present state	Next state				Output			
	00	01	11	10	00	01	11	10
1	1	3	1, 2, 3	4	0	×	×	1
2	1	3	2, 3	2	1	×	×	0
3	1	2	1, 4	1	1	×	×	0
4	1, 2	1, 2, 3, 4	2, 3	2, 3	0	×	×	1

switching function for the output Z is obtained by inspection:

$$\begin{aligned} T^X &= W'_n X_n + W_n X'_n Y_n, \\ T^Y &= W'_n Y_n + W_n Y'_n + W_n X'_n, \qquad (14.19) \\ Z_n &= W_n X_n Y_n. \end{aligned}$$

The implementation of the set of switching functions in (14.19) completes the design. The completed symbolic diagram is shown in Fig. 14.8. Note that clock pulses are omitted. ▲

EXAMPLE 14.3. Implement the state table shown in Table 13.14 with T-type flip-flops and diode gates.

The state table in Table 13.14 is redrawn in Table 14.7. This example is interesting because the designer has the opportunity and the responsibility of making judicious use of the optional next states available.

TABLE 14.8

Present state	Next state $A_{n+1}B_{n+1}$				Output			
A_n B_n	$x^1 = 0$ $x^2 = 0$	$x^1 = 0$ $x^2 = 1$	$x^1 = 1$ $x^2 = 1$	$x^1 = 1$ $x^2 = 0$	$x^1 = 0$ $x^2 = 0$	$x^1 = 0$ $x^2 = 1$	$x^1 = 1$ $x^2 = 1$	$x^1 = 1$ $x^2 = 0$
0 0	0 0	1 1	0 0 0 1 1 0	1 0	0	×	×	1
0 1	0 0	1 1	0 1 1 0	0 1	1	×	×	0
1 1	0 0	0 1	0 0 1 0	0 0	1	×	×	0
1 0	0 0 0 1	0 0 0 1 1 1 1 0	0 1 1 0	0 1 1 0	0	×	×	1

The partition approach is first attempted. Since there are four states to be implemented, it is certainly desirable to have a partition with the substitution property which has two blocks and each block contains two states. If this partition scheme is attainable, one flip-flop can then be used to differentiate the two blocks and another flip-flop used to differentiate the two states within each block. After an exhaustive search, this partition scheme is found to be nonexistent.

Since the state table has only four states, the guide lines developed in Section 14.3 do not offer much help in making the state assignment. The following assignment scheme is attempted:

$$\begin{array}{cc} 1 & 00 \\ 2 & 01 \\ 3 & 11 \\ 4 & 10 \end{array} \tag{14.20}$$

Table 14.8 is obtained by substituting (14.20) into Table 14.7. The first step to obtain switching functions for the two flip-flops A and B is to establish the maps shown in Fig. 14.9 for T^A and T^B.

The entries in cells which correspond to unique next states are established in a routine fashion. The entries for the ?-marked cells demand careful consideration. The ?-marked cells correspond to optional next

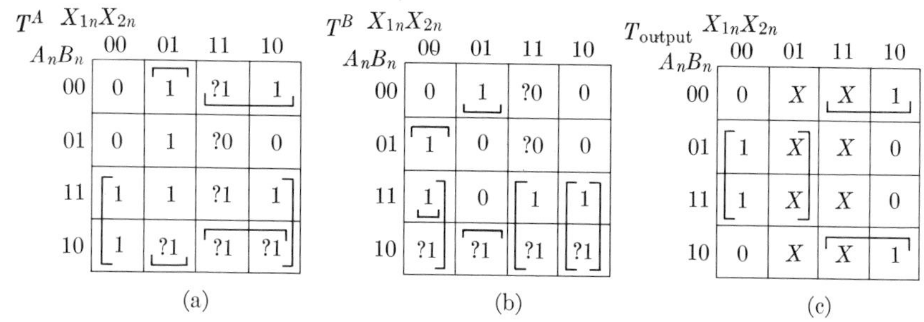

(a) T^A

A_nB_n \ $X_{1n}X_{2n}$	00	01	11	10
00	0	1	?1	1
01	0	1	?0	0
11	1	1	?1	1
10	1	?1	?1	?1

(b) T^B

A_nB_n \ $X_{1n}X_{2n}$	00	01	11	10
00	0	1	?0	0
01	1	0	?0	0
11	1	0	1	1
10	?1	?1	?1	?1

(c) T_{output}

A_nB_n \ $X_{1n}X_{2n}$	00	01	11	10
00	0	X	X	1
01	1	X	X	0
11	1	X	X	0
10	0	X	X	1

FIGURE 14.9

states. For example, when the present state is 4 ($A_n = 1$, $B_n = 0$) and the inputs are 01 ($x^1 = 0$, $x^2 = 1$), the next state can be 1, 2, 3, or 4.

In making a choice among available optimum next states, we have to examine all the relevant maps. In the present example, there are two maps, one for T^A and one for T^B. In determining the entries for cells 1000 in Fig. 14.9(a) and 14.9(b), we note that no matter which one of the two available optional next states we choose, A_{n+1} will be 0. Since $A_n = 0$, a 1 is entered in cell 1000 in Fig. 14.9(a). However, B_{n+1} can be either 1 or 0. 1 is tentatively entered in cell 1000 in Fig. 14.9(b).

Let us next consider cells 0011 in Fig. 14.9(a) and 14.9(b). It is desirable to have 1 entered in cell 0011 in (a). It can be done if the next state chosen is 4 (10). Note, however, that this also specifies that a 0 has to be entered in cell 0011 of (b). This explains why these two maps have to be considered concurrently.

Entries in other ?-marked cells are chosen in the same way, with the aim that the resultant set of switching functions for the flip-flops can be economically implemented.

For Example 14.3, the following set of switching functions are obtained through groupings in Fig. 14.9:

$$
\begin{aligned}
T^A &= A_n + X'_{1n}X_{2n} + B'_nX_{1n}, \\
T^B &= A_nX'_{2n} + A_nX_{1n} + B'_nX'_{1n}X_{2n} + B_nX'_{1n}X'_{2n}, \quad (14.21) \\
T_{\text{output}} &= B_nX'_{1n} + B'_nX_{1n}.
\end{aligned}
$$

The implementation of the switching functions is routine. ▲

Problems

14.1. Implement the simplified state table obtained in Problem 13.1 with RS-type flip-flops and diode gates. Show the assignment scheme made and the symbolic diagram of the circuit.

14.2. Implement the reduced state table obtained in Problem 13.2 with T-type flip-flops and direct-coupled transistor gates. Show the assignment scheme made and the symbolic diagram of the circuit.

14.3. Implement the minimum-row state table obtained in Problem 13.3 with JK-type flip-flops and diode-transistor gates. Show the assignment scheme made and the symbolic diagram of the circuit.

14.4. Implement the simplified state table obtained in Problem 13.4 with RS-type flip-flops and diode-transistor gates. Indicate the assignment scheme made and the symbolic diagram of the circuit.

14.5. Realize the state table obtained in Problem 13.6 with T-type flip-flops and diode gates. Indicate the assignment scheme chosen and the symbolic diagram of the circuit.

14.6. Realize the state table obtained in Problem 13.7 with JK-type flip-flops and direct-coupled transistor gates. Indicate the assignment scheme chosen and the symbolic diagram of the circuit.

14.7. Realize the state table obtained in Problem 13.8 with T-type flip-flops and diode gates. Show the assignment scheme chosen and the symbolic diagram of the circuit.

14.8. Realize the state table obtained in Problem 13.9 with RS-type flip-flops and diode-transistor gates. Indicate the assignment scheme chosen and the symbolic diagram of the circuit.

14.9. Implement the following state table with RS-type flip-flops and diode gates. Show the assignment scheme made and the symbolic diagram of the circuit.

Present state	Next state		Output	
	0	1	0	1
A	B	D	0	0
B	G	E	0	0
C	D	B	0	1
D	E	G	0	0
E	C	H	0	0
F	C	A	0	0
G	A	F	1	0
H	A	C	0	0

14.10. Realize the following state table with T-type flip-flops and direct-coupled transistor gates. Show the assignment scheme made and the symbolic diagram of the circuit.

Present state	Next state		Output	
	0	1	0	1
1	5	4	0	0
2	7	1	0	0
3	3	6	0	1
4	6	3	0	0
5	1	7	0	0
6	4	5	0	0
7	2	1	1	0

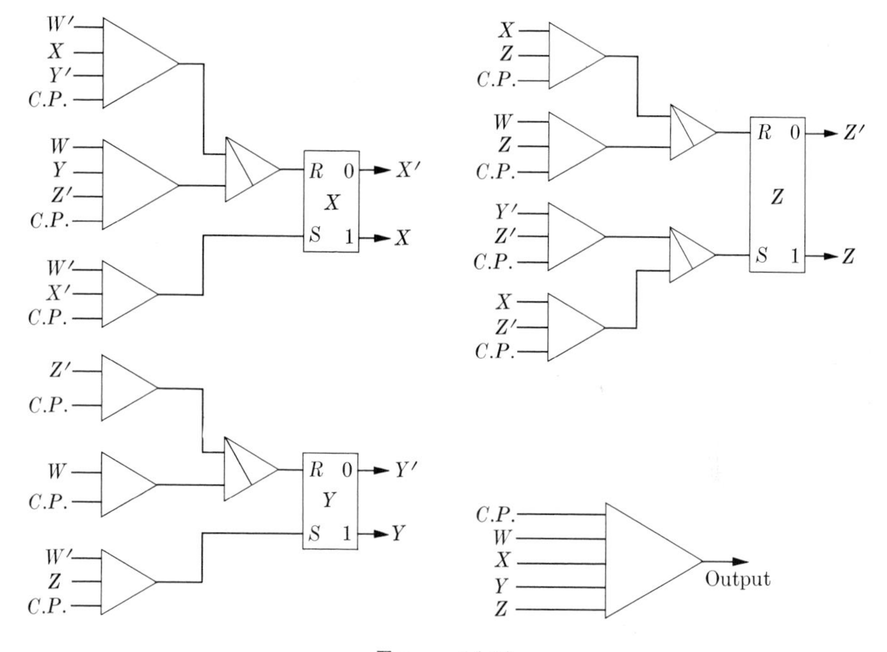

FIGURE 14.10

14.11. A synchronous sequential circuit is designed according to a given set of specifications. The symbolic diagram is shown in Fig. 14.10.

It is noted that only the R- and S-terminals of the flip-flops are used. Furthermore, it is felt that the original designer did not take full advantage of the approaches available. You are now asked to redesign the circuit in which only T-terminals of the flip-flops are used. State every step in your design process clearly. Show the diagram of your circuit.

14.12. Following a given set of specifications, a designer produced the following design.

Three flip-flops A, B, and C are used. The switching functions for their T-terminals are

$$\begin{aligned}
T^A &= W'A'B + W'BC' + A'BC' + AB'C + WB'C + WAC, \\
T^B &= W'A'C + W'A'B + A'BC + AB'C' + WB'C' + WAC', \\
T^C &= W'AC + W'B'C' + WBC + WA'C'.
\end{aligned}$$

The switching function for the output is

$$T_{\text{output}} = W'A'BC'.$$

It is felt that the implementation of these switching functions will be quite clumsy. Employ what you have learned to obtain a better design.

State every step in your design process clearly. Show the switching functions to be implemented.

CHAPTER 15

SEQUENTIAL CIRCUITS V: ASYNCHRONOUS CIRCUITS*

15.1 Introduction. In the previous four chapters, the theory and design of synchronous switching circuits are discussed. The block diagram of such circuits can be found in Fig. 11.1. In this chapter, asynchronous sequential circuits are discussed. The absence of the clock brings the designer face to face with some very interesting and important problems. It is obvious that additional considerations have to be made and additional approaches have to be developed. It should be pointed out, however, that the understanding of synchronous sequential circuits plays an essential role in the design of asynchronous sequential circuits.

15.2 Additional considerations in asynchronous sequential circuits. The block diagram of an asynchronous sequential circuit is shown in Fig. 15.1. Clearly it can be seen that the design of asynchronous sequential circuits involves the design of the memory and the design of a corresponding combinational switching circuit. In the following discussion, relays will be used as switching components. The application of electronic devices will be introduced later.

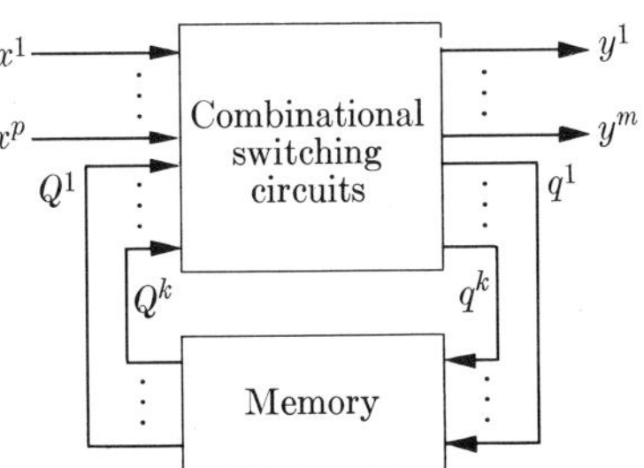

FIG. 15.1. Block diagram of an asynchronous sequential circuit.

It is recalled that in the design of synchronous switching circuits, flip-flops are used to form the memory. Each flip-flop is used to store one binary digit by virtue of its two stable operating states. A question might have been asked then: If two stable operating states are all that are needed, and a transistor can be used to achieve this because its conduction can be completely cut off or made to saturate, why then are the more expensive flip-flops employed? Note that in synchronous sequential circuits, the inputs to the memory, and consequently to its storage elements, are

* HU 3 and MU 1.

available only at the finite instants when the clock pulses appear. These inputs of finite duration are adequate to set or reset flip-flops, but they cannot keep the transistor or other switching components in either one of its two operating states.

In asynchronous sequential circuits, the clock is removed, and consequently simple switching components can be used to implement the memory. The block diagram of a relay asynchronous sequential circuit is shown in Fig. 15.2.

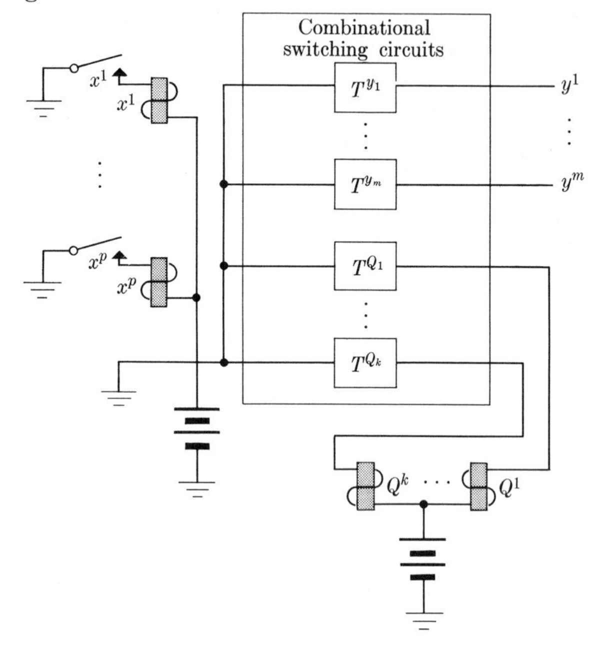

FIG. 15.2. Block diagram of a relay asynchronous sequential circuit.

A close correspondence between the block diagram in Fig. 15.2 and that in Fig. 15.1 is easily noted. The x-labeled relays are termed *primary* relays. An input is 1 if its correspondingly designated switch is closed; 0 if its correspondingly designated switch is open. Each Q coil is used to store one binary digit. Whenever a coil is excited, it is to be understood that a 1 is stored in the coil; whenever a coil is quiescent, a 0 is stored in that coil. Each input coil, as well as each Q coil, controls a set of contacts. These contacts are used to form switching circuits which control the Q coils. The Q-labeled relays which form the memory of the sequential circuit are termed *secondary* relays. The contacts of the primary and secondary relays are also used to implement switching functions, T^{y_1}, $T^{y_2}, \ldots, T^{y_m}$, which provide outputs.

15.3 Illustrative example. The approach developed to design the asynchronous sequential circuit resembles that used in designing the synchronous sequential circuit.* Additional considerations have to be made, however, because of the absence of the clock pulses in the feedback loop.

EXAMPLE 15.1 Design a counter which counts the number of times the truth value of a binary input changes. The counter is to return to its initial state after eight changes of the input value. The counter is to be implemented with relays.

The schematic diagram of the counter is that shown in Fig. 15.2, with $p = 1$. The truth value of the input is designated by x.

The first step in the design process is to construct the state diagram, also called the *flow diagram*, which is shown in Fig. 15.3.

Note that the outputs have not been considered at this stage. The initial state, where the truth value of x has been changed $8l$ times (l is an integer, zero included), is designated by 0. If the truth value of x, assumed to be 0, stays unchanged, the circuit remains at state 0. However, as soon as x is changed to 1, the state of the circuit is transferred from 0 to 1, where state 1 indicates that the truth value of x has been changed $8l + 1$ times. The remainder of the state diagram can be explained in the same way.

It is recalled that in the design of a synchronous sequential circuit, a state transition table can be obtained from the established state diagram.

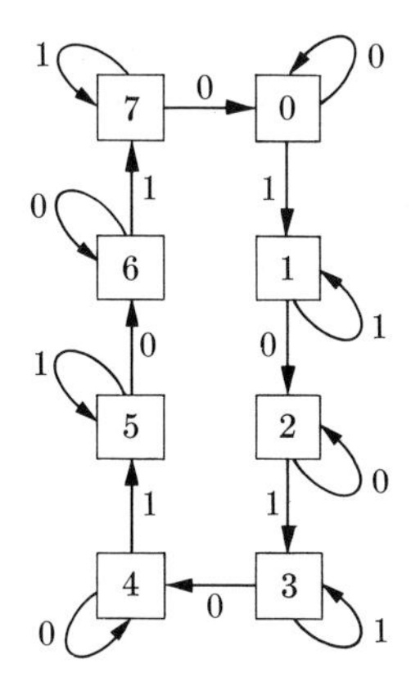

FIGURE 15.3

TABLE 15.1

Row	$x = 0$	$x = 1$
0	⓪	1
1	2	①
2	②	3
3	4	③
4	④	5
5	6	⑤
6	⑥	7
7	0	⑦

In the present case, a table (Table 15.1) can likewise be obtained from the state diagram in Fig. 15.3. However, certain modifications are made.

The most obvious modification is that there are no columns labeled "present state" or "next state." Certain entries are circled. These entries

* HU 3.

represent stable states. For example, if the circuit is at state 0 and $x = 0$, it will remain there until there is a change in the input value. When the input value does change to 1, the state of the circuit will change (or flow) from state 0 to state 1. Instead of being called the state transition table, it is generally referred to as a *flow table.* The flow table in Table 15.1 has another interesting characteristic. Each row has one and only one stable state. Such a flow table is termed a *primitive flow table.* A primitive flow table can be constructed directly from the given specifications of the problem.

The simplification of the flow table follows the same approaches developed in Chapter 13 to reduce the state transition table. Two identical rows can be merged into one. When a circled entry merges with an uncircled entry, the resultant entry should be circled. For example, the two rows

$$\textcircled{a} \quad b \quad \textcircled{c} \quad d$$
$$a \quad \textcircled{b} \quad c \quad d$$

can be merged into

$$\textcircled{a} \quad \textcircled{b} \quad \textcircled{c} \quad d.$$

One might have serious doubts about what was done. In reducing the state transition table of a synchronous sequential circuit, two rows can be merged only when their corresponding next state entries and output entries are identical. It seems that in reducing the flow table, no attention is paid to the output entries. This doubt can be dispersed by re-examining how outputs are produced in an asynchronous sequential circuit. In practice, the outputs from an asynchronous sequential circuit are observed when the circuit is in a stable state. The secondary relays, together with primary relays, control the circuit outputs. There is, therefore, no need to be concerned with the output entries.

Careful examination of Table 15.1 does not reveal that any two rows can be merged. The next task is the implementation of the flow table.

15.4 Secondary assignment. To implement the flow table (Table 15.1), we have to decide first how many secondary relays are to be used. Since there are eight rows in the flow table and each row is to be represented by a specific combination of operating conditions of the secondary relays, at least three relays are needed. These three relays are represented by three switching variables A, B, C. When $A = 1$, the coil of relay A is excited. When $A = 0$, the coil of relay A is not excited. Each one of the eight combinations of operating conditions of relays A, B, and C is to be assigned to represent one row of the flow table. To assign the available combinations to the rows of the flow table constitutes the *secondary assignment* problem.

A tentative assignment scheme is

Row	A	B	C
0	0	0	0
1	0	0	1
2	0	1	0
3	0	1	1
4	1	0	0
5	1	0	1
6	1	1	0
7	1	1	1

(15.1)

The assignment scheme (15.1) is a natural one, because each combination is the binary equivalent of its corresponding row designation. Up to this point, combinations of operating conditions of secondary relays have been assigned to the rows of a state table. The state representation can be easily derived from the row representation. Note that the row representation indicates the present operating conditions of the secondary relays. Since the secondary relays and primary relays dictate the operating conditions of the secondary relays, it is natural to give a state the same assigned representation as the row in which it is stable. For example, in Table 15.1, state 2 is stable in row 2, state 2 and row 2 are then represented by the same combination of operating conditions of secondary relays. More will be said about this point in the next section.

15.5 Racing in asynchronous sequential circuits. Substituting the assignment scheme (15.1) into the flow table (Table 15.1), we obtain Table 15.2.

In row 000, relays A, B, and C are not excited if the input value x is 0; the state of the circuit should be in 000. That is to say, relays A, B, and C should remain unexcited. The state of the circuit will stay at 000 indefinitely until there is a change in the input value. However, in row 000, if the input value is 1, the state of the circuit should be in 001; the operating condition of relay C should be changed from unexcited to excited. After this transition has taken place, the circuit again settles into a stable state 001, where the row designation and state designation are identical. Note that this transition involves only relay C.

When the state is in state 001 and $x = 1$, (row 2 of Table 15.2), no further transition will take place until the input value x is changed from

TABLE 15.2

Row	$x = 0$	$x = 1$
0 0 0	0 0 0	0 0 1
0 0 1	0 1 0	0 0 1
0 1 0	0 1 0	0 1 1
0 1 1	1 0 0	0 1 1
1 0 0	1 0 0	1 0 1
1 0 1	1 1 0	1 0 1
1 1 0	1 1 0	1 1 1
1 1 1	0 0 0	1 1 1

1 to 0. Table 15.2 indicates that the circuit should "flow" into the new stable state 010. This means that the following two changes must take place:

(a) Relay B, now unexcited, becomes excited.
(b) Relay C, now excited, becomes unexcited. (15.2)

At this point, it is vital to review the actual operation of a relay, especially the inevitable delay between the application of a voltage source across the coil and the actual closing or releasing of the contacts it controls. Let us examine a specific relay (Fig. 15.4). At $t = t_0$, a constant voltage source is applied across terminals C_1 and C_2. However, the normally open contact will not be closed at $t = t_0$, but rather at $t = t_0 + \Delta$. There is no reason to expect that the delay Δ developed in every relay is the same. This brings about a very interesting and important consideration in the design of asynchronous sequential circuits.

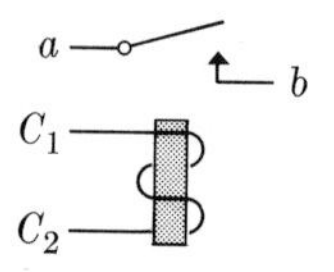

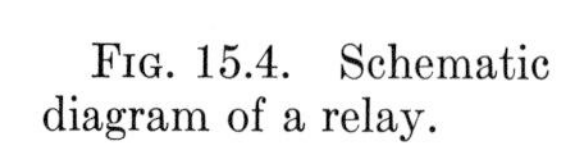
FIG. 15.4. Schematic diagram of a relay.

With this understanding, we can now investigate what will happen when the circuit is stable at state 001 and the input value is changed to 0. There are three possibilities.

(1) Changes (a) and (b) in (15.2) take place *simultaneously*. This enables the circuit to settle in a new stable state 010 as specified in Table 15.2.

(2) Change (b) happens faster than change (a). If this occurs, the secondary relays A, B, and C may all become unexcited. Consequently,

the circuit may go into the stable state 000. This, of course, violates the specification of the problem.

(3) Change (a) happens faster than change (b). If this occurs, the operating conditions of the secondary relays may be expressed by 011. Knowing that the input value x is 0, we can see from row 011 of Table 15.2, that further changes will take place, and it is highly unlikely that the desired stable state 010 will ever be reached.

The above analysis shows that the final state of the circuit, following an input value change, depends on the speeds of the different transitions involved. This is the *racing problem* in the asynchronous sequential circuit. Since the race, discussed above, may lead to erroneous results, it is called a *critical race*. There are also races which are *noncritical*. This is illustrated in the flow table of a relay circuit shown in Table 15.3.

TABLE 15.3

AB	$x = 0$	$x = 1$
00	00	11
01	01	11
11	01	11
10	00	11

Suppose that the circuit is at a stable state where the secondary relays A and B are not excited and the input x is 0. If the input x is changed from 0 to 1, the flow table specifies that the circuit should go into the stable state, where the secondary relays A and B are excited. Since this involves more than one secondary relay, a racing situation prevails. If the changes involving relays A and B happen simultaneously, the circuit will go into the desired stable state 11 directly. If the change in relay A happens first, the state of the circuit will move from row 00 to row 10, and subsequently settle in the desired stable state 11. If the change in relay B occurs faster, the stable state 11 can still be reached via 01. Such a race is considered noncritical, because the correct result is always achieved.

It now becomes apparent that in making a secondary assignment for an asynchronous sequential circuit, the designer should avoid creating any critical races. To meet this requirement, the transition between stable states should initiate a change in the operating condition of only one of the secondary relays, or, if more changes are necessary, the resultant race should be noncritical. The secondary assignment should always be made with the approaches developed in Chapter 14 and the consideration just presented.

Since the assignment in (15.1) does create critical races, a new assignment scheme is

Row	A	B	C
0	0	0	0
1	0	0	1
2	0	1	1
3	0	1	0
4	1	1	0
5	1	1	1
6	1	0	1
7	1	0	0

(15.3)

Substituting the assignment scheme (15.3) into the flow table of Table 15.2, we obtain Table 15.4.

TABLE 15.4

Row	$x = 0$	$x = 1$
0 0 0	0 0 0	0 0 1
0 0 1	0 1 1	0 0 1
0 1 1	0 1 1	0 1 0
0 1 0	1 1 0	0 1 0
1 1 0	1 1 0	1 1 1
1 1 1	1 0 1	1 1 1
1 0 1	1 0 1	1 0 0
1 0 0	0 0 0	1 0 0

A critical examination of Table 15.4 shows that there are no critical races present. It also reveals that the secondary assignment scheme (15.3) is made in such a way that any transition between two stable states will initiate a change in the operating condition of only one of the three secondary relays. For example, the circuit is stable at state 0 when secondary relays A, B, and C are not excited and the input x is 0; when the value of the input x is changed from 0 to 1, the state will settle into state 1. This is accomplished by altering only the operating condition of relay C, to change it from unexcited to excited.

15.6 Hazards in combinational switching circuits. The next task is to design the combinational switching circuits which control the coils of the secondary relays A, B, and C. This means that switching functions for three combinational switching circuits have to be established.

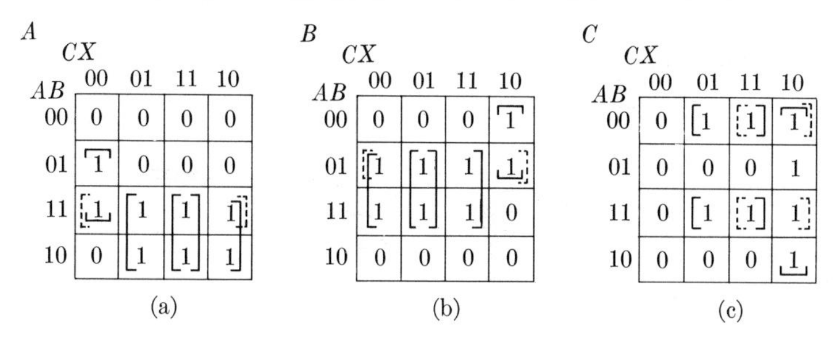

FIGURE 15.5

The reasoning used in Chapter 14 to obtain switching functions can be employed here. The three maps shown in Fig. 15.5 are obtained.

In the map for relay A, Fig. 15.5(a), the entry in cell 0000 is 0; this corresponds to row 000 and column 0 in Table 15.4. The entry in cell 0100 is 1; this corresponds to row 010 and column 0. The balance of the maps can be explained in the same way.

A set of three switching functions is obtained by proper groupings shown in Fig. 15.5:

$$A = BC'x' + Ax + AC, \tag{15.4a}$$

$$B = A'Cx' + Bx + BC', \tag{15.4b}$$

$$C = Cx' + ABx + A'B'x. \tag{15.4c}$$

If one does proceed to implement the switching functions (15.4) with contacts on relays A, B, C, and x, it is very likely that he will find the resultant sequential circuit does not function properly. This seems to be very discouraging because there is definitely no mistake in the design procedure. The cause of this trouble can be explained by examining the circuit in Fig. 15.6 for the coil of relay A.

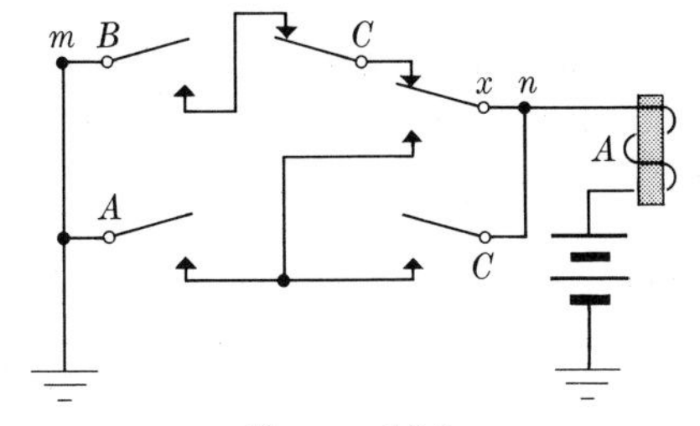

FIGURE 15.6

Assume that the circuit is at stable state 110. From Table 15.4, we see that $A = 1$, $B = 1$, $C = 0$, and $x = 0$. Examination of the circuit in Fig. 15.6 reveals that relay A is excited through the contactor path $BC'x'$. At this point, let us change the input value from 0 to 1. According to the flow table in Table 15.4, we see that relay C should become excited. Furthermore, relays A and B should remain excited. However, when x changes from 0 to 1, terminals m and n will remain connected *all the time*, only if the normally closed contact x' opens after or at the instant when the normally open contact x closes. This can be achieved, because either the path $BC'x'$ or the path Ax, or both, are available to transmit the ground. It is, however, possible that this requirement is not met. That is to say, it is very likely that the normally closed contact, x', opens before the normally open contact x closes. Consequently, there is a time interval when terminals m and n (Fig. 15.6) are not connected. If this interval is long enough, the normally open contact A will become open. This will leave relay A unexcited, even when the normally open contact x finally becomes closed. This indicates a hazard in the combinational circuit which prevents the sequential circuit from reaching the desired stable state.

There are several ways to forestall the hazard. Continuity transfer contacts* can be used in certain cases. Another approach is to provide a path which is independent of the variable being changed. Adopting this approach, an additional path, AB, is added between terminals m and n, as shown in Fig. 15.7.

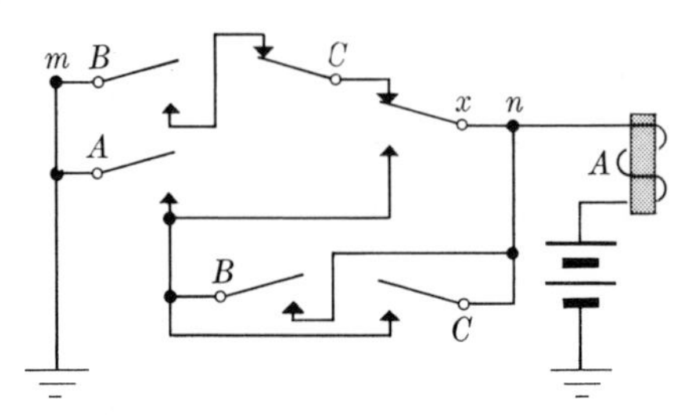

FIGURE 15.7

The first comment one would make is that this path is entirely redundant. This is absolutely true. However, by providing such a path, the connection between terminals m and n is independent of the transfer contact x during its transition.

The second comment is: How does one know to provide a path, characterized by AB, under the present situation? The clue lies in the groupings we made in the map of Fig. 15.5(a). Note that there were three groupings made, resulting in three terms shown in the right-hand side of Eq. (15.4a). The transition under discussion is initiated by the change

* A continuity transfer contact is designed so that for a short interval during transition, both the normally open and the normally closed contacts remain closed.

in x. It starts from cell 1100 and ends at cell 1101. Unfortunately these two cells belong to two separate groupings. This means that the connection between terminals m and n is passed from one path, $BC'x'$, created by the grouping containing 1100 to another path, Ax, created by another grouping containing 1101. Both paths are influenced by x. This brings about the hazard. To avoid it, a new grouping containing cells 1100, 1101, 1111, and 1110 is added. This new grouping suggests the path AB. When x changes from 0 to 1, the initiating cell and the terminating cell are contained in one grouping. The connection between terminals m and n is maintained throughout the transition by the path AB, which is independent of the changing x. To achieve this same end, we could have created a grouping containing only cells 1100 and 1101. Since this grouping would suggest a redundant path ABC', the previous grouping containing four cells is used.

The third comment is: Adding the path AB only avoids the hazard during this particular transition. Is there any other transition which will bring about hazardous results? This question can be answered by examining every possible transition. If both the initiating cell and the terminating cell are labeled 1, but they belong to one grouping, no hazard will occur and consequently no additional path is needed. So far as the switching circuit for relay A is concerned, path AB is the only one that is needed.*

The same reasoning is applied to the maps in Fig. 15.5(b) and 15.5(c). Instead of implementing the set of three switching functions shown in Eq. (15.4), the following set of functions is required:

$$A = BC'x' + Ax + AC + AB, \tag{15.5a}$$

$$B = A'Cx' + Bx + BC' + A'B, \tag{15.5b}$$

$$\begin{aligned} C &= Cx' + ABx + A'B'x + (AB + A'B')C \\ &= Cx' + (AB + A'B')(x + C). \end{aligned} \tag{15.5c}$$

The realization of these functions is omitted.

Up to this point we have not discussed how the outputs are produced. In the case of the counter design, three indicators, indicating the operating conditions of the three secondary relays, are all that are needed. In a general asynchronous sequential circuit design, the outputs are provided by combinational switching circuits, formed by contacts, controlled by the primary and secondary relays. ▲

---

* More discussion on hazards in combinational switching circuits can be found in HU 4.

15.7 Asynchronous electronic sequential circuits. In the previous discussion in this chapter, attention is paid to asynchronous relay sequential circuits. It can be shown with an example that the same reasoning is applicable in the design of asynchronous electronic sequential circuits.

EXAMPLE 15.2. Design an electronic switching circuit with two inputs, x^1 and x^2. The output is 1 when (a) $x^1 = 0$, $x^2 = 1$; and (b) x^1 becomes 0 before x^2 is made to be 1. The two input values do not change at the same instant.

In Example 15.1, a state diagram is established first. This is, however, not essential. We can start the design process by constructing the flow table. This is what is done in the present example (Table 15.5).

TABLE 15.5

Row	x^1x^2 00	01	11	10	Output
0	(A)	B	–	C	0
1	A	(B)	D	–	1
2	A	–	D	(C)	0
3	–	E	(D)	C	0
4	A	(E)	D	–	0

This table is initiated by naming the stable state of the circuit when the input combination is $00(x^1 = 0, x^2 = 0)A$. When x^2 changes from 0 to 1, we let the state of the circuit move from A to B. When the input combination becomes 10, the state of the circuit moves to C. A don't-care entry is made in row 0 and column 11. This is done because of the restriction that the two inputs do not change at the same time.

In row 1, the stable state is B. When the input combination changes from 01 to 00, we return the circuit to state A. When the input combination changes from 01 to 11, the circuit settles into state D. A don't-care entry is made under column 10, because the input combination cannot reach 10 from 01 in one step. Row 2 is completed in the routine fashion. It is interesting to examine the entries in row 3. The stable state of this row is D. When the input combination changes from 11 to 01, we let the circuit move to state E, rather than B. There is a definite reason for this. Note that state B is reached when the input combination changes from 00 to 01. In other words x^1 becomes 0 before x^2 is 1. In this situation, the output should be 1. When the input combination arrives at 01 from 11, x^2 becomes 1 before x^1 is 0. The output should be 0. A new stable state E is therefore created.

Note that in the flow table of Table 15.5, an output column is added. The output entry is related to the stable state of its corresponding row. That is why a 1 is entered in row 1, where B is the stable state.

The next task is to reduce the primitive flow table. Using the technique developed in Section 15.3, we see there are many possibilities of merging. They can be displayed by the approach developed in Section 13.3. It can also be done in the present situation by constructing a *merger diagram*, as shown in Fig. 15.8.

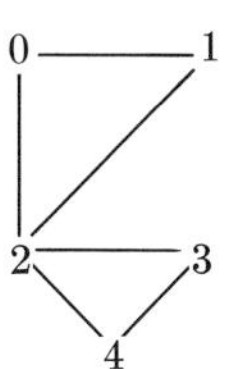

FIG. 15.8. A merger diagram for Table 15.5.

Rows 0 and 1 are connected by a line segment because they can be merged. The completed merger diagram shows that rows 0, 1, and 2 can be merged into one single row. It also indicates that rows 2, 3, and 4 can be replaced by a single row.

Following the above suggestions, we reduce the primitive flow table to that shown in Table 15.6. Row α is the resultant of merging rows 0, 1, and 2. Row β is the resultant of merging rows 3 and 4.

TABLE 15.6

Row	x^1x^2 00	01	11	10
α	(A)	(B)	D	(C)
β	A	(E)	(D)	C

Note that there is no output column in Table 15.6, because it might cause confusion. It should be understood that the output is 1 when the circuit is at state B.

The flow table in Table 15.6 indicates that we have to implement two rows. In the design of an asynchronous relay switching circuit, the operating conditions of the relay coils are used to implement the rows in a given flow table. It is quite obvious that operating conditions of transistors or other electronic devices can likewise be employed.

In the present example, there are only two rows to be implemented. One transistor, Y, is all that is needed. Row α is represented by having the transistor cut off ($Y = 0$). Row β is represented by having the transistor conduct in the saturation region ($Y = 1$). The switching function to operate the transistor Y can be obtained by substituting the above assignment scheme into the flow table of Table 15.6. The result is shown in Fig. 15.9.

Y \ x^1x^2	00	01	11	10
0	0	0	1	0
1	0	1	1	0

FIGURE 15.9

The switching function for Y is

$$Y = x^1x^2 + x^2Y. \tag{15.6}$$

No hazard is found in the combination circuit.* The output is 1 when the circuit is stable at B. The switching function for the output can be easily found:

$$T_{\text{output}} = (x^1)'x^2Y'. \tag{15.7}$$

The implementation of the switching functions in Eqs. (15.6) and (15.7) is quite straightforward. ▲

PROBLEMS

15.1. Design a counter which displays the number of times the truth value of a binary input varies. The counter is to return to its initial state after every four changes of the input value. This counter is to be implemented with relays. Show the flow table, the secondary assignment scheme, and the schematic diagram of the resultant circuit.

15.2. Implement the counter specified in Problem 15.1 with transistors. Show the secondary assignment scheme and the schematic diagram of the resultant circuit.

15.3. A counter which displays the number of times the truth value of a binary input varies is to be designed. The counter is to return to its initial state after every seven changes of the input value. This counter is to be implemented with relays. Show the flow table, the secondary assignment scheme, and the schematic diagram of the resultant circuit.

15.4. Realize the counter specified in Problem 15.3 with transistors. Show the secondary assignment scheme and the schematic diagram of the resultant circuit.

15.5. An asynchronous sequential circuit with one input is to be designed. The output is 1 whenever the input sequences assume the following pattern:

	t_n	t_{n+1}	t_{n+2}
Input	1	0	1

Implement the circuit with relays. Indicate the secondary assignment scheme and the schematic diagram of the resultant circuit.

---

* For more discussion on hazards in electronic combinational circuit, see HU 4, UN 1, and UN 2.

15.6. Try to implement the circuit specified in Problem 15.5 with transistors and diodes. Show the secondary assignment made and the symbolic diagram of the resultant circuit.

15.7. An asynchronous sequential circuit with two inputs, x^1 and x^2, is to be designed. Whenever the two inputs follow the pattern shown below, the output should be 1.

	t_n	t_{n+1}	t_{n+2}	t_{n+3}	t_{n+4}
x^1	0	———	1	———	0
x^2	———	1	———	0	———

Note that at any instant, only one input can be changed. The circuit is to be implemented with relays. Indicate the secondary assignment scheme and the symbolic diagram of the resultant circuit.

15.8. Implement the circuit specified in Problem 15.7 with transistors and diodes. Present the secondary assignment made and the symbolic diagram of the resultant circuit.

15.9. Design and implement an asynchronous sequential circuit with two inputs, x^1 and x^2. Whenever the two inputs follow the pattern shown below, the output is to be 1.

	t_n	t_{n+1}	t_{n+2}	t_{n+3}	t_{n+4}
x^1	1	———	0	———	1
x^2	———	0	———	1	———

Note that at any instant, only one input can be changed. Transistors and diodes are to be used. Indicate the secondary assignment scheme and the symbolic diagram of the resultant circuit.

15.10. Implement the circuit specified in Problem 15.9 with relays. Present the secondary assignment made and the schematic diagram of the resultant circuit.

BIBLIOGRAPHY

BIBLIOGRAPHY

AN 1 ANKRUM, P. D., *Principles and Applications of Electron Devices*, International Textbook Co., Scranton, Pa., 1959.

AR 1 ARMSTRONG, D. B., "On the Efficient Assignment of Internal Codes to Sequential Machines." *IRE Trans. on Electronic Computers*, Vol. EC-11, No. 5, October 1962, pp. 611–622.

AS 1 ASHENHURST, R. L., "The Decomposition of Switching Functions," *Bell Laboratories' Report No. 1*, 1953, pp. II-1–II-37.

AS 2 ASHENHURST, R. L., "The Decomposition of Switching Functions," *Proc. International Symp. on Theory of Switching*, pt. 1, Harvard University, Cambridge, Mass., April 1957, pp. 74–116.

AU 1 AUFENKAMP, D. D. and F. E. HOHN, "Analysis of Sequential Machines," *IRE Trans. on Electronic Computers*, Vol. EC-6, No. 4, December 1957, pp. 276–285.

AU 2 AUFENKAMP, D. D., "Analysis of Sequential Machines, II," *IRE Trans. on Electronic Computers*, Vol. EC-7, No. 4, December 1958, pp. 299–306.

BA 1 BARTEE, T. C , "The Automatic Design of Logical Networks," *Proc. Western Joint Computer Conference*, San Francisco, March 1959, pp. 103–107.

BA 2 BARTEE, T. C., "Computer Design of Multiple-Output Logical Networks," *IRE Trans. on Electronic Computers*, Vol. EC-10, No. 1, March 1961, pp. 21–30.

BI 1 BIRKHOFF, G. and S. MACLANE, *A Survey of Modern Algebra*, Macmillan, New York, 1948.

BO 1 BOOLE, G., *The Mathematical Analysis of Logic*, Cambridge, England, 1847 (Reprinted in 1948, Basil Blackwell, Oxford).

BO 2 BOOLE, G., *An Investigation of the Laws of Thought*, London, 1854 (Reprinted, Dover Publications, New York).

BU 1 BURKS, A. W., R. MCNAUGHTON, C. H. POLLMAR, D. W. WARREN, and J. B. WRIGHT, "The Folded Tree," *Journal of the Franklin Institute*, Vol. 260, No. 1, July 1955, pp. 9–24, No. 2, August 1955, pp. 115–126.

BU 2 BURKS, A. W. and H. WANG, "The Logic of Automata," *J. of Assoc. for Computing Machinery*, Vol. 4, Nos. 2 and 3, April and July 1957, pp. 193–218 and pp. 279–297.

CA 1 CALDWELL, S. H., "Recognition and Identification of Symmetric Switching Functions," *Trans. AIEE*, Vol. 73, pt. II, May 1954, pp. 142–146.

CA 2 CALDWELL, S. H., *Switching Circuits and Logical Design*, John Wiley and Sons, New York, 1958.

CA 3 Calingaert, P., "Multiple-Output Relay Switching Circuits," *Proc. International Symp. on Theory of Switching*, pt. 2, Harvard University, Cambridge, Mass., April 1957, pp. 59–73.

CA 4 Calingaert, P., "Two-Dimensional Parity Checking," *J. of Assoc. for Computing Machinery*, Vol. 8, No. 2, April 1961, pp. 186–200.

CH 1 Chao, S. C., "A Generalized Resistor-Transistor Logic Circuit and Some Applications," *IRE Trans. on Electronic Computers*, Vol. EC-8, No. 1, March 1959, pp. 8–12.

CH 2 Chu, J. T., "A Generalization of a Theorem of Quine for Simplifying Truth Functions," *IRE Trans. on Electronic Computers*, Vol. EC-10, No. 2, June 1961, pp. 165–168.

CH 3 Chow, C. K., "Boolean Functions Realizable with Single Threshold Devices," *Proc. IRE*, Vol. 49, January 1961, p. 370.

CO 1 Coates, C. L., R. B. Kirchner, and P. M. Lewis, "A Simplified Procedure for the Realization of Linearly-Separable Switching Functions," *IRE Trans. on Electronic Computers*, Vol. EC-11, No. 4, August 1962, pp. 447–458.

CO 2 Cohn, M. and R. Lindaman, "Axiomatic Majority-Decision Logic," *IRE Trans. on Electronic Computers*, Vol. EC-10, No. 1, March 1961, pp. 17–21.

CU 1 Curtis, H. A., *A New Approach to the Design of Switching Circuits*, D. Van Nostrand, Princeton, New Jersey, 1962.

CU 2 Curtis, H. A., "Multiple Reduction of Variable Dependency of Sequential Machines," *J. of Assoc. for Computing Machinery*, Vol. 9, No. 3, July 1962, pp. 324–344.

DU 1 Dunham, B. and R. Fridshal, "The Problem of Simplifying Logical Expressions," *J. Symbolic Logic*, Vol. 24, No. 1, March 1959, pp. 17–19.

EA 1 Earle, J., "Synthesizing Minimal Stroke and Dagger Functions," *IRE Trans. on Circuit Theory*, Vol. CT-7, Special Supplement, August 1960, pp. 144–154.

EI 1 Einhorn, S. N., "The Use of the Simplex Algorithm in the Mechanization of Boolean Switching Functions by Means of Magnetic Cores," *IRE Trans. on Electronic Computers*, Vol. EC-10, No. 4, December 1961, pp. 615–622.

EL 1 Elspas, B., "The Theory of Autonomous Linear Sequential Networks," *IRE Trans. on Circuit Theory*, Vol. CT-6, No. 1, March 1959, pp. 45–60.

ES 1 Estrin, B., B. Gilchrist, and J. H. Pomerene, "A Note on High-Speed Digital Multiplication," *IRE Trans. on Electronic Computers*, Vol. EC-5, No. 3, September 1956, pp. 140.

FO 1 Foss, F. A., "Use of a Reflected Code in Digital Control Systems," *IRE Trans. on Electronic Computers*, Vol. EC-3, No. 3, December 1954, pp. 1–6.

FR 1 FRIEDLAND, B., "Linear Modular Sequential Circuits," *IRE Trans. on Circuit Theory*, Vol. CT-6, No. 1, March 1959, pp. 61–68.

FR 2 FRAENKEL, A. S., "The Use of Index Calcus and Mersenne Primes for the Design of a High-Speed Digital Multiplier," *J. of Assoc. for Computing Machinery*, Vol. 8, No. 1, January 1961, pp. 87–96.

GA 1 GAZALE, M. J., "Irredundant Disjunctive and Conjunctive Forms of a Boolean Function," *IBM J. of Research and Development*, Vol. 1, April 1957, pp. 171–176.

GA 2 GARNER, H. L., "Generalized Parity Checking," *IRE Trans. on Electronic Computers*, Vol. EC-7, No. 3, September 1958, pp. 207–213.

GA 3 GABELMAN, I. J., "The Synthesis of Boolean Functions Using a Single Threshold Element," *IRE Trans. on Electronic Computers*, Vol. EC-11, No. 5, October 1962, pp. 639–642.

GI 1 GINSBURG, S., "A Technique for the Reduction of a Given Machine to a Minimal-State Machine," *IRE Trans. on Electronic Computers*, Vol. EC-8, No. 3, September 1959, pp. 346–355.

GI 2 GINSBURG, S., "A Synthesis Technique for Minimal State Sequential Machines," *IRE Trans. on Electronic Computers*, Vol. EC-8, No. 1, March 1959, pp. 13–24.

GI 3 GINSBURG, S., "Synthesis of Minimal State Machines," *IRE Trans. on Electronic Computers*, Vol. EC-8, No. 4, December 1959, pp. 441–449.

GI 4 GILCHRIST, B., H. POMERENE, and S. Y. WONG, "Fast Carry Logic for Digital Computers," *IRE Trans. on Electronic Computers*, Vol. EC-4, No. 4, December 1955, pp. 133–136.

GI 5 GILL, A., "Cascaded Finite-State Machines," *IRE Trans. on Electronic Computers*, Vol. EC-10, No. 3, September 1961, pp. 366–370.

GI 6 GIVONE, D. D., "A Tabular Method to Determine Simple Decompositions of Switching Functions," Ph. D. Thesis, Cornell University, Ithaca, N. Y., September 1963.

HA 1 HAMMING, R. W., "Error Detecting and Error Correcting Codes," *Bell System Tech. Journal*, Vol. 29, No. 2, April 1950, pp. 147–160.

HA 2 HARTMANIS, J., "On the State Assignment Problem for Sequential Machines I," *IRE Trans. on Electronic Computers*, Vol. EC-10, No. 2, June 1961, pp. 157–165.

HA 3 HARTMANIS, J., "Further Results on the Structure of Sequential Machines," *J. of Assoc. for Computing Machinery*, Vol. 10, No. 1, January 1963, pp. 78–88.

HA 4 HARRIS, B., "An Algorithm for Determining Minimal Representations of a Logic Function," *IRE Trans. on Electronic Computers*, Vol. EC–6, No. 2, June 1957, pp. 103–108.

HE 1 HENNIE, F. C., III, *Iterative Arrays of Logical Circuits*, MIT Press and John Wiley and Sons, New York, 1961.

HE 2 Hendrickson, H. C., "Fast High-Accuracy Binary Parallel Addition," *IRE Trans. on Electronic Computers,* Vol. EC-9, No. 4, December 1960, pp. 465–469.

HO 1 Hohn, F. E. and L. R. Schissler, "Boolean Matrices and the Design of Combinational Relay Switching Circuits," *Bell System Tech. Journal,* Vol. 34, No. 1, January 1955, pp. 177–202.

HO 2 Hohn, F. E., "2*N*-terminal Contact Networks," *Proc. International Symp. on Theory of Switching,* pt. 2, Harvard University, Cambridge, Mass., April 1957, pp. 51–58.

HO 3 Hohn, F. E., S. Seshu, and D. D. Aufenkamp, "The Theory of Nets," *IRE Trans. on Electronic Computers,* Vol. EC-6, No. 3, September 1957, pp. 154–161.

HU 1 Huntington, E. V., "Sets of Independent Postulates for the Algebra of Logic," *Trans. Am. Math. Soc.,* Vol. 5, 1904, pp. 288–309.

HU 2 Huntington, E. V., "New Sets of Independent Postulates for the Algebra of Logic," *Trans. Am. Math. Soc.,* Vol. 35, 1933, pp. 274–304.

HU 3 Huffman, D. A., "The Synthesis of Sequential Switching Circuits," *Journal of the Franklin Institute,* Vol. 257, Nos. 3 and 4, March and April 1954, pp. 161–190 and pp. 275–303.

HU 4 Huffman, D. A., "The Design and Use of Hazard-Free Switching Networks," *J. of Assoc. for Computing Machinery,* Vol. 4, No. 1, January 1957, pp. 47–62.

JU 1 Jury, E. I., *Sampled-Data Control Systems,* John Wiley and Sons, New York, 1958.

KA 1 Karnaugh, M., "The Map Method for Synthesis of Combinational Logic Circuits," *Trans. AIEE,* Communications and Electronics, Vol. 72, pt. I, November 1953, pp. 593–599.

KA 2 Karnaugh, M., "Pulse-Switching Circuits Using Magnetic Cores," *Proc. IRE,* Vol. 43, No. 5, May 1955, pp. 570–584.

KA 3 Kautz, W. H., "Constant-Weight Counters and Decoding Trees," *IRE Trans. on Electronic Computers,* Vol. EC-9, No. 2, June 1960, pp. 231–245.

KE 1 Keister, W., A. E. Ritchie, and S. H. Washburn, *The Design of Switching Circuits,* D. Van Nostrand, Princeton, New Jersey, 1951.

KE 2 Keller, H. B., "Finite Automata, Pattern Recognition and Perceptrons," *J. of Assoc. for Computing Machinery,* Vol. 8, No. 1, January 1961, pp. 1–20.

LE 1 Ledley, R. S., *Digital Computer and Control Engineering,* McGraw-Hill, New York, 1960.

LE 2 Lee, C. Y. and W. H. Chen, "Several-Valued Combinational Switching Circuits," *Trans. AIEE,* Vol. 75, pt. I, July 1956, pp. 278–283.

LE 3 Lehman, M., "High-Speed Multiplication," *IRE Trans. on Electronic Computers,* Vol. EC-6, No. 3, September 1957, pp. 204–205.

LU 1 Lucal, H. M., "Arithmetic Operations for Digital Computers Using a Modified Reflected Binary Code," *IRE Trans. on Electronic Computers,* Vol. EC-8, No. 4, December 1959, pp. 449–458.

MA 1 Mattson, R. L., "A Self-Organizing Binary System," *Proc. Eastern Joint Computer Conference,* Boston, 1959, pp. 212–218.

MA 2 MacSorley, O. L., "High-Speed Arithmetic in Binary Computers," *Proc. IRE,* Vol. 49, No. 1, January 1961, pp. 67–91.

MC 1 McCluskey, E. J., Jr., "Minimization of Boolean Functions," *Bell System Tech. Journal,* Vol. 35, No. 6, November 1956, pp. 1417–1444.

MC 2 McCluskey, E. J., Jr., and T. C. Bartee, *A Survey of Switching Circuit Theory,* McGraw-Hill, New York, 1962.

MC 3 McCluskey, E. J., Jr., "Iterative Combinational Switching Networks—General Design Considerations," *IRE Trans. on Electronic Computers,* Vol. EC-7, No. 4, 1958, pp. 285–291.

MC 4 McCluskey, E. J., Jr., and S. H. Unger, "A Note on the Number of Internal Variable Assignments for Sequential Switching Circuits," *IRE Trans. on Electronic Computers,* Vol. EC-8, No. 4, September 1959, pp. 439–440.

MC 5 McNaughton, R., "Unate Truth Functions," *IRE Trans. on Electronic Computers,* Vol. EC-10, No. 1, March 1961, pp. 1–6.

MC 6 McNaughton, R. and B. Mitchell, "The Minimality of Rectifier Nets with Multiple-Outputs Incompletely Specified," *Journal of the Franklin Institute,* Vol. 264, No. 6, December 1957, pp. 457–480.

MC 7 McNaughton, R. and H. Yamada, "Regular Expressions and State Graphs for Automata," *IRE Trans. on Electronic Computers,* Vol. EC-9, No. 1, March 1960, pp. 39–47.

ME 1 Meyerhoff, A. J. (ed.), *Digital Applications of Magnetic Devices,* John Wiley and Sons, New York, 1960.

ME 2 Mealy, G. H., "A Method for Synthesizing Sequential Circuits," *Bell System Tech. Journal,* Vol. 34, No. 5, September 1955, pp. 1045–1079.

MI 1 Millman, J. and H. Taub, *Pulse and Digital Circuits,* McGraw-Hill, New York, 1956.

MI 2 Minnick, R. C., "Linear-Input Logic," *IRE Trans. on Electronic Computers,* Vol. EC-10, No. 1, March 1961, pp. 6–16.

MO 1 Moore, E. F., "Gedanken Experiments on Sequential Machines" in *Automata Studies,* edited by C. E. Shannon and J. McCarthy, Princeton University Press, Princeton, New Jersey, 1956, pp. 129–153.

MO 2 Mott, T. H., Jr., "Determination of the Irredundant Normal Forms of a Truth Function by Iterated Consensus of the Prime Implicants," *IRE Trans. on Electronic Computers,* Vol. EC-9, No. 2, June 1960, pp. 245–252.

MU 1 Muller, D. E., and W. S. Bartky, "A Theory of Asynchronous Circuits," *Proc. International Symp. on Theory of Switching*, pt. 2, Harvard University, Cambridge, Mass., April 1957, pp. 51–58.

NE 1 Netherwood, D. B., "Minimal Sequential Machines," *IRE Trans. on Electronic Computers*, Vol. EC-8, No. 3, September 1959, pp. 339–345.

OB 1 O'Brien, J. A., "Cyclic Decimal Codes for Analogue to Digital Converters," *Trans. AIEE*, Vol. 75, pt. I, 1956, pp. 120–122.

OT 1 Ott, G. and N. H. Feinstein, "Design of Sequential Machines from Their Regular Expressions," *J. of Assoc. for Computing Machinery*, Vol. 8, No. 4, October 1961, pp. 585–600.

PA 1 Paull, M. C. and S. H. Unger, "Minimizing the Number of States in Incompletely Specified Sequential Switching Functions," *IRE Trans. on Electronic Computers*, Vol. EC-8, No. 3, September 1959, pp. 356–367.

PA 2 Paull, M. C. and E. J. McCluskey, Jr., "Boolean Functions Realizable with Single Threshold Devices," *Proc. IRE*, Vol. 48, July 1960, pp. 1335–1337.

PE 1 Petrick, S. R., "A Direct Determination of the Irredundant Forms of a Boolean Function from the Set of Prime Implicants," *Tech. Rept. No. 56–110*, AF Cambridge Research Center, Bedford, Mass., April 1956.

PE 2 Peek, R. L., Jr. and H. N. Wagar, *Switching Relay Design*, D. Van Nostrand, Princeton, New Jersey, 1955.

PE 3 Peterson, W., *Error-Correcting Codes*, John Wiley and Sons, New York, 1961.

PH 1 Phister, M., Jr., *Logical Design of Digital Computers*, John Wiley and Sons, New York, 1958.

PO 1 Povarov, G. N., "A Mathematical Theory for the Synthesis of Contact Networks with One Input and *k* Outputs," *Proc. International Symp. on Theory of Switching*, pt. 2, Harvard University, Cambridge, Mass., April 1957, pp. 74–94.

PR 1 Prather, R., "Computational Aids for Determining the Minimal Form of a Truth Function," *J. of Assoc. for Computing Machinery*, Vol. 7, No. 4, October 1960, pp. 299–310.

PY 1 Pyne, I. B. and E. J. McCluskey, Jr., "The Reduction of Redundancy in Solving Prime Implicant Tables," *IRE Trans. on Electronic Computers*, Vol. EC-11, No. 4, August 1962, pp. 473–482.

QU 1 Quine, W. V., "The Problem of Simplifying Truth Functions," *Am. Math. Monthly*, Vol. 59, No. 8, October 1952, pp. 521–531.

QU 2 Quine, W. V., "A Way to Simplify Truth Functions," *Am. Math. Monthly*, Vol. 62, No. 9, November 1955, pp. 627–631.

QU 3 Quine, W. V., "On Cores and Prime Implicants of Truth Functions," *Am. Math. Monthly*, Vol. 66, No. 9, November 1959, pp. 755–760.

RA 1 Ragazzini, J. R. and G. F. Franklin, *Sampled-Data Control Systems*, McGraw-Hill, New York, 1958.

RE 1 REITWIESNER, G. W., "The Determination of Carry Propagation Length for Binary Arithmetic," *IRE Trans. on Electronic Computers*, Vol. EC-9, No. 1, March 1960, pp. 35–38.

RI 1 RICHARDS, R. K., *Arithmetic Operations in Digital Computers*, D. Van Nostrand, Princeton, New Jersey, 1955.

RI 2 RICHARDS, R. K., *Digital Computer Components and Circuits*, D. Van Nostrand, Princeton, New Jersey, 1957.

RO 1 ROSENBLATT, F., "The Perceptron: A Theory of Statistical Separability in Cognitive Systems," *Report No. VG-1196-G-1*, Cornell Aero. Lab., 1958.

RO 2 ROGINSKIJ, V. N., "A Graphical Method for the Synthesis of Multiterminal Contact Networks," *Proc. International Symp. on the Theory of Switching*, pt. 2, Harvard University, Cambridge, Mass., April 1957, pp. 302–315.

RO 3 ROBERTSON, J. E., "A New Class of Digital Division Methods," *IRE Trans. on Electronic Computers*, Vol. EC-7, No. 3, September 1958, pp. 218–222.

SA 1 SAMSON, E. W. and B. E. MILLS, "Circuit Minimization: Algebra and Algorithm for new Boolean Canonical Expressions," *Tech. Report No. 54–21*, AF Cambridge Research Center, Bedford, Mass., April 1954.

SC 1 SCOTT, N. R., *Analogy and Digital Computer Technology*, McGraw-Hill, New York, 1960.

SE 1 SEMON, W., "Matrix Methods in the Theory of Switching," *Proc. International Symp. on Theory of Switching*, pt. 2, Harvard University, Cambridge, Mass., April 1957, pp. 13–50.

SE 2 SESHU, S., R. E. MILLER, and G. METZE, "Transition Matrices of Sequential Machines," *IRE Trans. on Circuit Theory*, Vol. CT-6, No. 1, March 1959, pp. 5–12.

SH 1 SHANNON, C. E., "A Symbolic Analysis of Relay and Switching Circuits," *Trans. AIEE*, Vol. 57, 1938, pp. 713–723.

SH 2 SHANNON, C. E., "The Synthesis of Two-Terminal Switching Circuits," *Bell System Tech. Journal*, Vol. 28, No. 1, January 1949, pp. 59–98.

SH 3 SHORT, R. A., "The Design of Complementary-Output Networks," *IRE Trans. on Electronic Computers*, Vol. EC-11, No. 6, December 1962, pp. 743–753.

SH 4 SHEFFER, H. M., "A Set of Five Independent Postulates for Boolean Algebras," *Trans. Am. Math. Soc.*, Vol. 14, 1913, pp. 481-488.

SI 1 SIMON, J. M., "Some Aspects of the Network Analysis of Sequence Transducers," *Journal of the Franklin Institute*, Vol. 265, June 1958, pp. 439–450.

SI 2 SIMON, J. M., "A Note on the Memory Aspects of Sequence Transducers," *IRE Trans. on Circuit Theory*, Vol. CT-6, No. 1, March 1959, pp. 26–30.

SI 3 SINGLETON, R. C., "A Test for Linear Separability as Applied to Self-Organizing Machines," *Self-Organizing Systems 1962*, Spartan Books, Washington, D. C., 1962, pp. 503–524.

SL 1 SLEPIAN, D., "A Class of Binary Signaling Alphabets," *Bell System Tech. Journal*, Vol. 35, No. 1, January 1956, pp. 203–234.

ST 1 STEARNS, R. E. and J. HARTMANIS, "On the State Assignment Problem for Sequential Machines II," *IRE Trans. on Electronic Computers*, Vol. EC-10, No. 4, December 1961, pp. 593–603.

TO 1 TOU, J. T., *Digital and Sampled-Data Control Systems*, McGraw-Hill, New York, 1959.

UN 1 UNGER, S. H., "A Study of Asynchronous Logical Feedback Networks," *Tech. Rept. No. 320*, Electronics Research Lab., M.I.T., Cambridge, Mass., 1957.

UN 2 UNGER, S. H., "Hazards and Delays in Asynchronous Sequential Switching Circuits," *IRE Trans. on Circuit Theory*, Vol. CT-6, No. 1, March 1959, pp. 12–26.

UN 3 University of Illinois, Digital Computer Laboratory, "On the Design of a Very High-Speed Computer," *Report No. 80*, October 1957, pp. 180–187.

UR 1 URBANO, R. H. and R. K. MUELLER, "A Topological Method for the Determination of the Minimal Forms of a Boolean Function," *IRE Trans. on Electronic Computers*, Vol. EC-5, No. 3, September 1956, pp. 126–132.

VE 1 VEITCH, E. W., "A Chart Method for Simplifying Truth Functions," *Proc. of Assoc. for Computing Machinery*, Pittsburgh, May 1952, pp. 127–133.

WA 1 WASHBURN, S. H., "Relay Trees and Symmetric Circuits," *Trans. AIEE*, Vol. 68, pt. I, 1949, pp. 582–586.

WH 1 WHITESITT, J. ELDEN, *Boolean Algebra and Its Applications*, Addison-Wesley, Reading, Mass., 1961.

YO 1 YOELI, M., "The Cascade Decomposition of Sequential Machines," *IRE Trans. on Electronic Computers*, Vol. EC-10, No. 4, December 1961, pp. 587–592.

INDEX

INDEX

385636

ABCDE69876